INDY
COFFEE
GUIDE

**INDEPENDENT COFFEE GUIDE
ENGLAND: SOUTH NO 8
IS SUPPORTED BY THESE
LOVELY PARTNERS**

blendsmiths

CAKESMITHS
CAKES FOR COFFEE SHOPS

ESPRESSO
SOLUTIONS

ROASTWORKS®
COFFEE Co LTD

Zettle
by PayPal

FOR BREW FREAKS, BEAN GEEKS

AND THE SIMPLY CURIOUS ...

Independent Coffee Guide team

Richard Bailey, Nick Cooper,
Charlotte Cummins, Tom Hampton,
Kathryn Lewis, Abi Manning,
Melissa Morris, Kirstie Newton,
Tamsin Powell, Jo Rees, Rosanna Rothery,
Melissa Stewart, Dale Stiling, Mark Tibbles,
Lara Watson and Selena Young.

Big thanks to the *Independent Coffee Guide*
committee (meet them on page 13) for
their expertise and enthusiasm, and to our
sponsors and supporters: Blendsmiths,
Brighton Coffee Festival, Bristol Coffee
Festival, Cakesmiths, Espresso Solutions,
Raw Material, Roastworks Coffee Co.,
Sucafina and Zettle by PayPal.

Coffee shops, cafes and roasteries are invited
to be included in the guide based on meeting
criteria set by the committee, which includes
the use of speciality beans, providing a
high-quality coffee experience for visitors
and being independently run.

For information on *Independent Coffee Guides*
for Ireland, Scotland, England – North,
Midlands & East, and Wales, visit:

INDYCOFFEE.GUIDE

indycoffeeguide

© Salt Media Ltd
Published by Salt Media Ltd 2024
saltmedia.co.uk
01271 859299
ideas@saltmedia.co.uk

salt

CONTENTS

Page

WELCOME

Welcome to the latest *Indy Coffee Guide* for the south of England.

In this new edition we're delighted to have spread the area we cover a little wider to include, for the first time, cafes and roasteries in Kent and Essex. It's always exciting to explore another coffee region and we're thrilled to share our finds with you.

We hope this little travel guide will be your invaluable aid to discovering top-notch speciality coffee in a sea of over-roasted beans and poor pours. Life's too short for bad coffee and that precious daily caffeine intake (before you get the jitters) deserves to be spent on a smooth and well-crafted sip.

We love to know where the guide takes you, so share your experiences with us on Instagram. And if there's a cafe or roastery you think deserves to be in the next guide, drop us a message via ideas@saltmedia.co.uk.

Indy Coffee Guide team
🄾 *indycoffeeguide*

L-R: Tamsin, Selena, Charlotte, Chris, Dale, Nick and Mark

✦ MEET THE COMMITTEE

The *Indy Coffee Guide* team work with a group
of industry experts to identify the best cafes
and roasteries to invite into the guide

ALEX ZEAL

Alex discovered his passion for speciality
coffee in New Zealand in 2015. He recently
became a member of the elected committee
of SCA UK as its judges coordinator and
now works at Extract Coffee Roasters in
Bristol as a wholesale manager.

TASH MURPHY

Tash's coffee career began 20 years ago when
she was a barista at RedRoaster, the first
indie second-wave roastery in Brighton. She
launched PHARMACIE Coffee Roasters in 2015.
In 2022 she left her role in sourcing and QC at
PHARMACIE to cross over to the green side by
joining Sucafina UK as a coffee trader.

COURTNEY OATES

In 2021, after over a decade of working as a barista in Kent, Courtney joined Yallah Coffee Roasters in Cornwall. Her interest in social and environmental sustainability was the perfect fit for the roastery, where she works closely with producers and importers who share her values.

WILL HARRIGAN

Will (pictured above, right) spent time in South and Central America, living and working with local coffee producers to learn about the industry from its roots before setting up River Coffee in Winchester in 2018. He continues to work closely with producers at origin through his speciality roastery.

JESSIE MAY PETERS

It was in France that barista Jessie May was introduced to the world of green coffee, which paved the way for her role as head of marketing at not-for-profit import and export company Raw Material. In 2019, she relocated from Paris to Margate.

CALLUM PARSONS

Our longest-standing committee member, Callum has spent many years in the speciality coffee competition circuit and trained thousands of baristas. He cemented his status in the coffee scene in 2020 when he opened Fire & Flow Coffee Roasters in Cirencester.

HOW TO USE THE GUIDE

COFFEE SHOPS

Coffee shops and cafes where you can drink top-notch speciality coffee. We've split the guide into areas to help you find places near you.

ROASTERIES

Meet the leading speciality coffee roasters and discover where to source beans. Find them after the cafes in each area.

MAPS

Every cafe and roastery is numbered so you can find them either on the area map at the start of each section or on the detailed city maps.

MORE GOOD FINDS

Discover more good coffee shops and roasteries at the end of each area section.

Follow us on Instagram:
indycoffeeguide

KEY

Symbols at the bottom of each cafe and roastery page provide further information on what you'll find at the venue.

Wifi

Dogs welcome

Bike friendly

Reusables accepted

Buy beans in store

Buy beans online

Outdoor seating

Cafe at the roastery

Roastery open to the public

Roastery visit by invite

Coffee courses

ESPRESSO
SOLUTIONS

AWARD-WINNING
CAFE & BARISTA TOOLS SUPPLIER

YOUR ADVENTURES START HERE

CORNWALL
COFFEE SHOPS

✪ CAFES

1 Loafs Bakery
2 Situ
3 Espressini
4 Strong Adolfos
5 Rising Ground – The Outlet
6 The Good Stuff
7 Liberty Coffee
8 Electric Bakery

✪ ROASTERIES

9 Yallah Coffee Company
10 The Roasting Room

Find more good coffee shops and
roasteries on page 37.

All locations are approximate

6 Boscastle

5 Wadebridge

4

CORNWALL

10 Zelah

TRURO

2 Penryn
9 Falmouth
Kergilliack
3

 Penzance

Bude

Launceston

I LOAFS BAKERY

63 Causewayhead, Penzance, Cornwall, TR18 2SR

loafsbakery.co.uk

loafsbakery

It's nigh on impossible to stroll past this cafe-bakery without stepping through the door. Its shop window – piled high with freshly baked sourdough loaves, cubed rubicon croissants, stuffed cruffins and creamy custard tarts – lures in even the most self-controlled passerby.

Of course, good pastries are best accompanied by a fresh brew, and Loafs' baristas know a thing or two about decent coffee. Self-confessed extraction-rate nerds and La Marzocco masters, the crew are adept at crafting first-rate flat whites from Square Mile's Red Brick beans. According to the team, the blend's fruity, chocolatey and nutty notes make it the perfect partner for a rubicon (croissant pastry shaped into a cube, stuffed with a custard filling and topped with a chocolate drizzle).

TIP PICK UP A "PASTRY NEVER SLEEPS" TOTE BAG TO CARRY YOUR HAUL HOME

The cafe-bakery has only been in business since April 2023 but has already gained a cult following thanks, in part, to its quirky branding, tattooed team, tongue-in-cheek Insta posts and innovative spin on all things pastry.

Word to the wise: swing by early if you want to get your hands on one of the daily specials – they disappear quickly.

Established
2023

Key roaster
Square Mile
Coffee Roasters

Brewing method
Espresso

Machine
La Marzocco
Linea PB

Grinder
Mahlkonig E65S
GbW

Opening hours
Mon–Sat
8am–5pm

2 SITU

The Warehouse, Commercial Road, Penryn, Cornwall, TR10 8AE

situcafe.co.uk

f situcafe *@ situcafe*

This popular coffee shop, eatery and events space run by Sham Mulji and Alexa Richardson started life in the pandemic, when Sham served coffee to his local community from a Piaggio Ape van. Drawing on his experience as an SCA-trained barista, chef and all-round food and drink pro, plus Alexa's background in events and hospitality, the project snowballed into a bricks-and-mortar venue in Penryn.

While Situ has grown and evolved since its inception, its guiding principles of heritage, culture and service remain unchanged. The dishes served at the eatery are inspired by Sham's Gujarati-Ugandan heritage and crafted using Cornish produce, plucked and grown from the surrounding coast and countryside.

TIP TRY THE TRADITIONAL MASALA CHAI, SERVED SHORT, SWEET AND SPICY

However, coffee is the bread and butter of Situ. There's always a variety of roasts available, including a seasonal espresso from Origin, a rotating single-origin espresso and a guest East African or Indian coffee prepared as batch or hand filter. Take a seat in the warehouse's modern interior and pair your coffee with a Nankhatai, a traditional Indian shortbread biscuit infused with cardamom.

Established
2023

Key roaster
Origin Coffee Roasters

Brewing method
Espresso, batch filter, Kalita Wave, Chemex, AeroPress

Machine
La Marzocco KB90

Grinder
Mahlkonig E65S GbW, Mahlkonig EK43

Opening hours
Mon-Sat
8am-4pm
Sun
9am-4pm

3 ESPRESSINI

37-39 Killigrew Street, Falmouth, Cornwall, TR11 3PW

07890 453705

f espressini *◎ espressini*

The bold pink frontage of this Falmouth coffee shop shouts loudly about Espressini's place at the forefront of a high-street rebellion championing creativity and independence in an ever-growing sea of chains.

The cafe's longstanding position at the heart of Falmouth is testament to the quality of its offering and draws in those seeking quality caffeination, delicious breakfasts and lazy brunches. Coffee is supplied by Cornish roastery Yallah, with which the Espressini gang have worked since day one. Out of this long-term relationship has sprung a signature espresso created especially for the cafe. The beans are a permanent fixture in the hopper, although finds from other roasteries that excite the team are also on offer occasionally, too.

TIP HIT UP A COLD BREW ON A HOT DAY

It's almost impossible to resist the pull of pairing a coffee with something to eat here; Espressini's locally sourced fodder is well-loved by locals. At the very least, nab a grab-and-go baked treat from the heaving countertop selection. If you're sticking around for brunch, ask the team for the day's waffle special (rum baba is a good shout), opt for tropical vegan granola with coconut yogurt, or go the whole hog with a meat or vegan Journeyman cooked brekkie.

Established
2012

Key roaster
Yallah Coffee Company

Brewing method
Espresso, V60, batch filter, Kalita Wave, cold brew, Chemex

Machine
Victoria Arduino Black Eagle

Grinder
Mythos One × 2, Mahlkonig EK43

Opening hours
Mon-Sat
7.30am-4.30pm
Sun
9am-4pm

4 STRONG ADOLFOS

Hawksfield, A39, St Breock, Wadebridge, Cornwall, PL27 7LR

strongadolfos.com | 01208 816949

f strongadolfos *©strongadolfos*

Since 2013, this award-winning indie cafe has been a haven for day-trippers and holidaymakers travelling the Atlantic Highway through Cornwall. However, unlike so many other roadside stops, Strong Adolfos is the kind of place you dream of breaking up a long journey.

Founders John and Mathilda Friström Eldridge have created a quirky and contemporary space where customers can relax and revive. Eye-catching additions to the sleek decor reference their passions for surf and motorcycle culture, and add a personal element to the experience.

TIP CHECK OUT THE COLLECTION OF RETAIL COFFEE KIT, HOMEWARES AND BOOKS

A long-term collaboration with pioneering Cornish roastery Origin sees a line-up of on-point espresso drinks served. Perfectly executed flat whites and lattes are complemented by an eye-widening selection of bakes, many of which are inspired by Mathilda's Scandinavian heritage, and all of which are baked in-house.

If something more substantial is needed to fuel onward adventures, there's an extensive cafe menu of breakfast, brunch and lunch dishes. House favourites include globetrotting collabs such as black forest pancakes, mexican brioche and kimchi 'shroom toast.

Established
2013

Key roaster
Origin Coffee
Roasters

Brewing method
Espresso

Machine
La Marzocco KB90

Grinder
Nuova Simonelli
Mythos One

Opening hours
Mon-Sun
8.30am-4pm

5 RISING GROUND - THE OUTLET

Unit 1 Clear Space Hub, Wadebridge, Cornwall, PL27 7FE

risingground.coffee | 01208 212110

f coffee.rg ☺ *risinggroundoutlet*

It's not often you get to quiz the roaster on the beans used to craft your brew or have a chance to taste a new coffee before it's released. However, that's exactly what's in store for the caffeine curious who make a pilgrimage to Rising Ground's HQ in Wadebridge.

Launched in spring 2023, The Outlet is where Rising Ground's baristas and roasters get to share the latest beans from the roastery next door. It started out as a weekday side-hustle but turned out to be so popular with locals that within a few months the team were slinging shots and pouring juicy batch filter on Saturdays too.

TIP ASK FOR DEETS ON THE NEXT PUBLIC CUPPING SESSION

The offer changes all the time, but the seasonal house Foundry blend is always ready and waiting to go on espresso. It's a well-rounded and full-bodied coffee which makes a knockout flat white and delivers notes of milk chocolate, caramel and stone fruits. An additional filter and espresso of the day – usually single origin and best served black – offer further opportunities for caffeinated exploration.

Established
2023

Key roaster
Rising Ground

Brewing method
Espresso,
batch filter,
pourover

Machine
Conti MC Ultima

Grinder
Compak Bolt

Opening hours
Mon–Sat
9am–2pm

6 THE GOOD STUFF

Harbour Light, The Harbour, Boscastle, Cornwall, PL35 0HL

thegoodstuffcafe.co.uk | 07894 069006

𝐟 *giveusthegoodstuff* ⊙ *giveusthegoodstuff*

Overlooking Boscastle's natural harbour at the point where the River Valency runs into the sea, the terrace of this beautifully rustic coffee shop offers an incredible backdrop for a morning brew.

Serving some of the best coffee in the area, The Good Stuff certainly lives up to its name. Working closely with Oxford roastery Missing Bean, owner Alice Attlee-Grant selects conversation-starting coffees and changes the house espresso regularly to keep customers delighted and surprised. Whether it's a chocolatey flat white made with Peruvian beans from the Chilchos Valley or a sweet and light filter such as the staff-fave Burundi, the beans are always single origin and direct trade.

TIP CHECK OUT THE REGULAR POP-UPS ON FRIDAY AND SATURDAY EVENINGS

The building has sat on the harbour for hundreds of years, so those who choose to sit in can soak up its historic vibe while they sip.

No trip is complete without perusing The Good Stuff's handpicked curation of provisions, which focuses on sustainable and ethical natural wines, snacks, handcrafted gifts and, of course, coffee beans.

Established
2021

Key roaster
Missing Bean Coffee Roasters

Brewing method
Espresso,
batch filter

Machine
La Marzocco
Linea PB ABR

Grinder
Mahlkonig EK43,
Mahlkonig E80S

Opening hours
Tue–Sun
9am–5pm

7 LIBERTY COFFEE

4 Northgate Street, Launceston, Cornwall, PL15 8BD
liberty-coffee.co.uk | 01566 776751
f LibCoffee *⊙ libcoffee*

It's a good indicator of the quality of a cafe when tables are hard to come by, the aroma of fresh coffee and homemade bakes fills the air and the baristas are engaged non-stop in crafting latte art. Liberty Coffee ticks all these boxes and has been perma-busy since it set up residence on Northgate Street in 2013.

Over the decade it's been in business, the team have built a great relationship with speciality coffee roasteries across the UK, resulting in an ever-changing line-up of exclusive guest beans. The strongest partnership is with pals at London roastery Kiss the Hippo, who supply the bespoke house blend: an organic coffee that bursts with fruity notes yet also pairs superbly with milk.

TIP IF THE SUN'S SHINING, TAKE YOUR ORDER TO THE NEW OUTDOOR SEATING AREA

Coffee isn't all that Liberty is renowned for, however: it's also heralded as the home of the best sausage rolls in the South West. It's a ballsy claim, but one backed by visitors who heap praise on variations such as the sun-dried tomato and fennel sausage roll served with runner bean chutney. There's lots more scrumptious fodder to get your chops around including pasties, homity pies and tiered cakes – don't miss the courgette and lime version.

Established
2013

Key roaster
Kiss the Hippo

Brewing method
Espresso,
batch filter

Machine
La Marzocco
Linea PB ABR

Grinder
Victoria Arduino
Mythos One

Opening hours
Tue–Sat
9am–4pm

8 ELECTRIC BAKERY

Unit 2 The Depot, Kings Hill, Bude, Cornwall, EX23 8PQ

electricbakery.co | 01288 356604

electricbakery

They say follow the locals to find the best food and drink, and that's certainly the case in Bude. Electric Bakery is a destination in itself in this seaside town, which was lacking in decent coffee prior to Electric's arrival in 2019. It's so beloved that it won a Food Reader Award in 2022 for Best Cafe in the South West – especially impressive when you consider it isn't really a cafe in the traditional sense.

Since the pandemic, the bakery has operated as a takeaway and outdoor-seating joint only, but that hasn't hampered the crowds who flock from far and wide for the coffee, sourdough loaves, overnight artisan breads and fresh pastries. It's '*food* we *want to eat,*' explains its director and speciality coffee buyer Christine Apiou.

TIP BOOK A PLACE ON CO-OWNER BENEDICT HARDING'S NEW SOURDOUGH COURSES

The ingredients are as local as it gets. The team cure and hand-slice bacon from local butcher Moores and use homemade hot sauce to turn it into next-level bacon sarnies. Grilled cheese is elevated with a blend of Cornish cheeses and Electric's own kimchi, while the wholemeal sourdough uses wheat grown and milled within three miles of the bakery. Cornwall's Origin provides the beans for the house roast, with rotating guests including We Are Here, Round Hill and Crankhouse.

Established
2019

Key roaster
Origin Coffee Roasters

Brewing method
Espresso, batch filter, cold brew

Machine
La Marzocco Linea PB

Grinder
Mahlkonig EK43, Mahlkonig E65S GbW, Victoria Arduino Mythos One

Opening hours
Wed-Sun
9am-2pm

BUDE

CORNWALL
ROASTERIES

9 YALLAH COFFEE COMPANY

Argal Home Farm, Kergilliack, Falmouth, Cornwall, TR11 5PD

yallahcoffee.co.uk | 01326 727383

f *yallahcoffee* **⊙** *yallahcoffee*

Many brands make noise about their sustainability ambitions, but this Cornish roastery is one of the minority that doesn't just pay lip service to the issue – it actually puts its money where its mouth is.

Freight-shipping beans to the UK from the world's coffee-growing regions makes a sizeable dent in indie roasteries' carbon footprint, yet the team at Yallah have found a solution to the problem: harnessing the power of wind. Working with New Dawn Traders, in May 2020 the team received their first sailboat consignment of beans from Colombia. Today, there are three sail-ship coffees in the core range of single origins.

Moving beans by boat is the long way around, but it's something founder Richard Blake and crew consider invaluable. In addition to cutting their emissions in this way, they're also committed to eliminating all single-use plastic and run a returnable cup scheme at the two Yallah cafes in St Ives and Penryn.

'THERE ARE THREE SAIL-SHIP COFFEES IN THE CORE RANGE OF SINGLE ORIGINS'

Coffees available to buy on the website change regularly, but customers can rest assured that every bag is sourced in accordance with the Yallah Buying Standards which ensures sourcing is honest and traceable – and the quality top-notch.

Established
2014

Roaster make and size
Virey Garnier 15kg

10 THE ROASTING ROOM

14 Lanteague Studios, Scotland Road, Zelah, Newquay, Cornwall, TR4 9JG

theroastingroom.co.uk | 07875 343465

© *theroastingroomcoffee*

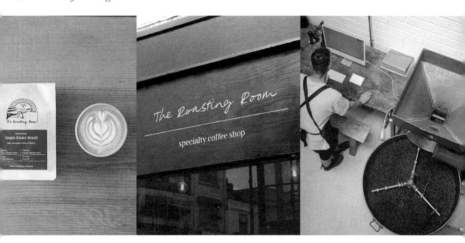

The Roasting Room's founder Olly Jones first caught the coffee bug in Raglan, New Zealand, when he worked in a surf shop adjoining a roastery. On his return to the UK he joined the fire service but, a few years later, when the opportunity to open a cafe with his partner Loz (a dentist at the time) came about, his interest in speciality was reignited.

Not long after launching the cafe on Newquay's Bank Street, Olly started roasting on a 4kg machine at the back of the shop. The cafe and its coffee were an instant hit with locals and visitors. Before long, demand had outpaced the original kit so, in 2022, the roasting operation moved to Lanteague Studios nearby.

'A ONE-OF-A-KIND VINTAGE VITTORIA RETROFITTED WITH MODERN TECH TO ENSURE CONSISTENCY'

The Roasting Room's range of sustainable coffees are now crafted on a one-of-a-kind vintage 1960s Vittoria roaster, which Olly has retrofitted with modern tech to guarantee consistency. Its 30kg capacity ensures the roastery can keep the cafe, plus its growing list of wholesale and consumer customers, stocked with top-notch blends and single origins. Check out the Featured Coffee on the website – it's usually something a little leftfield, like the recent fully washed Papua New Guinea single origin.

Established
2021

Roaster make and size
Vittoria 30kg

NEWQUAY

35

Tools to run
your coffee shop

Zettle

by PayPal

zettle.com/gb/contact-us

MORE GOOD FINDS IN CORNWALL

COFFEE SHOPS

45 QUEEN STREET
45 Queen Street, Penzance,
Cornwall, TR18 4BQ
45queenst.com

BEAR CORNWALL
St Mawes Castle Car Park, Castle Drive,
St Mawes, Cornwall, TR2 5DE

DARK PONY COFFEE
6 The Moor, Falmouth, Cornwall, TR11 3QA

FLORA
Trelowarren, Mawgan, Helston,
Cornwall, TR12 6AF
floranewyard.co.uk

GOOD VIBES CAFE
28 Killigrew Street, Falmouth,
Cornwall, TR11 3PN

GYLLY BEACH CAFE
Gyllyngvase Beach, Cliff Road, Falmouth,
Cornwall, TR11 4PA
gyllybeach.com

ORIGIN COFFEE ROASTERS - HARBOUR HEAD
Harbour Head, Porthleven, Helston,
Cornwall, TR13 9JY
origincoffee.co.uk

ORIGIN COFFEE ROASTERS - THE ROASTERY CAFE
The Roastery, 1 Treysa Place, Porthleven,
Helston, Cornwall, TR13 9FJ
origincoffee.co.uk

ST KEW FARMSHOP & CAFE
St Kew Highway, Bodmin,
Cornwall, PL30 3EF
stkewfarmshop.co.uk

THE ROASTING ROOM
65c Bank Street, Newquay,
Cornwall, TR7 1DL
theroastingroom.co.uk

THREE LITTLE BIRDS
Unit 2 Falmouth Business Park, Bickland
Water Road, Falmouth, Cornwall, TR11 4SZ
threelittlebirdscafe.co.uk

YALLAH CAFE - PENRYN
Commercial Road, Penryn,
Cornwall, TR10 8AF
yallahcoffee.co.uk

YALLAH CAFE - ST IVES
Court Arcade, St Ives,
Cornwall, TR26 1LF
yallahcoffee.co.uk

ROASTERIES

LARS & MARGO COFFEE ROASTERS
Unit 16 Holman Road, Liskeard,
Cornwall, PL14 3UT
larsandmargo.co.uk

ORIGIN COFFEE ROASTERS
The Roastery, 1 Treysa Place, Porthleven,
Cornwall, TR13 9FJ
origincoffee.co.uk

RISING GROUND
Unit 1 Clear Spave, Dunveth Business Park,
West Hill, Wadebridge, Cornwall, PL27 7FE
risingground.coffee

SABINS SMALL BATCH ROASTERS
Butterfly Barn, Hersham, Bude,
Cornwall, EX23 9LZ
sabinscoffee.co.uk

DEVON
COFFEE SHOPS

⊗ CAFES

⊗ ROASTERIES

Find more good coffee shops and
roasteries on page 69.

All locations are approximate

Woolacombe

Braunton

Barnstaple

Bideford

Chumleigh

DEVON

Willand

EXETER Topsham

Buckfastleigh

Totnes Paignton

PLYMOUTH

II TERRA NOVA

41 Chapel Street, Devonport, Plymouth, Devon, PL1 4DU

terranovacafe.co.uk | 01752 927888

f terranovadevonport *⊙ terranovadevonport*

Part of the Shred or Dead crew of cafes in and around Plymouth (see also Black Cat Surf Club and Rocket & Rascals), Terra Nova was named in honour of Devonport-born explorer Robert Falcon Scott and his ill-fated voyage to the South Pole.

A spirit of adventure runs through each of the Shred or Dead venues, and this social space within the former Crown Hotel hosts all kinds of intrepid visitors – from cyclists exploring the South West to seafaring folk docked at the nearby marina. Whatever your mode of transport, the prize for finding your way to Terra Nova's door is reviving speciality coffee and endurance-fuelling homemade bakes.

TIP HIRE THIS DYNAMIC SPACE FOR A KNEES-UP

The team recently started working with Cornish roastery Origin and have installed a new La Marzocco to do justice to the quality beans. Those needing more than a caffeine jolt to recharge their batteries should order the Mocha Mania smoothie which pairs espresso with vanilla ice cream, banana, hazelnut syrup, chocolate and milk. Leave room for brunch though – sourdough toast with sobrassada (spreadable salami) and honey is an unmissable house special.

Established
2022

Key roaster
Origin Coffee Roasters

Brewing method
Espresso

Machine
La Marzocco

Grinder
Nuova Simonelli GX 85

Opening hours
Mon-Sat
9am-5pm
Sun
9am-4pm

12 ROCKETS AND RASCALS

7 Parade, Plymouth, Devon, PL1 2JL

rocketsandrascals.co.uk | 01752 927555

f *rocketsandrascalsuk* *⊙* *rocketsandrascals*

In 2023, this Barbican favourite celebrated a decade of serving silky espresso to Plymouth's cyclists, tourists and indie supporters. A lot has changed in the past ten years – most notably the addition of two sister venues – but its focus on adventure, friends and good coffee remains unchanged.

The team recently switched up the coffee offering, enlisting the help of Cornwall's Origin Coffee Roasters to keep the grinders topped up with high-spec beans. They also upgraded their kit and now pull espresso through a shiny new La Marzocco machine.

TIP HIRE THE QUIRKY ROCKETS AND RASCALS BUILDING FOR YOUR NEXT EVENT

Join the two-wheeled adventurers for a cortado pit stop under the alfresco awning or stick around for brunch to fuel your day's activities. The aptly named Sprinter's Breakfast (all the best bits of a full English) will power your cycling up and down Devon's hills or your day exploring Britain's ocean city on two feet.

Inspired by the cycling jerseys and paraphernalia decorating the cafe? Hire a bike from the shop for the afternoon and reward yourself with a post-pedal cake and coffee.

Established
2013

Key roaster
Origin Coffee Roasters

Brewing method
Espresso

Machine
La Marzocco

Grinder
Nuova Simonelli, Fiorenzato

Opening hours
Mon-Fri
9am–4pm
Sat
8am–5pm
Sun
9am–5pm

PLYMOUTH

43

13 BLACK CAT SURF CLUB

31 The Broadway, Plymstock, Plymouth, Devon, PL9 7AF

blackcatsurfclub.com | 01752 927999

f blackcatsurfclub *⊙ blackcatsurfclub*

Riding the wave of demand for indie coffee spots that also do a gnarly brunch, in 2020 the team at Shred or Dead (a collective of adventure-fuelled caffeine venues in and around Plymouth) opened Black Cat Surf Club in Plymstock.

The reception from local surfers, walkers and holidaymakers was off the hook so, in 2022, the crew expanded next door to double the cafe's capacity. A blend of Moroccan, Californian and Devonian surf culture, the interior is bright, spacious and studded with boards and other gear.

TIP PICK UP A BLACK CAT SURF CLUB TEE OR HOODIE IN STORE

Early risers fresh from a dawn patrol arrive from 9am to get stuck into brekkie plates such as The Pipeline Breakfast of smashed avo, beans, mushrooms, veggie sausages, tomato, hash browns and spinach. At midday the lunch line-up kicks in, delivering a crowd-pleasing menu of superfood salads, toasties, flatbreads and wraps. This good eating is matched by speciality coffee from pioneering Cornish roastery Origin, as well as restorative smoothies such as The Recovery: a mash-up of banana, protein powder, peanut butter, granola and skimmed milk.

Established
2020

Key roaster
Origin Coffee Roasters

Brewing method
Espresso

Machine
La Marzocco

Grinder
Nuova Simonelli GX 85

Opening hours
Mon–Sun
9am–4pm

PLYMOUTH

44

14 VOYAGER COFFEE

Unit 6 Mardle Way Business Park, Buckfastleigh, Devon, TQ11 0JL

voyagercoffee.co.uk | 01364 644440

@ *popupvoyager*

A small industrial estate on the fringes of Dartmoor isn't the first place you'd expect to find a slick coffee trailer serving interesting single-origin brews. Yet that's where you'll find Voyager's converted American camper, parked up outside its Buckfastleigh HQ.

TIP HIRE THE CHROME COFFEE TRAILER FOR YOUR NEXT EVENT

The roastery is known across the south of England and beyond for its fully traceable speciality beans, and this new permanent pop-up enables the roasters to get instant feedback on their latest batch. The core range of blends is available to-go as espresso drinks, although the trailer also showcases new single origins before they appear elsewhere.

The quality coffee is complemented by cakes from Exploding Bakery in Exeter – its salted caramel brownie making a perfect partner to Voyager's Native flat white. In summer, keep 'em peeled for the chrome wagon at festivals and events across the region.

Established
2021

Key roaster
Voyager Coffee

Brewing method
Espresso

Machine
Sanremo Verona RS

Grinder
Fiorenzato SR70

Opening hours
Mon-Fri
8.30am-2pm

15 THE HAIRY BARISTA

82 High Street, Totnes, Devon, TQ9 5SN
thehairybarista.co.uk | 07397 817535
f *thehairybarista* @ *the.hairy.barista*

This Totnes favourite recently closed its doors. However, any panic among The Hairy Barista regulars was soon averted when it became clear that owner Roee Yekutiel had simply moved his coffee shop to roomier premises a few doors up the High Street.

The same lively bohemian vibe for which the original venue was known and loved prevails at number 82, but now there's more space to kick back and enjoy the coffee and atmosphere. Roee continues to stock the grinders with award-winning speciality beans from London's Mission Coffee Works and supplements them with guest roasts from Campbell & Syme, Square Mile and Colonna.

TIP ALL CAFFEINED OUT? TRY A VIBRANT SUPERFOOD LATTE

Vegans are well looked after at The Hairy Barista: white coffees are served with oat milk as standard (soy, almond and Riverford Dairy are also available) and the foodie bill is exclusively plant-based. The seasonal menu of smoothies, toasties, soups and cakes is crafted from ethically sourced, nutritious ingredients. Check out The Hairy Barista's Insta page for info on its next after-hours event, such as live-music nights hosted by sister company Adama.

Established
2017

Key roaster
Mission
Coffee Works

Brewing method
Espresso, V60,
cafetiere,
turkish pot

Machine
Sanremo Opera 2

Grinder
Mythos One,
Mahlkonig EK43,
Mahlkonig
E65S GbW,
Mahlkonig
E80S GbW

Opening hours
Mon-Sat
9am-5pm
(seasonal opening hours)

TOTNES

46

16 GAIA COFFEE

39 Winner Street, Paignton, Devon, TQ3 3BN
gaiagiving.com | 07428 324781
f *gaiacoffee39* ⊙ *gaiacoffee_*

From the minute you step into this not-for-profit, family-run cafe and see the smiles of its punters, you sense you're in for an authentic and unusual coffee experience.

While the quality of coffee that's roasted, brewed and served here is the top priority, the friendly team don't see Gaia as just a place to enjoy a great brew. For them, it's somewhere connections form, friendships blossom and visitors leave feeling uplifted.

TIP SUN SHINING? TAKE A SEAT IN GAIA'S COMMUNITY GARDEN

Good vibes emanate from this stylish space with its verdant houseplants, pink benches and colourful cushions. Visitors can also explore a packed calendar of mental health and anxiety support groups, yoga classes, meditation sessions, wellbeing walks and coffee-roasting experiences. Profits are reinvested into the local community.

Director and head roaster Ceri Ashford works closely with her husband, mother-in-law and sister to keep the workshops running and the grinders topped up. The family recently turned their hands to roasting, the results of which can be tasted in the signature house blend, Gaia's Helping Hand. If you're swerving caffeine, try the soothing Brazilian decaf.

Established
2020

Key roaster
Gaia Coffee Roasters

Brewing method
Espresso, cold brew

Machine
La Spaziale S5

Grinder
Compak E5, Compak E6

Opening hours
Mon-Sat
9am-3pm

17 LILAC BAKERY

59 Cowick Street, Exeter, Devon, EX4 1HR

07925 285872

⊙ lilacbakery.exeter

You'd have to possess otherworldly levels of self control to resist adding a warm-from-the-oven bake to your flat white order at this contemporary bakery in Exeter. From Wednesday to Sunday, the city's discerning foodies head there early and queue to get first pick of the lemon meringue pie cruffins, peach-bejewelled danishes, and pistachio and mascarpone brioche.

Owners Eddie and Jenn Goodwin handcraft all the baked goods (including sourdough, sausage rolls, focaccia sarnies, cakes and laminated pastries) from scratch at dawn each day and use high quality, ethically sourced ingredients.

TIP A RECORDING STUDIO IS IN THE WORKS AND WILL BE AVAILABLE TO HIRE FROM THE END OF 2024

There's no better pairing to a sweet bake than an expertly prepared coffee, and the Lilac Bakery team know their way around a brew bar as well as they do a kitchen. Visitors can choose between the house roast (from Obadiah in Edinburgh) or a guest coffee (switched up every fortnight) before selecting their fave serve style from a line-up of brewing methods including espresso, batch filter, V60 and AeroPress.

Decision made, kick back in the cool environs of the cafe with your order – always served on beautiful crockery for an extra dusting of delectation.

Established
2021

Key roaster
Obadiah

Brewing method
Espresso, V60, batch filter, AeroPress

Machine
Victoria Arduino Black Eagle

Grinder
Mahlkonig E65S GbW

Opening hours
Wed-Fri
8am-2pm
Sat
9am-2pm
Sun
9.30am-1pm

EXETER

18 SACRED GROUNDS

McCoy's Arcade, Fore Street, Exeter, Devon, EX4 3AN

sacredgrounds.co | 01392 791440

f exetersacredgrounds *⊙ sacredgroundsvegancafe*

Walk five minutes out of Exeter's chain-dominated city centre towards the River Exe and you'll find yourself in the indie quarter, home to this contemporary cafe. Located in the light-filled atrium at the back of McCoy's Arcade, Sacred Grounds is a beautiful space in which to relax, meet friends and let the creative juices flow.

Alongside coffee, an innovative and exciting plant-based menu is the focus here, but ardent carnivores shouldn't let that put them off. Head chef Maxim Wortley dabbles in all sorts of scientific sorcery to create mind-bending dishes from seasonal ingredients. The award-winning vegan poached "eggs", for example, took three months to perfect and are the most authentic version you'll find that doesn't involve the help of a chicken.

TIP BOOK TALKS, A SUPPER CLUB AND ART MARKETS ARE HOSTED IN THE ATRIUM AFTER DARK

On the coffee front, the team collab with local indie Roastworks. Its roasters have created a blend to complement the cafe's chosen alt milk (Oatly Barista Edition, although other options are available), which also tastes delicious served black.

Established
2018

Key roaster
Roastworks
Coffee Co.

Brewing method
Espresso, V60

Machine
Victoria Arduino
Eagle One

Grinder
Victoria Arduino
Mythos 2

Opening hours
Mon-Sat
9am-3pm
Sun
10am-3pm

EXETER

49

19 130 BASEMENT

Basement, 130 Fore Street, Exeter, Devon, EX4 3JQ
crankhousecoffee.co.uk | 07828 076596
@ crankhouse130b

As you'd expect from South West speciality stalwart Crankhouse, this roastery-cafe in Exeter's indie hub is pleasingly particular about the coffee it serves, while the vibe remains completely chilled.

There's a neighbourhood quality to 130 Basement, thanks to its choice tunes on the stereo, impeccable coffee, plethora of tempting cakes baked in the open kitchen and super-friendly service. You'll want to move in.

TIP CHECK OUT THE RANGE OF BREWING EQUIPMENT WHILE YOU WAIT FOR YOUR COFFEE

Pick a pew and order a warm cardamom bun or the staff-fave toasted banana bread with vanilla ice cream, then peruse the coffee menu. The offering at this West Quarter landmark is endlessly interesting. The beans are switched up daily, but there's always a range of easy-drinking blends, more complex single origins and coffees that have undergone unusual processes to bring out the juiciest, fruitiest flavours.

All the coffees are roasted omni, which means they can be sampled in a variety of serves. The baristas know their stuff, so ask for their recommendation when you're choosing from the seasonal offering.

Established
2020

Key roaster
Crankhouse Coffee

Brewing method
Espresso, Clever Dripper, batch filter

Machine
La Marzocco Linea PB

Grinder
Victoria Arduino Mythos One × 2, Mahlkonig EK43 S

Opening hours
Mon–Fri
8am–4pm
Sat
9am–4pm

20 THE COMMON BEAVER

59 Magdalen Road, Exeter, Devon, EX2 4TA

07725 620116

f *thecommonbeaver* ⓘ *thecommonbeaver*

Be prepared to queue for your coffee at this uber-popular hangout on Exeter's indie-centric Magdalen Road. Don't let the prospect of a short wait put you off, however, as The Common Beaver's caffeine and bagels are worth every second spent in line.

The foundation of the always on-point espresso drinks is Fire & Flow's Aurora blend: a Brazil/Burundi split yielding notes of chocolate, caramel and nuts when paired with dairy, and milk chocolate, maple and pecan when matched with oat milk. On batch, expect to encounter fruit-forward roasts from the likes of Hard Lines, Foundation and New Ground.

TIP WHATEVER'S ON BATCH WILL ALSO BE AVAILABLE TO BUY AS BEANS IN THE RETAIL SECTION

Homemade bagels make up the bulk of the food offering and the glossy rings of springy dough are stuffed with fillings such as pulled local pork and slaw; broad-bean guac, tomato chutney and smoky marinated tofu; and golden halloumi, mushroom and aioli.

Exploding Bakery's irresistible traybakes and brownies – try the dense and dark lumberjack cake – are a satisfying way to round off any visit.

Established
2018

Key roaster
Fire & Flow
Coffee Roasters

Brewing method
Espresso,
batch filter,
cold brew

Machine
La Marzocco
Linea PB

Grinder
Compak F8

Opening hours
Mon-Fri
7.30am–4pm
Sat
8am–4pm
Sun
9am–3pm

21 CIRCLE

37 Fore Street, Topsham, Devon, EX3 0HR

circletopsham.com | 07735 683839

 circletopsham

Topsham's Fore Street is a hub of interesting indie eateries and shops, and at its southern end – a stone's throw from the quayside – is a beautiful little hangout that combines the two.

A cafe, plant shop and gallery rolled into one, Circle is a haven of greenery, caffeine and creativity. It's likely you'll pop in for a flat white and leave with your coffee, a bag of treasures from local makers and a new Monstera for the living room. You can even pick up a Coffee Arabica plant to start growing your own green beans.

TIP TRY A SLICE OF HOMEMADE CAKE OR ORDER A WEDGE OF EXPLODING BAKERY TRAYBAKE

Co-founder Fay Clement worked at Exploding Bakery, one of Devon's first speciality cafes, before setting up Circle in 2021, so a dynamite coffee is guaranteed. As well as a house espresso from Roastworks in Willand, Fay and partner David source beans from other top South West roasteries including Crankhouse and Sweven.

'We pick wild and wonderful guest coffees to offer something that's quite different to our crowd-pleasing house roast,' says Fay.

Established
2021

Key roaster
Roastworks Coffee Co.

Brewing method
Espresso, V60

Machine
Victoria Arduino Eagle One

Grinder
Mahlkonig E65

Opening hours
Mon-Fri
8.30am-4pm
Sat
9am-4pm
Sun
9.30am-3pm

TOPSHAM

22 COW & CACAO CAFE

Darts Farm, Topsham, Devon, EX3 0QH
dartsfarm.co.uk | 01392 878200
f dartsfarm *◎ dartsfarm*

For over two decades, Darts Farm near Topsham has been a destination for foodies in Devon and beyond but, in 2022, it also put a pin in the South West's speciality-coffee map when it opened its own cafe, chocolaterie and gelateria.

In keeping with their homemade ethos (all the chocolate and gelato is made in-house), the team recently started roasting speciality-grade coffee in the very roaster they use to craft their range of artisan bean-to-bar chocolate. The new own-roasted single-origin beans are supplemented by top-notch guest roasts from local indies such as EXE, Roastworks and Wogan.

TIP BALANCED BRUNCH OPTIONS INCLUDE AÇAÍ BOWLS, BAKED EGGS AND BANANA BREAD

Sample the coffee in a range of espresso drinks or, for the ultimate indulgence, order an affogato of silky homemade vanilla gelato showered in crema-rich espresso. Push the boat out entirely with a hot choc crafted from Cow & Cacao's own-roasted 40 per cent milk chocolate.

The accompanying edibles are equally unctuous. Feast on waffles piled with seasonal toppings, toasted gelato-stuffed croissants or sourdough pizza cooked over flame in the wood-fired oven.

Established
2022

Key roaster
Cow & Cacao

Brewing method
Espresso

Machine
La Marzocco
Linea PB

Grinder
Mahlkonig E65

Opening hours
Mon-Sat
9am-5.30pm
Sun
9.30am-4pm

23 THIS MUST BE THE PLACE

North Devon

f *thismustbetheplacecoffee* *thismustbethe.place_*

In 1983, Talking Heads sang: 'Home is where I want to be but I guess I'm already there' on their track *This Must Be the Place*. The song was the inspo for this mobile speciality coffee shop and how the team hope their customers feel on discovering TMBTP at events, markets and festivals across North Devon.

TIP BOOK THIS MUST BE THE PLACE FOR YOUR PRIVATE EVENT IN NORTH DEVON OR BEYOND

Molly Hutchings purchased the horsebox in 2022 and lovingly converted it into this brew bar on wheels, which serves quality espresso drinks, cakes and pastries.

She stocks the hoppers with beans from Devon's Roastworks and has plumped for its The Truth blend (Brazil and Peru) and Sugarcane Decaf (Colombia) as the house specials. Seasonal drinks keep the offering fresh, such as the maple and pecan latte (double-shot latte with spiced maple syrup, topped with cream and pecans) which provides an extra dose of cosiness during the chilly months.

Molly is keen to do all she can to support other local indies, whether that's through organising joint events or stocking their products. Recent collaborations include using milk from Bideford's Webbery Moos and roping in Barnstaple's Baked Well at Home to provide sweet bites.

Established
2022

Key roaster
Roastworks
Coffee Co.

Brewing method
Espresso

Machine
Fracino Contempo
Electronic Dual Fuel

Grinder
HeyCafé HC-600

Opening hours
Local events
and festivals
(seasonal opening hours)

NORTH DEVON

24 SUNSHINE AND SNOW

40 Mill Street, Bideford, Devon, EX39 2JW
sunshineandsnowshop.com | 01237 459110
f sunshineandsnow *◎ sunshineandsnowshop*

With its canary-yellow alfresco furniture, bright blue door and multicoloured shopfront, this coffee bar, lifestyle store and events space on Bideford's Mill Street is impossible to miss.

Sunshine and Snow's vibrant exterior mirrors the fun community vibe within. Take a seat in the cafe space and you'll be surrounded by friends grabbing a coffee after their yoga class in the studio upstairs, creative types browsing the curated homewares and books in the lifestyle store, and locals who've popped in to enjoy a speciality brew from a sunny window seat. There's also a beautifully curated clothing section.

TIP CHECK OUT BROTHER BRAND IAN SNOW, WHICH SELLS EXQUISITE FURNITURE ONLINE

Cornish roastery Origin provides a clean and contemporary blend to match this cool environment. It's served alongside traybakes and brownies from Exploding Bakery, which rustles up a seasonal selection of toothsome bites that pair perfectly with coffee.

Founder India Snow plans to offer evening small plates and natural wine soon, further broadening this multifaceted venue's allure.

Established
2021

Key roaster
Origin Coffee
Roasters

Brewing method
Espresso, V60, drip

Machine
La Marzocco
Linea PB

Grinder
Victoria Arduino
Mythos One

Opening hours
Mon-Sat
9.30am-5pm

25 THE FEEL GOOD LARDER

7 Bridge Buildings, Boutport Street, Barnstaple, Devon, EX32 8LW
thefeelgoodlarder.co.uk | 07789 865107
f thefeelgoodlarder *@ thefeelgoodlarder*

Healthy, quick and genuinely appealing food is often difficult to come by when you're ravenous and in a rush. Feel Good owners Sam and Stu Walker knew that feeling well and, uninspired by their local options and with bags of hospitality experience, the conscious foodies decided to establish their own health-focused cafe to nourish the time-poor of Barnstaple.

Every last crumb at The Feel Good Larder is gluten-free and made in-house by Stu and Sam. The menu headliner is the daily salad plates, which are dictated by the vibrant fruit and veg that arrives in the local produce box each morning. Other offerings include frittatas, loaded banana bread and warm cheese scones served with cheddar and Hogs Bottom chutney.

TIP DON'T MISS THE SEASONAL SUPPER CLUBS – TICKETS DON'T HANG AROUND

Traffic-light lattes (beetroot, turmeric and matcha) provide further nourishment for visitors – or stick to the organic house espresso from Bristol pioneer Extract. Its Honduran-Peruvian blend delivers a rich, chocolatey coffee that tastes great with both dairy and alt milks. Pair your brew with a naturally sweetened slice of cake (try the cacao and beetroot loaf) to highlight the coffee's caramel characteristics.

Established
2022

Key roaster
Extract Coffee
Roasters

Brewing method
Espresso,
batch filter

Machine
La Marzocco
Linea Classic S

Grinder
Mahlkonig
E80S GbW

Opening hours
Tue-Sat
8am-3pm

BARNSTAPLE

26 BEATSWORKIN

9 Queen House, Queen Street, Barnstaple, Devon, EX32 8HJ

beatsworkin.net | 01271 321111

f beatsworkinuk *⊙ beatsworkin*

This north Devon stalwart was doing the multifunctional thing way before the trend went mainstream. A skate shop, clothing store and coffee house rolled into one, Beatsworkin curates the interests of founder Glenn Field – and its customers – under one roof.

It's almost impossible to miss this Queen Street hangout: just look for the wood-clad shopfront and window revealing a wall bedecked with eye-catching skateboards. Browse the array of decks, caps and streetwear before taking a break to enjoy a cup of organic Beanberry coffee.

TIP CHECK OUT THE NEW BEATSWORKIN ONLINE SHOP AND ORDER SKATE KIT AND GARMS TO YOUR DOOR

The small-batch beans are roasted in Surrey and then prepped as espresso by Glenn. Order your coffee to-go or grab a seat outside under the covered shopfront and watch the world go by. Those interested in coffee kit should check out the Sanremo machine that's been fitted with custom portafilter handles crafted from an old skateboard.

Established
2015

Key roaster
Beanberry Coffee Company

Brewing method
Espresso

Machine
Sanremo

Grinder
Mahlkonig K30 Air

Opening hours
Wed-Sat
10am-7pm

27 51 DEGREES NORTH COFFEE CO.

Unit 7-9 Velator Way, Braunton, Devon, EX33 2FB

51degreesnorthcoffee.com | 07403 944544

f 51degreesnorthcoffee **◎** 51degreesnorthcoffee

It's probably a safe bet to assume that 51 Degrees founder Justin Duerden was the kind of kid who couldn't sit still. Since he started serving speciality brews from a solar-assisted cart in 2017, he's been enthusiastically spreading the word about good coffee throughout north Devon and developing a mini caffeine empire.

This coffee shop in Braunton opened at the height of the pandemic and served as a neighbourhood hub where locals could pick up delicious brews and see a friendly face. It's still a pillar of the community, where Justin now roasts a selection of high-grade beans for coffee shop customers and local retailers.

TIP TOO HOT FOR STEAMED MILK? TRY ONE OF THE JAPANESE-STYLE ICED COFFEES

Single origins from the 51 Degrees roastery are served alongside coffees from the likes of Origin, Round Hill, Coffee Factory and Girls Who Grind. There are usually at least two options to choose from: a more traditional roast and something a little funkier – the baristas will suggest the best serve style to suit.

If you're planning on ordering your coffee to-go, don't forget to pack a reusable as the cafe has recently ditched single-use takeaway cups.

Established
2020

Key roaster
Multiple roasteries

Brewing method
Espresso, V60, AeroPress, batch filter, cold brew

Machine
La Marzocco

Grinder
Mazzer Major, Anfim SCODY II, Mahlkonig K30

Opening hours
Mon-Fri
7am-5pm
Sat
8.30am-5pm
Sun
9.30am-5pm

BRAUNTON

28 THE WORX BRAUNTON

8 The Square, Braunton, Devon, EX33 2JD

theworxbraunton.co.uk | 01271 813897

f theworxbraunton *@ theworxbraunton*

Holidaymakers heading to north Devon for a dose of sun, sea and surf can rest assured their caffeine needs will be expertly covered at this coffee house, kitchen and bar.

Located in Braunton, a buzzy village a stone's throw from the area's best beaches, The Worx focuses on doing simple things well. The coffee menu centres around espresso and the team use Exe Coffee Roasters' Neighbourhood blend to create smooth, cocoa-rich flat whites, lattes and americanos.

TIP LOOK OUT FOR SEASONAL SPECIALS SUCH AS PUMPKIN-SPICE LATTES

The food offering is equally uncomplicated. For morning visitors, there's an enticing line-up of cafe classics, from American-style pancakes with bacon and maple syrup to eggy bread with berries. At lunchtime, a menu of signature sandwiches, toasties and sharing plates has broad appeal.

On sunny days, enjoy your coffee in the private walled courtyard. If it's past noon you can pimp your order with a cocktail or lace a Worx hot chocolate with Baileys or Disaronno.

Established
2019

Key roaster
Exe Coffee Roasters

Brewing method
Espresso

Machine
La Spaziale S5

Grinder
Mahlkonig E65S

Opening hours
Mon-Fri
8.45am-4pm
Sat
9am-4pm
Sun
10am-2pm

There's even more to life than good coffee

Food Lifestyle magazine is your seasonal guide to special and off-the-beaten-track places to stay, dine, shop and visit in the South West

Subscribe to the quarterly magazine or read online at food-mag.co.uk

29 MERAKI COFFEE CO.

12 South Street, Woolacombe, Devon, EX34 7BB

07411 205222

f *merakicoffeeco* **○** *merakicoffeecompany*

Consistency is king at this coastal coffee shop. No matter how far the queue snakes down the street in summer, or how chilled the pace in winter, its espresso is always on-point.

Located a few hundred metres from Woolacombe Beach, Meraki is a busy hive of activity when the sun's shining. Surfers prop their boards against the whitewashed exterior while they sip a flat white, walkers grab a seat to refuel with brekkie sourdough rolls or stuffed croissants after a stomp through the dunes, and locals drop in to buy locally grown flowers.

TIP TRY ONE OF THE BEAUTIFULLY ARRANGED GRANOLA OR BIRCHER BREAKFAST BOWLS

In the colder months, the cafe becomes a cosy hub as the log burner roars to life and refreshing summer drinks are replaced with seasonal lattes and hot chocolates. These quieter days also free up the baristas to talk regulars through the latest guest roasts and recommend their favourites from a collection of homemade cakes that line the counter.

Established
2018

Key roaster
The Devon
Coffee Company

Brewing method
Espresso

Machine
Barista Attitude
Tempesta

Grinder
Mahlkonig
E80 GbW,
Mahlkonig
E65S GbW,
Anfim Pratica

Opening hours
Mon–Sun
8am–4pm

WOOLACOMBE

DEVON
ROASTERIES

30 THE DEVON COFFEE COMPANY

195 Faraday Mill, Plymouth, Devon, PL4 0ST

devoncoffeecompany.com | 01752 222567

f devoncoffeecompany | *devoncoffeecompany*

Over the past year, the team at Devon Coffee Company have taken a huge stride towards fulfilling their sustainability pledges by committing to roasting only organic-certified beans. This, coupled with the roastery's continued support of causes such as Food 4 Farmers through its 1% for the Planet membership, demonstrates their commitment to environmental protection and sustainable sourcing.

'TASTE OF THE WEST AWARD-WINNING BLENDS THE AMERICAS, SUPER EIGHT AND GUMDROP ARE ALL CERTIFIED ORGANIC'

Two current coffee highlights are Chelbesa from Ethiopia, a fruit bomb that sees cherries placed on drying beds for up to 35 days to deliver a sweet, floral coffee; and Sierra Nevada, sourced from Colombian agro-ecological producers who are helping reclaim social, economic and cultural rights for their communities.

Taste of the West award-winning espresso blends The Americas, Super Eight and Gumdrop have all recently been certified organic. Packaged in fully compostable pouches (including the labels), these delicious coffees are delivered to local indie businesses by the roastery's fleet of electric vehicles.

Established
2011

Roaster make and size
BESCA 15kg

PLYMOUTH

64

3I VOYAGER COFFEE

Unit 6 Mardle Way Business Park, Buckfastleigh, Devon, TQ11 0JL

voyagercoffee.co.uk | 01364 644440

f *voyagercoffeeroasters* **@** *voyagercoffee*

From its days as a one-man startup to the thriving coffee business it's become, Voyager has always taken inspiration from its surrounding wild Dartmoor landscape. In order to look after the environment beyond the immediate vicinity, the Voyager team are on a mission to achieve peak sustainability. Coffee is sourced from small farms and importers, packaging is compostable and a zero-landfill policy is firmly observed. The roastery also recently became a partner in Buckfastleigh's social supermarket by making surplus beans available to locals at an affordable price.

Established
2015

Roaster make and size
Genio 30kg, Genio 15kg

'NEW AND EXCITING SINGLE ORIGINS SOURCED FROM BRAZIL TO UGANDA'

Coffees are hand roasted in small batches to guarantee quality, and the carefully curated collection of beans is supplemented regularly by new and exciting single origins sourced from Brazil to Uganda.

Home brewers should check out the new Roasters' Choice subscription for high-quality, sustainably sourced single origins from the award-winning roastery. Voyager boasts Great Taste and Food Drink Devon awards, including golds for two of its blends, the training facilities and sustainability.

BUCKFASTLEIGH

32 CRANKHOUSE COFFEE

Basement, 130 Fore Street, Exeter, Devon, EX4 3JQ

crankhousecoffee.co.uk | 07588 020288

f *crankhousecoffee* ⊙ *crankhouseroast*

Committed to the craft and science of speciality since 2014, Crankhouse founder Dave Stanton loves delving into the geekiest realms of coffee and recently completed a post-grad qualification on the subject through Zurich University.

Inspired by the roastery-cafes he visited while living in Australia, he came home keen to replicate that experience in the South West. The first incarnation of this saw him roasting in a small garage in Exeter, followed by a move to a converted barn on the edge of Dartmoor. Then, in 2019, he moved the operation to a roomy site in Exeter's West Quarter which has both a roastery and cafe on-site.

'CRANKHOUSE'S OMNI-ROAST STYLE KEEPS THE OPTIONS OPEN'

Dave buys beans in small quantities to keep his offer intriguing, so those looking for rare and interesting single origins or easygoing all-rounders will find something to suit. Crankhouse's omni-roast style keeps the brew-method options open for pros and home set-ups too.

The roastery recently became a Rocket Espresso Experience Centre and has a range of the beautiful machines in its training space. Those keen to up their home espresso game can get in touch to arrange a demo.

Established
2014

Roaster make and size
Loring S15 Falcon 15kg,
IKAWA Pro V2

33 ROASTWORKS COFFEE CO.

Unit 7 Blackdown Park, South View Estate, Willand, Cullompton, Devon, EX15 2FS

roastworks.co.uk | 01884 829400

f *roastworkscoffeeco* ⓞ *roastworks_coffee_co*

This Devon roastery is a great success story that's brought speciality coffee to the masses – without compromising on quality or equality. Roastworks beans can be found in 237 Waitrose stores across the UK, as well as at some of the best coffee shops in the country, yet the team's promise to pay farmers a fair price remains unbroken.

'We believe in nurturing longstanding relationships with our producers and working with them through thick and thin,' says founder Will Little. This supportive relationship means if a farm's crop suffers because of adverse weather, Will and team aren't going to leave the farmers high, dry and out of pocket.

'A SUCCESS STORY THAT'S BROUGHT SPECIALITY COFFEE TO THE MASSES'

Part of the brand's broad appeal – beyond the outstanding quality of its coffee – is its simple categorisation, which ditches the jargon and makes buying coffee online a breeze. Three tiers (Classic, Curious and Contemporary) enable customers to find seasonal beans based on their preferences. Those who like to geek out over funky processes and far-out flavour profiles should head to the single-origin section of the shop to discover the roasters' latest finds and experiments.

Established
2014

Roaster make and size
G.W. Barth Menado 60kg,
Probat LG 12kg

34 51 DEGREES NORTH COFFEE CO.

Unit 1 Compass House, Velator, Braunton, Devon, EX33 2DX

51degreesnorthcoffee.com | 07403 944544

f *51degreesnorthcoffee* ⊚ *51degreesnorthcoffee*

The name of this north Devon roastery refers to the coordinates of a point along the River Torridge where, in 2017, founder Justin Duerden decided to turn his interest in coffee into a career.

First came a solar-assisted coffee van which he pitched up at various spots in the area to serve top-notch espresso. Then in 2020, after becoming a stalwart of the local community, Justin opened his first bricks-and-mortar coffee shop in Braunton.

'EACH COFFEE HAS ITS OWN CHARACTER'

After building the business and its reputation, the natural next step was to start roasting. In 2022, the 51 Degrees roastery was established and the first yields from the fully electric Toper roaster shared with the coffee van and shop's loyal customers.

The focus of this small-batch roastery is single-origin coffee – Justin prefers not to blend because *'each coffee has its own character'*. Most of the beans are sourced from Africa, although a collaboration with Karst Organics has introduced a series of washed Timorese beans. Expect fruity, funky and complex coffees, best served black and savoured slowly. Be among the first to try the latest releases at one of the community coffee-tasting events.

Established
2022

Roaster make and size
Toper 2kg,
Kaleido Sniper M6
Dual System 600g

BRAUNTON

MORE GOOD FINDS IN DEVON

COFFEE SHOPS

ANNIE AND THE FLINT
126 High Street, Ilfracombe,
Devon, EX34 9EY
annieandtheflint.co.uk

BLOCK - BARNSTAPLE
12-14 Butchers Row, Barnstaple,
Devon, EX31 1BW
eatatblock.com

CAFE CROYDE BAY
Baggy Lodge, Moor Lane, Croyde,
Devon, EX33 1PA
cafecroydebay.co.uk

HEARTBREAK HOTEL COFFEE
Unit 4 West Cross, Caen Street,
Braunton, Devon, EX33 1AQ
heartbreakhotelcoffee.com

THE DEVON COFFEE TRAVELLER
The Old Manor, Old Torquay Road, Preston,
Paignton, Devon, TQ3 2QZ

THE EXPLODING BAKERY
1-2 The Crescent, Queen Street,
Exeter, Devon, EX4 3SB
explodingbakery.com

VEG BOX
7 Piazza Terracina, Haven Road,
Exeter, Devon, EX2 8GT
vegboxcafe.com

BATH & SOMERSET
COFFEE SHOPS

⊗ CAFES

⊗ ROASTERIES

Find more good coffee shops
and roasteries on page 85.

*All locations are approximate

SOMERSET

BATH

41
40
39

42

Frome

37
38

36

Glastonbury

TAUNTON

35

Yeovil

35 FINCA – YEOVIL

11 High Street, Yeovil, Somerset, BA20 1RG

fincacoffee.co.uk | 01305 300400

f *fincayeovil* 🅞 *scouting4coffee*

This Yeovil site opened in 2016, following the success of Finca's flagship Dorchester cafe-roastery. It's strikingly similar to the original, with a wood-clad exterior, bi-fold windows and buckets of rustic charm.

Not long after launching this second venue, the founders got the keys to a dedicated roastery space from which to craft an expanded selection of single origins for the cafes. From those early days, the indie brand has gone from strength to strength and now includes six cafes and a roastery producing more than 40 coffees each year.

TIP IN SUMMER, GRAB A SEAT AT ONE OF THE ALFRESCO BIERKELLER TABLES

Pay a visit to this High Street venue to try the latest roasts as espresso, and then pick up a bag of beans to experiment with at home. The team prefer a single-origin approach so you'll find an array of countries on offer – mostly Latin American and African.

A counter crowded with decadent brownies, golden pastel de nata, springy banana bread and more from the Finca bakery in Poundbury tempts visitors to indulge. The fruit-studded tiffin is a particularly tasty match for the choc-nut-forward Latin American espresso.

Established
2016

Key roaster
Finca Coffee Roasters

Brewing method
Espresso

Machine
La Marzocco

Grinder
Eureka Olympus

Opening hours
Mon–Sat
8am–5.30pm
Sun
10am–3pm

YEOVIL

36 FINCA - GLASTONBURY

14 Market Place, Glastonbury, Somerset, BA6 9HJ

fincacoffee.co.uk | 01305 300400

f *fincaglastonbury* **◎** *scouting4coffee*

The latest addition to Finca's growing family of speciality coffee shops across Somerset and Dorset, this Glastonbury baby was born in spring 2024.

The Finca crew have secured a fantastic corner spot, with floor-to-ceiling windows, on the town's bustling Market Place. Like its siblings, it focuses on serving a rolling selection of single-origin coffees which have been roasted at the Finca HQ in Dorchester.

Curious caffeine fans will love the constantly shifting menu. The Finca roasters like to mix things up and experiment with different processes and origins; in 2023 they roasted 40 different coffees for their cafes and legion of online customers. Choose between three espresso options: a nutty Latin American, a fruity African and a single-origin decaf.

TIP THE ROASTERS ARE ALWAYS WORKING ON SOMETHING NEW; ASK THE BARISTAS FOR THEIR RECS

The homemade theme continues with the food offering as all pastries and cakes are crafted each morning at the Finca bakery in Poundbury. Drool over a counter brimming with the likes of oaty traybakes, springy cinnamon buns and soft banana bread – the challenge is choosing just one.

Established
2024

Key roaster
Finca Coffee Roasters

Brewing method
Espresso

Machine
La Marzocco

Grinder
Eureka Olympus

Opening hours
Mon-Sat
8am-5pm
Sun
10am-3pm

37 MOO AND TWO

27 Catherine Hill, Frome, Somerset, BA11 1BY

mooandtwo.com | 07816 311452

@ *mooandtwo*

Cobbled Catherine Hill is a hive of indie activity in the Somerset town of Frome. Halfway up, sandwiched between vintage, houseplant and local makers' shops is Moo and Two, a small but perfectly formed speciality coffee bar and tea emporium.

Spend a morning dipping in and out of the shops before settling in at Moo and Two for a reviving brew. Its Unit Fourteen house espresso is roasted by the team at Round Hill in Radstock and updated quarterly to reflect seasonal harvests. Or try a selection of the roastery's filter coffees, which are prepared as Moccamaster batch, V60, cold brew or AeroPress.

TIP CHECK OUT THE LIVE MUSIC EVENTS, SOME HOSTED IN COLLAB WITH NEIGHBOURS STILL LIFE GIN

Those who appreciate the nuanced notes of speciality teas should explore the collection of loose-leaf blends. Founder Euan Barker sources them directly from growers in South India and blends them in-house. They're also available, alongside a selection of beans from Round Hill, to brew at home.

Take time to imbibe your drink in the cosy confines of the wood-panelled cafe. A record player spinning mostly country music adds to the relaxed charm of this coffee go-to.

Established
2016

Key roaster
Round Hill Roastery

Brewing method
Espresso, V60,
batch filter,
AeroPress,
cold brew

Machine
La Spaziale S9

Grinder
Mahlkonig
E65S GbW,
Victoria Arduino
Mythos One

Opening hours
Mon-Sat
9am-4pm
Sun
9am-1pm

FROME

38 THE RIVER HOUSE

Black Swan Arts, 2 Bridge Street, Frome, Somerset, BA11 1BB

riverhousefrome.co.uk | 07921 852785

𝐟 *theriverhousefrome* 	⃝ *riverhousefrome*

Celebrating its tenth birthday in 2024, this quirky coffee house in the indie-centric Somerset town of Frome prides itself on being an inclusive space where coffee lovers from all walks of life can congregate to enjoy good brews, food and conversation.

The fun, relaxed and shamelessly silly vibe at The River House is contagious. The playlist is never boring, the brunch line-up littered with cheeky puns (get your chops around a Posh Muff or sample the Lovely Baps) and there's a schedule of lively events including drag quiz nights.

TIP PLANT-BASED VISITORS WILL FIND LOTS OF VEGAN OPTIONS ON THE BRUNCH MENU

Fuelling all this madness is own-roasted coffee from sister roastery Loud Mouth. Its cafe customers get first dibs on the latest single origins and blends, which are updated regularly by the experimental roasters. Ask the baristas what's new and for their recommended serve style.

The food offering is refreshed every six months to keep River House's followers on their toes. Expect to chow down on deliciously indulgent dishes such as the Hash Gordon – golden hash browns piled with chorizo, fried eggs and romesco.

Established
2014

Key roaster
Loud Mouth Coffee

Brewing method
Espresso,
cold brew,
batch filter

Machine
Astoria Valina

Grinder
Fiorenzato F64 EVO,
La Cimbali Magnum

Opening hours
Mon-Sat
9am-5pm
Sun
10am-4pm

39 THE COLOMBIAN COMPANY - BATH

6 Abbey Gate Street, Bath, BA1 1NP

thecolombiancompany.com | 07534 391992

f thecolombianco *@ thecolombianco*

Located under a honeyed-stone archway in Bath city centre, this is the OG premises of The Colombian Company, which was founded by Colombian-born Jhampoll Gutierrez Gomez. The venture was inspired by his love for his mother country and an appreciation of its quality coffee, and the result has proved such a hit that Jhampoll now has two coffee shops in Bath and two in Bristol.

The own-roasted house Finca Las Cruces coffee is sourced in micro-lots from a family-run farm in the Risaralda region of Colombia and prepped as espresso, V60 or AeroPress. There's a decent decaf available too.

TIP ON A SUNNY DAY, NAB A TABLE OUTSIDE AND ADMIRE THE VIEWS OF ABBEY GREEN

Commuters make a pre-work pit stop here to pick up their morning caffeine fix and peruse the wooden counter laden with fresh-from-the-oven pastries. Midmorning and lunchtime sippers adopt a more leisurely pace, taking a pew at a window stool or at one of the outside tables where they can watch the world go by while gorging on springy sourdough toasties.

With walls and countertops decked in natural wood, luscious green plants hanging from the ceiling and chilled Colombian beats on the stereo, this is a welcome sanctuary away from the city buzz.

Established
2017

Key roaster
The Colombian Company

Brewing method
Espresso, V60, AeroPress

Machine
La Marzocco Linea Classic S

Grinder
Compak E10

Opening hours
Mon–Fri
8am–5pm
Sat
8am–5.30pm
Sun
9am–5pm

40 COLONNA & SMALL'S

6 Chapel Row, Bath, BA1 1HN
colonnacoffee.com | 07766 808067
⊙ *colonnacoffee*

This multi-award-winning coffee shop should be on everyone's bucket list – whether they're into speciality or not. For devout coffee followers it's a mecca of rare and interesting beans, while for the uninitiated it's an opportunity to get closer to understanding the art and science of the speciality movement.

When three-time UK Barista Champion Maxwell Colonna-Dashwood opened Colonna & Small's in 2009, it was one of the first venues in the South West to serve high-scoring coffee roasted by independent roasteries. In the years that have followed, the shop has come to represent cutting-edge innovation.

TIP ORDER COLONNA COFFEES – INCLUDING SPECIALITY-GRADE PODS – FOR HOME DELIVERY

Alongside the list of house-roasted Colonna single origins is a freezer menu of limited and highly sought-after coffees. Beans from the world's best producers are sourced in ultra-small batches, then weighed and frozen, ready to be ground to order and prepared as either espresso, AeroPress or low-pressure lungo (somewhere between an espresso and filter).

'We're often described as more of a customer experience centre rather than a coffee shop,' says Maxwell. *'We've tailored it to showcase the complexity and intrigue of speciality coffee.'*

Established
2009

Key roaster
Colonna Coffee

Brewing method
Espresso,
AeroPress, lungo

Machine
Modbar

Grinder
Mahlkonig EK43

Opening hours
Mon-Fri
8.30am-5.30pm
Sat
9am-5.30pm
Sun
10am-4pm

TO MAKE THE BEST COFFEE, YOU HAVE TO BUY THE BEST COFFEE.

ROASTWORKS®

COFFEE C° LTD

HEAD OVER TO OUR WEBSITE
TO FIND OUT MORE:

ROASTWORKS.CO.UK

41 PICNIC COFFEE

9 Saracen Street, Bath, BA1 5BR
picniccoffee.co.uk | 01225 330128
f *picniccoffee* **◎** *picnic_bath*

In 2023, to celebrate its tenth birthday, Picnic Coffee collaborated with PLOT Roasting to create a limited-edition release of its Virunga house espresso. The beans, which are sourced from the Virunga National Park in DRC, not only taste great but also support the local economy at origin – including rangers who look after the mountain gorillas that call the park home.

Since being established in 2013, Picnic has been a central part of the Bath coffee community and ridden the wave of speciality trends and developments. Founder Tim Starks has always been keen to keep the coffee menu at the innovative end of the scale and recently started experimenting with roasting in-house.

TIP PICK UP ONE OF THE NEW PICNIC BRANDED CHILLY'S REUSABLES FOR YOUR FLATTIE TO-GO

The own-brand coffee is available to sample in a plethora of brew methods, alongside guest roasts from the likes of Skylark, Assembly, Red Bank and Yallah. If you want an in-depth intro to the new house beans, tag along to one of the regular public cupping sessions at the cafe. Ask a barista or check socials for the latest line-up of events.

Established
2013

Key roaster
PLOT Roasting

Brewing method
Espresso, V60, AeroPress

Machine
Victoria Arduino Eagle One

Grinder
Mahlkonig E65S GbW, Mahlkonig EK43 S

Opening hours
Mon-Fri
8am-4.30pm
Sat
8.30am-5pm
Sun
9am-4pm

BATH & SOMERSET
ROASTERIES

42 LOUD MOUTH COFFEE ROASTERS

Unit J3 Jenson Court, Frome Commerce Park, Frome, Somerset, BA11 2FQ

loudmouthcoffee.com

f *loudmouthcoffee* © *loudmouthcoffee*

If it's character you're after, you'll find it at Loud Mouth Coffee. The team promise to provide 'proper belter coffee without the nobby nonsense'.

The gang strive to make coffee accessible and affordable for both die-hard coffee fans and speciality freshers by cutting out the scary jargon and keeping things fun. The feelgood coffee is created with a conscience: Loud Mouth's owners are passionate about mental health and support counselling and talking-therapy charities, which empower people to speak about their experiences and challenges. As they like to say: 'Drink it Loud, say it proud.'

'FEELGOOD COFFEE CREATED WITH A CONSCIENCE'

The roastery is an offshoot of partner cafe The River House and provides caffeinated excellence from a variety of origins including Peru, Burundi and Timor-Leste. The team work with Falcon to source impeccable beans as well as buying direct from farms with which they've formed long-lasting partnerships.

New for 2024 is a training academy delivering SCA-accredited courses, barista training, cupping workshops and roastery tours.

Established
2018

Roaster make and size
BESCA BSC-05 5kg, Toper 3kg

MORE GOOD FINDS IN BATH & SOMERSET

COFFEE SHOPS

BLOCK - TAUNTON
4-6 Magdalene Lane,
Taunton, Somerset, TA1 1SE
eatatblock.com

BRAZIER COFFEE ROASTERS
Unit 10-11 Tonedale Mill
Business Park, Wellington,
Somerset, TA21 0AW
braziercoffeeroasters.co.uk

CASSIA
Unit 1 Sovereign Point,
Bath, BA2 3GJ
cassiacollective.co.uk

CRUMBS OF KEYNSHAM
10 High Street, Keynsham,
Somerset, BS31 1DQ
crumbs.company.site

NOOK - BATH
12a Old Bond Street,
Bath, BA1 1BP
nooktheshop.co.uk

NOOK - FROME
14 King Street, Frome,
Somerset, BA1 1BH
nooktheshop.co.uk

STRANGERS WITH COFFEE
31 St Cuthbert Street, Wells,
Somerset, BA5 2AW

THE COLOMBIAN COMPANY - WIDCOMBE, BATH
9a Claverton Buildings,
Widcombe, Bath, BA2 4LP
thecolombiancompany.com

FORUM COFFEE HOUSE
3-5 Forum Buildings,
St James Parade,
Bath, BA1 1UG
forumcoffeehouse.com

ROASTERIES

BRAZIER COFFEE ROASTERS
Unit 10-11 Tonedale Mill Business Park,
Wellington, Somerset, TA21 0AW
braziercoffeeroasters.co.uk

BRISTOL
COFFEE SHOPS

✖ CAFES

✖ ROASTERIES

Find more good coffee shops
and roasteries on pages 116-117.

All locations are approximate

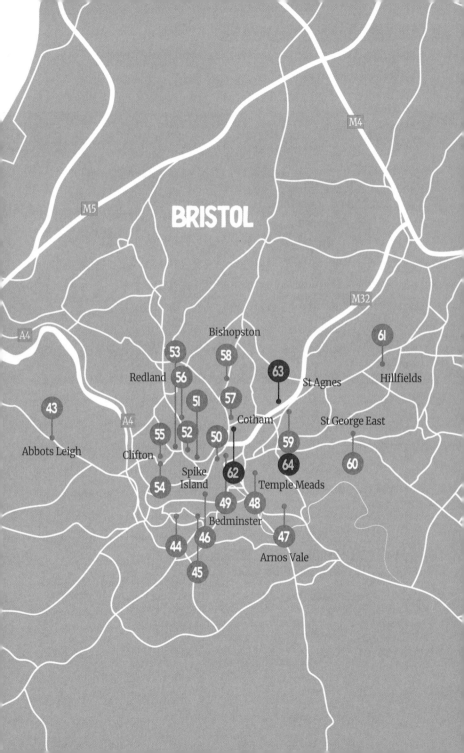

BRISTOL

M4

M5

M32

A4

Bishopston

53

58

63

61

Redland

56

St Agnes

Hillfields

51

57

43

52

50

Cotham

St George East

Abbots Leigh

55

59

A4

Clifton

54

Spike
Island

62

64

60

Temple Meads

49

48

Bedminster

44

46

47

45

Arnos Vale

43 THE BIKE SHED CAFE

1 Manor Road, Abbots Leigh, Somerset, BS8 3RP

bikeshed.cafe | 07437 211655

thebikeshedcafe

Sharing space with the 17th-century George Inn, The Bike Shed Cafe is a hidden gem that's cosy in winter – thanks to its woodburner – yet rocks a beer-garden vibe in summer.

As its name suggests, this drive-by serves a large local cycling community, although walkers and runners are just as drawn to its top-quality caffeine output.

Bristol roastery Extract is the main supplier of Bike Shed coffee and keeps the hoppers topped up with its single-origin Cast Iron beans (named after the roastery's reclaimed and restored vintage roasters). Guest roasts are supplied by London roastery Union.

TIP VISIT ON A FRIDAY FOR DELECTABLE DOUGHNUTS FROM SWINDON INDIE, PIPPIN & CO

Refuelling cycle tours and runs requires decent fare and the team at this Somerset cafe have it covered. House faves include a bacon and avocado roll with chilli oil and fresh lime, and the current bestseller: the fish-finger doorstep sarnie. The savouries may be hearty but save a little room to sample the quality bakes and cakes from the ever-changing counter – you can work it off later.

Established
2021

Key roaster
Extract Coffee Roasters

Brewing method
Espresso, batch filter

Machine
La Marzocco Linea PB

Grinder
Compak F8

Opening hours
Mon-Tue
8am-3.30pm
Wed-Sat
8am-4pm
Sun
9am-4pm

ABBOTS LEIGH

44 TINCAN COFFEE CO - BEDMINSTER

234 North Street, Bedminster, Bristol, BS3 1JD
tincancoffee.co.uk | 01179 633979
f *tincancoffeeco* ⊙ *tincancoffeeco*

Community has always been at the heart of this North Street venue so, when the vibe went slightly off kilter in 2023, the team were keen to get it back on track. They decided to free the cafe's big communal tables of laptops (they're still welcome on the smaller tables), and within days the chatting and socialising recommenced.

And there's plenty to talk about here. Whether it's striking up a conversation about the house coffee (a Brazilian single origin with notes of chocolate, hazelnut and honey) from local roastery Triple Co or asking for recommendations on the day's brunch bill (chorizo huevos rancheros or vegetable bruschetta are good calls), table neighbours often start nattering with each other.

TIP ORDER BRUNCH OR LUNCH TO-GO FROM THE LOADED MAIN MENU

The baristas are equally friendly and enthusiastic. Ask them for the low-down on the latest guest coffee available as espresso or batch — it's usually something on the fruitier side to contrast with the nutty notes of the house espresso.

Established
2016

Key roaster
Triple Co Roast

Brewing method
Espresso,
batch filter

Machine
La Marzocco
Linea PB

Grinder
Mahlkonig E80 GbW

Opening hours
Mon-Fri
8am-5pm
Sat-Sun
9am-5pm

45 NOOK

24 North Street, Bedminster, Bristol, BS3 1HW
nooktheshop.co.uk | 01174 621683

f nooktheshop *ⓘ nooktheshop*

Inspired by the laid-back coffee culture of east-coast Australia, Nook is a shot of sunny Byron Bay in the heart of Bedminster. While travelling in 2018, founder Millie couldn't get enough of the speciality coffee, healthy food and chilled vibe of Australia's coastal cafes and, on returning home to Frome, decided to recreate the experience in the Somerset town.

Nook's colourful açaí bowls, superfood smoothies and vibrant poke salads were such a hit that in 2021 Millie launched a second shop in Bath, which was followed in 2023 by this Bristol outpost. Hampshire-roasted River Coffee provides the house espresso at all three cafes and is the perfect base for a killer oat flat white. Other UK roasteries fill a monthly guest filter spot, and homemade cold-pressed juices offer caffeine-free refreshment.

TIP TRY THE CACAO AÇAÍ BOWL, OR THE "CRACK BOWL" AS IT'S KNOWN BY REGULARS

Millie and team are determined to change the fast-food scene by producing healthy and delicious gluten-free takeaway dishes (made using seasonal ingredients) which are ready in a matter of minutes. For brekkie, try the toasted banana bread with coconut yogurt, blueberry compote, maple syrup, banana and toasted almonds – one of the many vegan options. At lunch, dive into a bowl of bang bang chicken with broccoli, sweetcorn salsa, rainbow slaw and pickled red onions.

Established
2023

Key roaster
River Coffee

Brewing method
Espresso,
batch filter

Machine
Expobar Crem EX3

Grinder
HeyCafé HC-600

Opening hours
Tue–Sun
8am–4pm

46 LITTLE VICTORIES

7 Gaol Ferry Steps, Wapping Wharf, Bristol, BS1 6WE
littlevics.co.uk

 littlevicsbris

Some of Bristol's best food and drink can be found at Wapping Wharf, and nestled among the indie restaurants is this contemporary coffee bar serving a selection of the city's best beans.

Little Victories is the younger sibling of Small Street Espresso (one of Bristol's first speciality coffee shops) and big brother to Small Goods which deals in artisan doughnuts and caffeine and is situated a stone's throw from Temple Meads station. Each venue has its own individual character, and this harbourside outpost enjoys bags of natural light thanks to its towering glass windows.

TIP VISIT AFTER DARK FOR CRAFT BEER AND ESPRESSO MARTINIS

The house espresso is roasted in the city by Bristol pioneer Clifton Coffee, while the rotating guest filter spot showcases roasteries from further afield such as Hard Lines, Crankhouse, River and Moon Roast. For pourover the team use a Hario Switch, and, in warmer weather, craft cold-brew drip for refreshing summer pours.

Small Goods doughnuts are available on Wednesdays and Fridays and include creative flavour combos such as chocolate Guinness cake, raspberry lemonade and vietnamese iced coffee.

Established
2016

Key roaster
Clifton Coffee
Roasters

Brewing method
Espresso, V60,
cold brew, pourover

Machine
Victoria Arduino
Black Eagle

Grinder
Mahlkonig E65S × 3,
Mahlkonig EK43

Opening hours
Mon-Thu
8am-5pm
Fri
8am-11pm
Sat
9am-11pm
Sun
9am-5pm

47 COFFEE CLUB

The Airstreams, Central Road, Paintworks, Bath Road, Bristol, BS4 3EH

07584 038067

☉ *coffeeclubpaintworks*

If you like your coffee with a dose of quirk, make a beeline for the converted Airstreams at Bristol's Paintworks. Coffee Club's South Carolina campers have been fitted out as lively mobile cafes that serve coffee with a vinyl soundtrack. That's in the daytime; come night they're a hub for super-intimate gigs and monthly socials. It's a winning combo that's been drawing the community together since May 2023.

Coffee Club is part of a growing enterprise and there's a sister cafe on Bristol Marina, which opened in 2020. The two unite in one goal: to provide an excellent coffee experience in a relaxed environment by working with local, like-minded suppliers.

TIP JOIN THE CLUB! MEMBERSHIP EQUALS PURSE-PLEASING DISCOUNTS

The Club's house blend is Rocket Espresso from Bristol's Extract Coffee Roasters. It's supplemented by guest filters from local indies such as Radical, whose lush light-medium roast from Ethiopia features notes of black tea, peach and elderflower. The coffees are best paired with vegan pastries from The Forest Bakery.

Being a music lover is part of the job description for the friendly baristas who are always happy to chat about what's on the decks.

Established
2020

Key roaster
Extract Coffee
Roasters

Brewing method
Espresso,
batch filter

Machine
Sanremo Zoe

Grinder
Sanremo SR70

Opening hours
Mon–Fri
8am–3pm

48 SMALL GOODS

Unit 3, 2 Glass Wharf, Temple Quay, Bristol, BS2 0EL

smallgoods.co.uk

smallgoodsbristol

You don't need science to tell you that coffee tastes better with a doughnut on the side, but if you want to test the hypothesis a trip to this Bristol bakery and coffee shop is the perfect place to do it.

Each morning, the Small Goods bakers craft row after row of springy doughnuts stuffed with homemade fillings. And, as if the house classics (raspberry jam, vanilla custard and dark chocolate) weren't tempting enough, each week brings a new tray of creative seasonal specials (including a vegan option) such as sticky toffee pudding, coconut macaroon and matcha with white chocolate and blueberries.

TIP ORDER CLICK-AND-COLLECT DOUGHNUTS FOR YOUR NEXT BIRTHDAY BASH

These plump spheres of joy are the perfect accomplice to a smooth Clifton Coffee espresso and elevate the raisin, chocolate and marzipan notes of the bespoke house blend. Alternatively, opt for a cup of juicy batch brew (usually a single origin from the Bristol roastery) alongside your dough for just £5.50 all in.

The bakers are also pretty good at turning out other bread-based delicacies; bag a stuffed focaccia sarnie or glossy brioche bun for lunch.

Established
2021

Key roaster
Clifton Coffee
Roasters

Brewing method
Espresso,
batch filter

Machine
Victoria Arduino
Black Eagle

Grinder
Mahlkonig E65S × 3,
Mahlkonig EK43

Opening hours
Mon-Fri
8am-3pm

49 DARESHACK

Vintry Building, Wine Street, Bristol, BS1 2BD

dareshack.com | 01179 298216

dareshack

Dareshack, meaning literally 'a place for daring', has to be one of Bristol's most enterprising ventures. The coffee shop/studio is on a mission to fuel a creative revolution, one cup at a time, by using a percentage of its coffee sales for creative projects.

At the heart of Dareshack's city-centre building is its industrial-style coffee shop. It also has a studio (for gigs, exhibitions and filming), meeting rooms and a gallery.

TIP CHECK OUT THE NEW SISTER SITE AT 4 CHRISTMAS STEPS, BRISTOL

'No two days are ever the same,' says co-founder Gui Petrini, who set up the company with partner Adda Cohn. *'One day you might find a film crew on-site and the next a band doing a soundcheck for a show in the studio. The space radiates a genuine creative atmosphere and features art exhibitions and installations, which are often open to the public.'*

Alongside the house blend Triple Dare (from Bristol's Triple Co Roast), visitors will find a rotation of guest coffees served as espresso, filter and batch from roasteries such as Manhattan, Assembly and New Ground.

The crew also love to vacuum seal and freeze some of the rarer coffees they've discovered, resulting in a top-shelf library of frozen finds to thrill the fussiest of connoisseurs.

Established
2020

Key roaster
Triple Co Roast

Brewing method
Espresso,
Kalita Wave,
batch filter

Machine
Modbar
Espresso AV

Grinder
Mahlkonig
E80 Supreme,
Mahlkonig E65S,
Mahlkonig EK43

Opening hours
Mon-Fri
7.30am-5.30pm
Sat-Sun
9am-5.30pm

50 SMALL STREET ESPRESSO

23 Small Street, Old City, Bristol, BS1 1DW

smallstreetespresso.co.uk

smallstespresso

One of the first shops in Bristol to serve speciality-grade coffee, Small Street Espresso celebrated its eleventh birthday in December 2023. The intimate venue has been a beacon in the city's constantly evolving speciality scene for over a decade, during which it's served reliably great coffee from the UK's best roasteries.

TIP VISIT WEDNESDAY AND FRIDAY FOR FRESH DOUGHNUTS FROM SISTER STORE SMALL GOODS

While the venue has expanded by taking over the shop next door, and spilled out onto the street thanks to the pedestrianisation of the Old City, its style has stayed pretty consistent. Small Street's signature sky-blue La Marzocco is still stacked with classic cups of the same colour, the menu continues to be displayed on a black peg-letter board and the exposed-brick walls remain uncovered to create a cosy vibe.

The team's ongoing collaboration with Clifton Coffee is also unwavering, although novelty seekers will be delighted to know that the consistent house blend is kept company by a guest single origin from the likes of Radical Roasters, New Ground and Hard Lines.

Established
2012

Key roaster
Clifton Coffee Roasters

Brewing method
Espresso, V60, cold brew

Machine
La Marzocco FB80

Grinder
Mahlkonig E65S × 3, Mahlkonig EK43

Opening hours
Mon-Fri
8am-4pm

5| COFFEE UNDER PRESSURE – PARK STREET

76 Park Street, Bristol, BS1 5LB

coffeeunderpressure.co.uk | 01174 521075

f *coffeeunderpressure* **◎** *coffeeundrpressure*

Park Street is home to some of Bristol's most iconic indie brands, so when baristas and cafe owners Maria Fyssaki and Nasos Nasios picked up the keys to number 76 they knew their coffee shop would be in good company.

Launched in 2020, this is the third Coffee Under Pressure site and the first outside of Reading, where the project began in 2015. Each venue has its own character which reflects its specific setting, and this beautifully refurbished Grade II-listed building (which was almost obliterated during the second world war) is no exception. An overarching industrial style with bleached-wood highlights signals its membership of the Coffee Under Pressure family.

TIP ON DRIZZLY DAYS, NAB A SPOT IN THE WINDOW AND COSY UP WITH A WHITE CHOCOLATE MOCHA

This is a single-origin-only set-up and visitors are treated to a choice of up to ten direct-trade coffees at any time (two espresso, two filter and six retail). The baristas are extremely knowledgeable about the line-up so can recommend the best beans to suit your taste and favoured serve style.

Established
2020

Key roaster
Missing Bean Coffee Roasters

Brewing method
Espresso, AeroPress, V60

Machine
Victoria Arduino Eagle One

Grinder
Mythos One × 2, Mahlkonig EK43

Opening hours
Mon–Sun
9am–5pm

52 LITTLE BAGEL CO.

80 Queens Road, Bristol, BS8 1QU

littlebagelco.co.uk | 01173 048118

@ littlebagelcouk

Bristol is a melting pot of cultures, and on Queens Road a bite of the Big Apple awaits at Little Bagel Co. From the fresh chewy bagels to the on-point coffee, this busy takeaway captures New York's food'n'coffee to-go culture.

Each morning, the LBC crew rise before dawn to bake the day's batch of bagels, which are always served fresh – never toasted or frozen – for an authentic NYC taste. Get there early to beat the queue and grab breakfast faves such as the BEC (bacon, egg and cheese). Classic combos are dished out all day and accompanied by seasonal specials inspired by events such as Chinese New Year and Day of the Dead.

TIP CAN'T MAKE YOUR MIND UP? ORDER A TRADITIONAL SALMON LOX OR REUBEN

The team at Fire & Flow in the Cotswolds roast a bespoke espresso blend to complement the bagels, and the beans have proven to be so popular they're now sold in the cafe in 1kg bags so customers can get a taste of the experience at home. There's also a guest coffee spot that welcomes a shifting selection of beans from specialist roasteries, including Bristol's own Radical Roasters and Clifton Coffee.

Established
2022

Key roaster
Fire & Flow
Coffee Roasters

Brewing method
Espresso,
batch filter

Machine
Conti Monte Carlo

Grinder
Compak F8,
Compak PK100

Opening hours
Mon-Fri
7.30am-4pm
Sat
9am-4pm
Sun
9am-3pm

53 STARLINGS

99 Queens Road, Clifton, Bristol, BS8 1LW
starlingsuk.co.uk | 07444 922490
f Starlings, Clifton ⓘ starlings_bristol

In 2022, Edward Starling left the corporate world to follow his dream of starting a hospitality venture in the heart of Clifton. Word of mouth made his eponymous cafe gain instant success for its upmarket brunches and delicious coffee, cocktails and cakes. It even helped Starlings earn a finalist position in the Best New Business category at the Bristol Life Awards 2023.

Visitors dropping by will find a house blend crafted by Triple Co Roast alongside a roster of ever-changing guest coffees – regulars include Origin, Radical and Wogan – so there's always a tantalising new special to sample.

TIP TRY THE BOTTOMLESS BRUNCH – 90 MINUTES OF PROSECCO, BUCKS FIZZ, APEROL SPRITZ OR BLOODY MARY WITH A MEAL FOR £35

Customers rave about Starlings' beautiful interiors, picture-perfect food and hybrid business model. By day it's a stylish brunch/lunch spot; by night, a flexible dining venue hosting everything from singles' nights to supper clubs and pop-up feasting events to wine tastings. Come sundown, coffee can be swapped for locally produced craft beer or wine.

Established
2022

Key roaster
Triple Co Roast

Brewing method
Espresso

Machine
La Marzocco
Linea Classic

Grinder
Anfim Pratica

Opening hours
Tue-Fri
8am–4pm
Sat
9am–5pm
Sun
10am–4pm

BRISTOL

54 FOLIAGE CAFE

17 Regent Street, Bristol, BS8 4HW

foliagecafeclifton

If you like to take your daily cup with an ample helping of clean air, Foliage Cafe in Clifton Village could be your new watering hole. That's because it's adorned with lush greenery (all of which you can buy) draped over every surface and cascading from the ceiling.

The cafe is a home-from-home for its customers – around 90 per cent are regulars – who visit for the top-notch coffee experience as much as the botanical vibe. City roastery Clifton Coffee provides the house espresso and filter as well as special guest roasts, and the entire offering is refreshed monthly to spotlight coffees from eight different origins.

TIP GRAB A WARM, DOUBLE-BAKED BANANA, NUTELLA AND ALMOND CROISSANT WITH YOUR BREW

This indoor-jungle bar has recently enjoyed a makeover, but friendly service remains a constant. The chatty staff remember customers' names, welcome canine friends and draw smiley faces on babyccinos.

Up the endorphins further with a plate of something delicious from a seasonal menu that features hearty Insta-worthy brunches, mighty sandwiches and Foliage's take on the classic croque monsieur. Chase it with one of the scrumptious cakes, which are switched up as often as the daily changing soup.

Established
2019

Key roaster
Clifton Coffee Roasters

Brewing method
Espresso, V60, AeroPress, Chemex

Machine
La Marzocco Linea Classic

Grinder
Mahlkonig E65, Compak E6

Opening hours
Mon-Fri
8am–4pm
Sat-Sun
8am–5pm

55 TWELVE

12 King's Road, Clifton, Bristol, BS8 4AB

01179 738684

◎ *twelve_clifton*

Take a pause from shopping in Clifton Village or a stomp across the Downs to swing by this charming cafe on King's Road for exceedingly good coffee and homemade cake.

Founder Jen Nicholls keeps the offering stripped-back and straightforward so she can focus on quality. The former UK Latte Art Championship competitor prefers to explore a range of quality roasteries rather than fixing on one house roast, so the beans used to make the espresso change all the time. And while many coffee shops in the area use Bristol roasteries, Twelve provides an opportunity to explore further afield. Sample coffees from Fire & Flow in the Cotswolds, Dark Woods in Huddersfield, London's Kiss the Hippo, River in Hampshire and more.

TIP GOT A PARTY TO PLAN? ASK THE TWELVE TEAM TO BAKE YOU A CAKE

Great coffee needs to be paired with great carbs and Twelve's counter is crammed with cake stands groaning under the weight of all manner of homemade bakes. Enjoy a dose of nostalgia in the form of lemon drizzle, victoria sponge, bakewell tart or carrot cake.

Visitors are greeted by head of customer enjoyment Oscar, a black lab who's known to accept belly rubs as tips. He's super friendly and happy to welcome other dogs to the cafe too.

Established
2015

Key roaster
Multiple roasteries

Brewing method
Espresso

Machine
La Marzocco
Linea PB

Grinder
Mahlkonig E65S
GbW, Compak E6

Opening hours
Wed-Fri
8am-2pm
Sat-Sun
8.30am-2pm

BRISTOL

56 THE COLOMBIAN COMPANY - BRISTOL

121 Whiteladies Road, Bristol, BS8 2PL

thecolombiancompany.com | 07534 391992

f *thecolombianco* ⓘ *thecolombianco*

With its distinctive black and white tiled floor, black walls, natural wood shelving, hanging plants and tree trunk tables, The Colombian Company in Clifton is a lush oasis where visitors can savour the flavours of Colombian coffee.

The cafe is loved for its smiley staff who craft slick latte art on espresso drinks made from the house Finca Las Cruces coffee – imported direct from Colombia by cafe owner Jhampoll Gutierrez Gomez. In the mood for something sweet? Try a rich and smooth Colombian hot chocolate or a chai latte made with Bath-based Henny & Joe's masala chai.

TIP THE RETAIL SHELVES ARE STOCKED WITH TREATS IMPORTED FROM COLOMBIA AND SPAIN

Brews are best accompanied with generous slabs of homemade cake (made by Jhampoll's partner, Veronica) or toasties oozing with unctuous fillings. Customers looking for something stronger will also find beers from Venezuela and Spain.

In summer, pull up a chair on the pavement outside and watch the crowds stream from Clifton Down railway station – a spot of people-watching is always a good pairing with a caffeine hit.

Established
2019

Key roaster
The Colombian Company

Brewing method
Espresso, V60, AeroPress

Machine
Conti

Grinder
Compak E10

Opening hours
Mon-Fri
8am-5pm
Sat
9am-5.30pm
Sun
9am-6pm

BRISTOL

57 POQUITO COFFEE

116 Cheltenham Road, Stokes Croft, Bristol, BS6 5RW

poquitocoffee.co.uk

f poquitocoffee *© poquitocoffee*

This newcomer in bustling Stokes Croft represents a fresh start in a new city for owner Sam Janes, who spent 12 years working in Manchester's nightclub scene.

He's quickly made an impression on the locals with Poquito's chalky black shopfront, sleek interior, consistently good coffee and perfect pastries. On fine days, the bi-fold windows are opened wide so the space is open to passersby – a friendly invitation welcoming everyone to come inside.

Uber-local Clifton Coffee Roasters does the honours with the house offering and its Suspension Espresso forms the base of the drinks menu. There's also a rotating list of guest roasts including the delicious Colombian Huila sugarcane decaf, Kenya Gicherori AA and Panama Black Cat Typica.

TIP ALREADY EATEN? PICK UP A VEGAN OR GLUTEN-FREE PASTRY FOR LATER

South West suppliers are key to Poquito's success, with pastries from Wiltshire's Pano Bakehouse, bagels courtesy of Bagelry Box and cakes from 404 Bakes (both Bristol). Even the greenery is for sale, thanks to a collab with local indie Bush Plants.

Established
2023

Key roaster
Clifton Coffee
Roasters

Brewing method
Espresso, pourover

Machine
La Marzocco
Linea Classic

Grinder
Mahlkonig E65S,
Mahlkonig EK43 S

Opening hours
Mon-Fri
7.30am-4pm
Sat-Sun
8.30am-4pm

58 TINCAN COFFEE CO - BISHOPSTON

157 Gloucester Road, Bishopston, Bristol, BS7 8BA

tincancoffee.co.uk | 01179 232076

f tincancoffeeco *⊙ tincancoffeeco*

Bristol has always been fiercely independent and Gloucester Road, in the north of the city, is one of the longest streets of indie stores in Europe. At its heart sits Tincan, a stalwart of the city's speciality coffee scene.

This Bishopston site is a sister to the original bricks-and-mortar cafe in Bedminster, which was established in 2016 following the success of Tincan's fleet of vintage Citroën coffee vans. If you're deciding which cafe to visit, North Street is your destination for creative brunch dishes paired with top-notch coffee, while this Gloucester Road outpost is more pared back and focuses on sourdough toasties, salads and Forest Bakery pastries.

TIP ALL THE GORGEOUS FOREST BAKERY PASTRIES ARE NOW VEGAN

The team recently mixed up the coffee offering and introduced a new single-origin house pour from Triple Co Roast. The beans, which are grown in the Cerrado Mineiro region of Brazil, produce a bold and sweet cup with flavours of cacao, honey and hazelnut. Take it as espresso or filter – or check out what's on the guest list from the likes of Kickback.

Established
2018

Key roaster
Triple Co Roast

Brewing method
Espresso,
batch filter

Machine
La Marzocco
Linea PB

Grinder
Mahlkonig E80 GbW

Opening hours
Mon-Fri
8.30am-5pm
Sat
9am-5pm
Sun
10am-5pm

59 RADICAL ROASTERS

60-62 St Marks Road, Easton, Bristol, BS5 0LR

radicalroasters.co.uk | 01231 456789

radicalroastersuk

The creative crew at this roastery-cafe describe its style as 'Granny's living room meets Irish bar,' so if that sounds right up your street, be sure to stop by next time you're in Easton.

This inclusive space is truly one of a kind. Cups and plates are a mismatch of retro finds, the shutters are decorated with unconventional animal-themed murals and near the bar you'll find the world's first (according to the RR team) speciality coffee vending machine, which dispenses bags of beans and filter papers as well as radical literature.

TIP PICK UP PACKAGING-FREE BEANS FROM THE REFILL STATION

There's something to catch the eye in every inch of space here, yet one sip of the own-roasted coffee will focus the senses on its main appeal. The women-led roasting crew select the highest quality beans that not only taste fantastic but also empower as many people as possible. Sample them as espresso or filter, or opt for one of the guests supplied by roasteries that also prioritise making a difference in the industry.

Vegan pastries, breakfast baps and events such as life-drawing classes give visitors the excuse to extend their stay and soak up the radical vibe.

Established
2022

Key roaster
Radical Roasters

Brewing method
Espresso,
batch filter

Machine
La Marzocco
Linea PB

Grinder
Mahlkonig E80

Opening hours
Thu-Fri
8am-4pm
Sat
8.30am-4pm
Sun
9am-4pm

BRISTOL

60 THE ORCHARD COFFEE & CO

20 Clouds Hill Road, St George, Bristol, BS5 7LA
theorchardbristol.co.uk | 07484 355238
f orchardcoffeeco *theorchardcoffeeco*

No two days are ever the same at this Bristol coffee house and bakery. Whether it's introducing a new guest roast on filter, masterminding a novel pastry or zhuzhing up the brekkie bill, the baristas, bakers and chefs love to keep the offering fresh and funky.

One of Britain's most beautiful coffee venues, the gorgeous old building features a cloud-skimming vaulted ceiling and showers visitors with light from expansive arched windows. On the mezzanine, above the wooden bar that runs the length of the room, is the house bakery which turns out all the sourdough, pastries and cakes that adorn the counter.

TIP GIVE THE GIFT OF GOOD COFFEE WITH AN ORCHARD VOUCHER

Locals and visitors gather in this dynamic space (check out the line-up of events) to drink proper coffee, sink their teeth into crisp pastries and feast on contemporary brunch dishes. The house beans are bronzed on-site in the new roaster, with backup from guest roasteries Airhead and Radical (both Bristol). Baked goods include the likes of Biscoff cruffins, and breakfast plates range from homemade hash with mushrooms and kimchi to sourdough piled with smoked salmon, capers, dill and confit-garlic yogurt.

Established
2018

Key roaster
The Orchard
Coffee & Co

Brewing method
Espresso,
batch filter

Machine
Rancilio
Speciality RS1

Grinder
Mahlkonig E65S

Opening hours
Mon-Sun
8am-4pm

BRISTOL
20 24
COFFEE FESTIVAL

14 SEPTEMBER 2024
AT BRISTOL BEACON

A CELEBRATION OF
ALL THE CONTENT
OF THIS GUIDE AND
MORE...

www.bristolcoffeefestival.co.uk
bristolcoffeefestival

61 MI CAFÉ SU CAFÉ

Bristol and Bath Railway Path, Hockey Lane, Bristol, BS16 3RX

micafe.club | 07979 844467

f micafesucafe *⊙ micafe2020*

Pedal along the Fishponds stretch of the Bristol and Bath Railway Path to discover Céline, a 1970s Citroën van that provides caffeinated sustenance to passing cyclists and walkers.

Established in 2020 by Adam Streames, Mi Café Su Café (My Cafe, Your Cafe in Spanish) has become a roving favourite on the city's speciality scene. Adam serves two coffees which are made exclusively for the cafe by nearby Blind Owl Coffee Co. Pick the El Café blend from Colombia and El Salvador for warm apple-pie flavours and a smooth hazelnut-praline finish, or go decaf with the De Café blend of Colombian and Brazilian beans to relish notes of dark chocolate, nutmeg and sweet frangipane.

TIP BOOK CÉLINE AND ADAM TO SERVE COFFEE AT YOUR NEXT EVENT

A recent addition to the set-up is refillable retro-style coffee cans, so fans can craft their own Mi Café-inspired coffee experience at home – and receive a cracking deal on beans when they top up.

Grab a homemade seasonal cake or snack (we're talking spinach and feta 'schnuffels', ginger cake, lemon drizzle, sausage rolls) to provide an energy boost for the next leg of the trail.

Established
2020

Key roaster
Blind Owl Coffee Co.

Brewing method
Espresso

Machine
Fracino FCL2 LPG

Grinder
Mazzer Super Jolly

Opening hours
Wed–Sat
7.30am–3.30pm
Sun
8.30am–3pm

BRISTOL
ROASTERIES

62 LOST HORIZON COFFEE

The Basement Space, City Road Baptist Church, Stokes Croft, Bristol, BS2 8TP

losthorizoncoffee.com | 07946 488383

☐ *losthorizoncoffee*

For five years, this Bristol micro-batch speciality roastery has been hand-delivering coffee by cargo bike and offsetting more than double the carbon footprint emitted from farm to cup (including the energy taken to boil the kettle to brew the coffee).

'KIT'S WORKING THE SPIRITUAL CONNECTION FURTHER BY MOVING INTO THE BASEMENT OF CITY ROAD BAPTIST CHURCH'

Lost Horizon's founder Kit Nisbet named his business after the 1933 novel by James Hilton that depicted the utopia of Shangri-La, where people achieved long, happy lives by eating stimulating berries. Kit's working the spiritual connection further by moving his business into the basement of City Road Baptist Church.

The new premises will include a brew bar where customers can sample seasonal single origins from the four corners of the globe, as well as a range of processing methods, varietals and roast styles.

For a regular fix, sign up for a tailored subscription package – delivered to your door by pedal power if you live in Bristol.

Established
2019

Roaster make and size
Proaster 10kg

63 EXTRACT COFFEE ROASTERS

Roastery Works, Unit 1 New Gatton Road, Bristol, BS2 9SH

extractcoffee.co.uk | 01179 554976

f *extractcoffee* ⊚ *extractcoffee*

Extract has come a long way since it started roasting speciality-grade coffee in 2007. The Bristol roastery has added training and education spaces in London and Manchester, while its speciality team continues to grow and includes some of the industry's top coffee judges and competition baristas.

The roastery focuses on innovation and works directly with growers to showcase new processes while also highlighting the effects of climate change and gender inequality in the industry. Its catalogue of coffees has something for everyone, the flagship Hero range of easy-drinking brews supplemented by experimental single origins.

'THE TEAM INCLUDES SOME OF THE INDUSTRY'S TOP COFFEE JUDGES AND COMPETITION BARISTAS'

The team pride themselves on building longstanding relationships with growers – some of which span almost a decade. Once in Bristol, the beans are roasted in a trio of refurbished vintage Probat roasters and then delivered to Extract's wholesale customers, which include some of the UK's most prestigious hotels, bars and coffee shops.

Retail customers can also order coffee online and take a quiz to discover which beans will best suit their tastes and brew set-up.

Established
2007

Roaster make and size
Probat G120 120kg,
Probat UG60 60kg,
Probat LE12 12kg

64 RADICAL ROASTERS

60-62 St Marks Road, Bristol, BS5 0LR

radicalroasters.co.uk

☉ *radicalroastersuk*

In 2021 Cat O'Shea decided that, having roasted coffee for other people for years, she'd take the plunge and launch her own business. What started in a small shed on a 1kg roaster soon evolved – with the help of a council grant – into a fully blown cafe-roastery with a 5kg Diedrich and a team of equally passionate roasters and baristas.

Established
2021

Roaster make and size
Diedrich IR-5 5kg

'WHEN NOT WORKING IN COFFEE, CAT PLAYS IN A PUNK BAND CALLED KISS ME, KILLER'

Radical's success is no surprise: Cat's a Great Taste coffee judge, has twice been a UK Barista Championship semi-finalist, came fourth in the UK Coffee Roasters Championship, was an SCA UK Sensory Coffee judge and is a certified Q Grader. She buys coffee from trusted small-scale importers and works with marginalised groups to provide free skill sharing. When not working in coffee, Cat plays in a punk band called Kiss Me, Killer.

As its name suggests, Radical is inclined towards the intriguing and unusual, sourcing extraordinary coffees from across the globe. One such find is an experimental micro-lot from grower Jairo Arcila in Colombia. Jairo adds dehydrated mandarin skin during green bean fermentation to produce notes of citrus and brown sugar.

MORE GOOD FINDS IN BRISTOL

COFFEE SHOPS

1B PITVILLE
1b Pitville Place, Cotham, Bristol, BS6 6JZ

BAKEHOUSE AT CAKESMITHS
St Philips Road, Bristol, BS2 0JZ
bakehousebristol.com

BAKESMITHS
65 Whiteladies Road, Bristol, BS8 2LY
bakesmiths.co.uk

BOONA BOONA COFFEE ROASTERS
152 Wells Road, Totterdown,
Bristol, BS4 2AG
boonaboona.co.uk

BURRA - NORTH STREET
223 North Street, Bristol, BS3 1JJ
burrabristol.co.uk

BURRA - REDLAND
7 Lower Redland Road, Bristol, BS6 6TB
burrabristol.co.uk

COFFEE + BEER
16 Cotham Hill, Bristol, BS6 6LF
coffeeandbeer.co.uk

FULL COURT PRESS
59 Broad Street, Bristol, BS1 2EJ
fcp.coffee

INTERLUDE COFFEE
145 St Michael's Hill, Bristol, BS2 8DB

JOZI
3 Worrall Road, Clifton, Bristol, BS8 2UF
jozibristol.co.uk

NEW CUT COFFEE
The Art Warehouse, Wapping Wharf,
Bristol, BS1 4RN
newcutcoffee.com

ODD SHOP
45 Whiteladies Road, Bristol, BS8 2LS

ORIGIN COFFEE ROASTERS - VICTORIA STREET
36 Victoria Street, Redcliffe,
Bristol, BS1 6BY
origincoffee.co.uk

SPICER + COLE AT THE RWA
Queens Road, Bristol, BS8 1PX
spicerandcole.co.uk

SPICER + COLE - CLIFTON VILLAGE
9 Princess Victoria Street, Bristol, BS8 4DX
spicerandcole.co.uk

SPICER + COLE - FINZELS REACH
Counterslip, Bristol, BS1 6BX
spicerandcole.co.uk

SPICER + COLE - QUEEN SQUARE
1 Queen Square Avenue, Bristol, BS1 4JA
spicerandcole.co.uk

SWEVEN COFFEE
12 North Street, Bedminster,
Bristol, BS3 1HT
swevencoffee.co.uk

THE COLOMBIAN COMPANY - CITY CENTRE, BRISTOL
Dominions House, 23-25 St Augustine's
Parade, Bristol, BS1 4UL
thecolombiancompany.com

ROASTERIES

BOONA BOONA COFFEE ROASTERS
Unit 17 Station Road Workshops,
Station Road, Bristol, BS15 4PJ
boonaboona.co.uk

CLIFTON COFFEE ROASTERS
Island Trade Park, Bristow Broadway,
Avonmouth, Bristol, BS11 9FB
cliftoncoffee.co.uk

SWEVEN COFFEE
12 North Street, Bedminster,
Bristol, BS3 1HT
swevencoffee.co.uk

TRIPLE CO ROAST
Unit 11 Montpelier Central, Station Road,
Bristol, BS6 5EE
triplecoroast.com

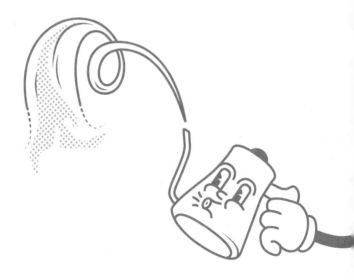

DORSET & WILTSHIRE
COFFEE SHOPS

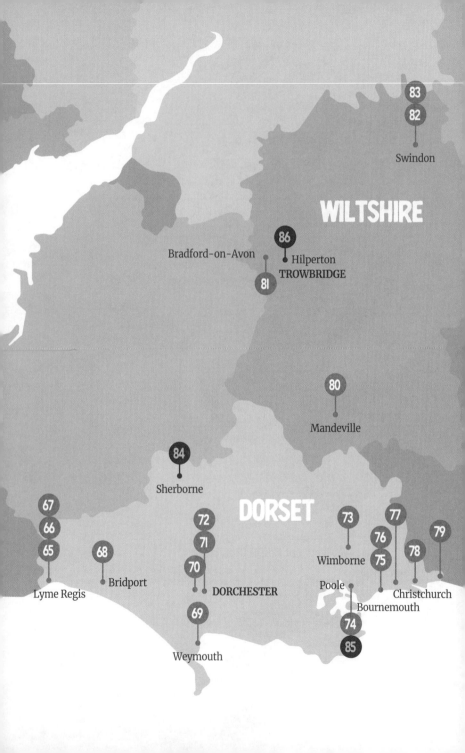

83
82
Swindon

WILTSHIRE

86
Bradford-on-Avon
Hilperton
TROWBRIDGE
81

80
Mandeville

84
Sherborne

DORSET

67
66
65
Lyme Regis

68
Bridport

72
71
70
DORCHESTER

69
Weymouth

73
Wimborne

77
76
75
Poole

79
78
Christchurch
Bournemouth

74
85

⊗ CAFES

⊗ ROASTERIES

Find more good coffee shops
and roasteries on page 147.

All locations are approximate

65 AMID GIANTS & IDOLS

59 Silver Street, Lyme Regis, Dorset, DT7 3HR
07898 074305

f *giantsandidols* ⊚ *amid_giants_and_idols*

It may be a bit of a climb up Lyme Regis' Silver Street to reach Amid Giants & Idols, but it's worth it for the quality caffeination to be found at the top – courtesy of owners Tom and Hayley Michael and their band of baristas.

A stalwart of Dorset's speciality scene since 2014, the shop partners with Somerset's Brazier Coffee Roasters for its house blend Coast: a rich coffee ringing with notes of chocolate and marzipan. If you love what you taste in the cafe, pick up a bag of beans to enjoy at home (the team will grind it for your preferred brew method). Coffee lovers who are more adventurous have plentiful options too, and can explore a collection of naturally processed single origins from Ethiopia, Nicaragua, Rwanda and more.

TIP ALL THE CAKES AND BAKES ARE HOMEMADE, SO IT WOULD BE RUDE NOT TO INDULGE

Linger longer in this laid-back spot for brunch or lunch. Catch some rays in the hidden courtyard garden or stay indoors to admire the hessian coffee sacks lining the ceiling while you munch on dishes packed with local ingredients. A perennial favourite is the sweetcorn fritters with avocado salsa, grilled halloumi, poached eggs and chilli.

Established
2014

Key roaster
Brazier Coffee Roasters

Brewing method
Espresso, V60, woodneck, Chemex, AeroPress

Machine
La Marzocco

Grinder
Mazzer × 2

Opening hours
Tue–Sat
9am–4pm
Sun
10am–3pm

66 THE WHOLE HOG LYME BAY

6a Broad Street, Lyme Regis, Dorset, DT7 3QD

thewholehog.co.uk | 07967 338995

☉ *thewholehoglyme*

This tiny takeaway hatch has become an institution in Lyme Regis, yet its success has spread way beyond the foodie seaside town. In 2023, it was named Best Cafe in the South West at the Food Reader Awards, fending off competition from some of the most established venues in the region.

For founder Cheryl Alner, the recipe for success was straightforward: keep the quality high and the proposition simple. Consequently, The Whole Hog's menu features just three key items – speciality coffee, roast baps and artisan doughnuts – and almost everything is crafted from scratch on-site each morning.

TIP NOT INTO PORK? NO PROBLEM. TRY ONE OF THE CHICKEN OR VEGAN ROAST BAPS

Arrive early to avoid missing out on a warm-from-the-oven glossy bun stuffed with slow-roasted pork and drizzled with apple sauce, as they sell out most days. Add a Monmouth Coffee flat white (batch filter is also available) and box of doughnuts (flavours include salted caramel, chocolate and homemade raspberry jam, plus seasonal specials) to your order and head to the shore to scoff your bounty on the beach.

Established
2019

Key roaster
Monmouth
Coffee Company

Brewing method
Espresso,
batch filter

Machine
La Marzocco

Grinder
Victoria Arduino
Mythos One

Opening hours
Mon–Sun
8.30am–2pm
(seasonal opening hours)

67 TOWN MILL BAKERY

Coombe Street, Lyme Regis, Dorset, DT7 3PY

townmillbakery.co.uk | 01297 444754

f *townmillbakerylymeregis* @ *townmillbakery*

This hub in the heart of Lyme Regis is where locals congregate to pick up loaves of Taste of the West gold-award-winning organic sourdough and steaming cups of Bristol-roasted speciality coffee.

A bakery, deli and cafe, Town Mill Bakery is a one-stop shop from which visitors can grab brunch at the same time as picking up a truckle of cheese, a jar of local honey and a bunch of blooms.

TIP BEAT THE QUEUE BY PRE-ORDERING YOUR LOAVES FROM THE ONLINE SHOP

Take a seat at one of the refectory-style tables and savour a plate of turkish eggs or creamy mushrooms on toast from a line-up that includes all the usual brekkie favourites. The vegan Green Brunch is perennially popular, and combines sugar snap peas and Tenderstem broccoli with avocado, roasted tomatoes and hummus on sourdough toast, topped with salad and dukkah.

The team are as passionate about the coffee as they are the food and serve Extract's Cast Iron Guatemalan brew (notes of black cherry and cocoa). The beans are roasted on Betty, a restored 1955 cast-iron Probat roaster.

Established
2019

Key roaster
Extract Coffee Roasters

Brewing method
Espresso, batch filter, cold brew

Machine
La Marzocco

Grinder
Compak, Mahlkonig EK43, Victoria Arduino Mythos One

Opening hours
Thu-Mon
8.30am-2.30pm
(seasonal opening hours)

68 SOULSHINE

76 South Street, Bridport, Dorset, DT6 3NN

wearesoulshine.co.uk | 01308 422821

f *wearesoulshine* ◎ *wearesoulshine*

In 2021, this Bridport favourite was taken over by friends and former River Cottage colleagues Andy Tyrrell and Joel Gostling. While Soulshine had long been known as a delicious destination for coffee and brunch, the duo raised its gourmet game with the introduction of an evening menu and a regular supper club.

Creative dishes crafted with wholesome ingredients are now available all day. Utilising their River Cottage experience, almost everything is made from scratch in-house (including some of the jams, breads and cakes) and there's a preference for all things pickled and preserved. The breakfast menu revolves around eggs, sourdough, pancakes and the like, while the lunch and dinner line-ups focus on small plates of local, seasonal produce.

TIP MAKE YOUR WAY THROUGH THE SHOP AND CAFE TO THE SPACIOUS COURTYARD DINING AREA

The food isn't the only thing to get a glow-up: the coffee is now roasted in-house under the Goose & Badger brand. The micro-roastery cooks up a short bill of seasonal single origins, which are available to sample in the cafe alongside guest roasts from larger outfits such as Crankhouse, Friedhats and Full Court Press.

Established
2021

Key roaster
Goose & Badger

Brewing method
Espresso, V60,
batch filter,
cold brew

Machine
La Marzocco
Linea PB

Grinder
Mahlkonig E65S
GbW,
Mahlkonig EK43

Opening hours
Mon–Sat
9.30am–3pm,
6pm–11pm
Sun
9.30am–3pm

69 FINCA - WEYMOUTH

13 St Thomas Street, Weymouth, Dorset, DT4 8EW

fincacoffee.co.uk | 01305 300400

f *fincaweymouth* ⓘ *scouting4coffee*

A blend of exposed brick, wood cladding and pendant lighting creates a pleasingly cosy vibe at this Weymouth coffee shop. The rustic aesthetic is shared by all of Finca's six West Country venues — along with the use of own-roasted coffee and homemade bakes.

Finca's roasting team are passionate about single origins and roast up to 40 different varieties each year. There are usually three available to sample at the cafes, including something floral and fruity from Africa; a nutty, chocolate-forward roast from Latin America; and a crowd-pleasing decaf. Recent favourites include Rocky Mountain from Ethiopia and Arcangel from Bolivia.

TIP CHECK OUT THE LATEST ADDITION TO THE FINCA FAMILY IN GLASTONBURY

On the counter sits an expansive selection of goodies from the sister bakery in Poundbury: try a slice of flavoursome carrot cake, a wedge of rich brownie or pair your brew with one of a plethora of buttery pastries. In summer, bi-fold windows are drawn back so customers can sit and sip while enjoying a cool coastal breeze.

Established
2019

Key roaster
Finca Coffee Roasters

Brewing method
Espresso

Machine
La Marzocco

Grinder
Eureka Olympus

Opening hours
Mon-Sat
8am-5pm
Sun
10am-3pm

WEYMOUTH

70 FINCA - POUNDBURY

24 Buttermarket, Poundbury, Dorchester, Dorset, DT1 3AZ

fincacoffee.co.uk | 01305 300400

f *fincapoundbury* ⊙ *scouting4coffee*

It's nigh on impossible to order just a coffee at Finca's Poundbury outpost, thanks to the on-site bakery forging a constant stream of intoxicating scents. Resistance is futile, so instead submit to the call of bejewelled tiffin, golden pastel de nata and aromatic cinnamon buns.

The bakers arrive at dawn to craft an army of sourdough loaves, focaccia, traybakes and buns for Finca's six coffee shops across Dorset and Somerset. This venue is arguably the looker of the family, residing within the historic hexagonal building at the centre of the town's Buttermarket. It's also the spot to sample the baked goods while they're still warm from the oven.

TIP DON'T LEAVE WITHOUT PICKING UP A LOAF OF SOURDOUGH OR A SLAB OF SPRINGY FOCACCIA

The coffee on offer is also an in-house operation, roasted at Finca's HQ in Dorchester. There are usually three single-origin espresso options available (a chocolatey Latin American, a fruity and floral African and a seasonal decaf), but the selection shifts all the time. An extended catalogue of Finca coffees to brew at home is available from the retail shelves.

Established
2017

Key roaster
Finca Coffee Roasters

Brewing method
Espresso

Machine
La Marzocco

Grinder
Eureka Olympus

Opening hours
Mon-Sat
8am-4pm
Sun
10am-3pm

41 Great Western Road, Dorchester, Dorset, DT1 1UF

fincacoffee.co.uk | 01305 300400

f fincadorchester *⊙ scouting4coffee*

This Dorchester store is where it all began for the Finca team and from where, in just under a decade, they have built a six-strong collective of speciality coffee shops and a roastery.

The gang might work with some of the highest-quality coffee in the world but they started their roasting journey bronzing beans each evening on a tiny 1kg roaster — before getting up at dawn to bake the day's cakes for the cafe. Fortunately, the hard graft paid off and the community coffee shop soon developed a legion of devoted customers.

TIP THE COFFEE MENUS CHANGE MONTHLY, SO ASK THE BARISTA FOR THE LOW-DOWN ON THE LATEST ROASTS

In 2016, demand outpaced the capacity of their little red roaster and they invested in a 10kg Toper and a new HQ to house it in. Now the team roast an astonishing range of single origins (up to 40 each year) to supply their growing fleet of cafes, and have also opened the Finca bakery in Poundbury.

Visit this flagship venue to taste the latest roasts and morning's pastries while perched on a bench at the window. When the weather's good, the bi-fold windows are pulled back and the good vibes spill out onto the street.

Established
2014

Key roaster
Finca Coffee
Roasters

Brewing method
Espresso

Machine
La Marzocco

Grinder
Eureka Olympus

Opening hours
Mon–Sat
8am–5pm
Sun
10am–3pm

DORCHESTER

72 FINCA - DORCHESTER, SOUTH STREET

50a South Street, Dorchester, Dorset, DT1 1DQ

fincacoffee.co.uk | 01305 300400

f *fincadorchestertown* 📷 *scouting4coffee*

Over the past decade, Finca's flagship Great Western Road coffee shop has garnered a dedicated local following for its own-roasted beans and house bakes. Now the people of Dorchester can get a second bite of the cherry at this new town-centre site.

Roomier than the original venue, the South Street cafe has plenty of seating on its first floor as well as outside on bierkeller tables. It's the perfect spot to flop after a busy morning of shopping or chill out with the papers and a top-notch flat white.

TIP ORDER A SLICE OF THE COFFEE CAKE, FEATURING A PUNCHY ⅓ SHOT OF OWN-ROASTED ESPRESSO IN EACH SERVE

All the coffees – there are at least three to choose from at any time – are crafted in town at the Finca roastery. The team like to keep the offering fresh, so the single-origin options are updated every few weeks. Visitors can also buy Finca beans to brew at home from the retail collection – or order the full spectrum of high-quality beans online.

Established
2023

Key roaster
Finca Coffee
Roasters

Brewing method
Espresso

Machine
La Marzocco

Grinder
Eureka Olympus

Opening hours
Mon-Sat
8am-5pm
Sun
10am-3pm

73 SONDER COFFEE

48 High Street, Wimborne, Dorset, BH21 1HT

sondercoffee.co.uk

f *sondercoffee35* **⊙** *sondercoffeewimborne*

The word 'sonder' describes the feeling you experience when realising every passing stranger has a life as intricate as your own: full of ambitions, anxieties and affection. And for cafe founder Ebony Paz that chimed perfectly with the vein of compassion and connectivity she wanted to run through her own coffee shops.

This venue is the younger sibling of a big sister in Salisbury and, since it launched in spring 2023, has become a popular spot for remote workers who visit to sip while blasting through emails. They're in luck: the Salisbury venue's co-working space has been such as success there are now plans to introduce a dedicated working area in Wimborne.

TIP THE INCREDIBLE GOODIES ON THE COUNTER ARE FROM LOCAL INDIE SCARLET BAKES CAKES

Ebony keeps her customers expertly caffeinated via beans from Extract. She chose the roastery for its sustainable ethos and now works exclusively with the Bristol outfit, using Rocket for the house espresso. A beguiling blend of black cherry, caramel, cocoa and liquorice flavours, it's good served with or without milk – and even better with a locally made cruffin or Nutella knot from Orchard Bay Bakery.

Established
2023

Key roaster
Extract Coffee
Roasters

Brewing method
Espresso

Machine
La Marzocco

Grinder
Compak F8

Opening hours
Mon-Sat
8am-6pm
Sun
9am-4.30pm

74 GROUNDED COFFEE ROASTERS

12 Kingland Crescent, Poole, Dorset, BH15 1TB

groundedcoffeeroasters.com | 07572 377336

f *groundedcoffeeroasters* *ⓘ* *groundedcoffeeroasters*

This Poole cafe's roots burrow back to 2015 when Rosie and Jon Rowe, inspired by their shared love of coffee, converted a rusty Land Rover into a coffee truck (named Arthur).

Fast forward to today and the husband-and-wife team have grown a fully fledged fleet. Arthur is backed up by fellow coffee trucks George, Flynn and Rupert, all of which rep Grounded at hundreds of events each year, from music festivals to corporate dos. Rosie and Jon then opened this roastery-cafe in 2020, from which the pair and their knowledgeable band of baristas serve own-roasted coffee as espresso and V60. And things keep expanding: the roasting operation has outgrown the space at the back of the shop and is upping sticks to its own unit next door.

🆃🅸🅿 TRY THE LOLA, A SUPER SWEET AND STRONG COFFEE NAMED AFTER ROSIE AND JON'S DAUGHTER

Sweet Breeze (an Ethiopian and Guatemalan blend) is a fruity tonic in warmer months, while Autumn Fire (a smoky Guatemalan and Indian mix) and Winter Nights (Brazilian, Honduran and Papua New Guinean beans delivering smooth brown sugar and caramel notes) delight when the temperature drops. There's also a shifting selection of single origins for those keen to try something new. Be sure to pair your pick with one of the goodies from the countertop collection of cakes and pastries.

Established
2020

Key roaster
Grounded Coffee Roasters

Brewing method
Espresso, V60

Machine
Crem EX3

Grinder
Crem Pulse 65

Opening hours
Mon-Sat
9am-5pm
Sun
10am-4pm

POOLE

75 ESPRESSO KITCHEN

69 Commercial Road, Bournemouth, Dorset, BH2 5RT

espressokitchen.co.uk | 01202 790123

f espressokitchen *o espressokitchen*

Step into the charming world of Espresso Kitchen and you'll find yourself captivated by its cosy, quirky vibe. This curious coffee shop in the heart of Bournemouth showcases a riotous mix of eye-catching and fascinating objects: walls are pasted with newspapers while surfaces are adorned with clashing cushions, surfboards, coffee tins, postcards and more.

Everything served in this unique hideaway is a celebration of quality, flavour and sustainability. Espresso drinks are crafted from organic coffee beans sourced directly from farms at origin and roasted in Dorset by the pros at Beanpress.

TIP LUNCH LIKE A LOCAL WITH A CHEDDAR, BLACK OLIVE AND SUN-BLUSHED TOMATO SCONE

Pair your pour with something savoury from the cracking line-up of veggie, gluten-free, dairy-free and organic options. Or, if you're craving a slice of sweetness, choose one of the delectable homemade bakes such as classic carrot cake or a zesty lemon tart.

Perch downstairs in the bustle of the bar or, to get stuck into a book or catch up with friends, take refuge in the snug upstairs. Don't be surprised if the music, warming drinks and gentle babble of conversation soothe you into staying longer than anticipated.

Established
2012

Key roaster
Beanpress
Coffee Co.

Brewing method
Espresso

Machine
La Marzocco FB70

Grinder
Compak E8

Opening hours
Mon-Fri
8am-5pm
Sat
8am-6pm
Sun
9am-5pm

BOURNEMOUTH

76 SOUTH COAST COFFEE

24 Richmond Hill, Bournemouth, Dorset, BH2 6EJ

southcoastcoffee.co.uk | 01202 093577

f *wearesouthcoastcoffee* ⊙ *south.coast.coffee*

South Coast Coffee and Bad Hand Roastery are near neighbours in Bournemouth and both rep the speciality scene in the seaside town. SCC – renowned for its plant-based menu, funky decor and merchandise by local artist Mirek Lucan – uses Bad Hand's Shaka roast as its house blend, the Colombian and Peruvian beans' chocolatey notes creating a delicious espresso both with and without milk.

Grab a window seat and treat yourself to a mocha made with hot chocolate from another local company, Green Label Kitchen. A variety of alternative roasts from Bad Hand are also on offer via batch, so drop in to find out what's in the hopper.

TIP EVERYTHING ON THE MENU IS AVAILABLE TO TAKE AWAY

SCC's chefs use locally sourced ingredients to switch up their seasonally changing brunch and lunch menus. Check out the sweetcorn chowder topped with crispy vegan bacon, or plump for the customer fave South Coast Brunch. Whatever you go for, it's nigh on impossible to resist rounding off your visit with something sweet from the ever-changing selection of cakes.

Established
2010

Key roaster
Bad Hand
Coffee Roasters

Brewing method
Espresso,
batch filter

Machine
La Marzocco

Grinder
Compak

Opening hours
Mon–Sat
8am–4pm
Sun
9am–3pm

77 WILD

651a Christchurch Road, Boscombe, Bournemouth, Dorset, BH1 4AP

wildboscombe.com | 01202 985398

f *wildboscombe* ◎ *wild_boscombe*

This teeny tiny coffee shop in the Bournemouth suburb of Boscombe may be small, but its good vibes and friendly charm are larger than life.

There are a handful of cosy seats within Wild's bare-brick interior, yet its takeaway hatch opening onto bustling Christchurch Road is where most of the action happens. Ethically roasted coffee from Beanpress in Poole flies out of the serving window in a range of espresso drinks, paired with organic local milk or a dairy-free alternative.

TIP THERE ARE LOTS OF OPTIONS FOR VEGANS – TRY THE PLANT-BASED BLUEBERRY BAKEWELL SLICE

The stripped-back coffee offering is accompanied by a line-up of freshly pressed juices and superfood lattes, including turmeric and matcha. Less superfood and more super-tempting is the cake cabinet, packed to the rafters with coffee-shop classics such as almond-flaked croissants, vegan cinnamon buns and frosting-topped carrot cake slices. Those looking for something more filling will like the range of stuffed bagels (the pastrami, gouda and gherkin combo is unreal) or the house-special avo on toast.

Established
2020

Key roaster
Beanpress
Coffee Co.

Brewing method
Espresso

Machine
La Marzocco Linea

Grinder
Compak

Opening hours
Mon–Sun
8am–5pm

78 COAST COFFEE

74 High Street, Christchurch, Dorset, BH23 1BN

coastcoffeeshop.com | 01202 096260

f coastcoffee74 *◎ coastcoffee74*

This popular indie coffee shop on Christchurch High Street is a go-to for a breakfast of streaky-bacon sarnies, warming porridge or stacks of fluffy American-style pancakes. Pair your pick of the edibles with the house coffee blend, Shaka, which is roasted in Bournemouth by Bad Hand. Its notes of chocolate, orange and molasses make it a superb match for food and a gratifyingly smooth way to start the day.

TIP WELSH RAREBIT WITH REAL-ALE CHUTNEY IS A MUST-TRY HOUSE SPECIALITY

Lunch is equally popular and features dishes such as the beetroot-falafel salad alongside wraps layered with juicy chicken, smoked bacon and red onion. A daily drop from BakeHouse24 in Ringwood delivers fresh-from-the-oven doughy deliciousness, including bagels served with the likes of brie, red onion and mango chutney.

Cakes on the counter change regularly so there's always a slice of something sweet to try. Favourites include Dorset apple cake, and salted caramel and honeycomb brownies.

The crew at Coast Coffee go all out to ensure everything – from the freshly prepared soups to creative latte art – is top notch, so it's no surprise the venue was named Best Coffee House in Christchurch 2023 by Restaurant Guru.

Established
2015

Key roaster
Bad Hand
Coffee Roasters

Brewing method
Espresso

Machine
La Spaziale

Grinder
Compak E8

Opening hours
Mon-Fri
8am–4pm
Sat
8am–4.30pm
Sun
9am–4pm

79 THE PADDLE CAFE

397 Waterford Road, Highcliffe, Christchurch, Dorset, BH23 5JN

thepaddle.co.uk | 01425 275148

f thepaddlecafe 🄾 *thepaddlecafe*

Overnight oats adorned with fruits and seeds, towering pancake stacks dressed in indulgent toppings, skillet-pan shakshuka sprinkled with feta and herbs: brunch is more than a weekend treat at The Paddle, it's a way of life.

Creative, seasonal and thoroughly Instagrammable is the brief followed by the chefs at this contemporary Highcliffe cafe, a short walk from the shore. They deliver every time, using local produce to craft an elevated menu of brunch classics and innovative specials. The homemade hash browns are so good they've earned a cult following, while the ever-popular french toast changes its accompaniments to fit the season.

TIP CHECK OUT THE PADDLE'S SISTER VENUES IN MILFORD ON SEA AND BROCKENHURST

Food this good deserves a companion of equal standing, and happily the coffee hits the mark. Roasted in Bournemouth by the team at Bad Hand, the Shaka house blend has notes of chocolate, orange and molasses to complement a wide range of flavours. There's also a cracking Brazilian decaf which delivers a rich hit of nutty caramel sweetness.

Established
2013

Key roaster
Bad Hand
Coffee Roasters

Brewing method
Espresso,
cafetiere

Machine
Conti MC Ultima

Grinder
Markibar Izaga

Opening hours
Mon, Wed-Sat
8am-3.30pm
Sun
9am-2.30pm

CHRISTCHURCH

80 THE STALLS CAFE

Manor Farm, Sutton Mandeville, Salisbury, Wiltshire, SP3 5NH

thestallscafe.com | 07849 495592

f thestallscoffee *@ the_stalls_coffee*

Located in an expanse of verdant fields in the Wiltshire countryside, The Stalls Cafe excels at serving small-batch-roasted coffee and wholesome home-cooked fare with limited food miles.

The 16th-century barn was transformed into a cafe by Anna Strang and Maggie Kerr, who met while travelling the world researching plastic pollution. Keen to channel their eco experience into a new venture, they created a community-focused space with sustainability at its heart on the farm where Anna grew up.

TIP DON'T MISS THE MENU OF ANTIPODEAN BRUNCH DISHES

The cafe's interior is authentically rustic with stone walls, Douglas fir beams, cobblestone floors, horse carts suspended from the ceiling and wooden tables handcrafted by local makers.

Ingredients are sourced as locally as possible, with beef from the farm and unhomogenised whole milk from a local dairy. The latter is delivered in kegs and dispensed from a converted beer barrel to eliminate packaging completely, while the house espresso beans from The Roasting Party in Winchester arrive in large refillable containers for the same reason. They're turned into silky smooth coffees to provide feelgood sipping opportunities from breakfast to mid-afternoon coffee breaks.

Established
2022

Key roaster
The Roasting Party

Brewing method
Espresso, V60,
batch filter

Machine
Sanremo Verona RS

Grinder
Mazzer

Opening hours
Wed-Sun
9am-3pm

81 LITTLE RITUALS

7 Silver Street, Bradford-on-Avon, Wiltshire, BA15 1JY

little-rituals.co.uk | 077435 820009

 little_rituals_boa

This new addition to Silver Street broadened Bradford-on-Avon's coffee culture when it opened in summer 2023. With its shifting selection of speciality beans from the UK's leading roasteries, it's a novel spot to discover interesting coffees you haven't yet sampled.

Little Rituals founders Toby McLaren and Isabelle Mulvany favour roasteries that push the boundaries on flavour, so beans from the likes of Sweven, Skylark, Red Bank and Girls Who Grind often feature. Head to the cafe's Insta page to find out what's brewing (the gang usually post their favourite new picks on the grid) and then pop in to try it as espresso, batch filter or AeroPress.

TIP DON'T MISS THE SUNDAY SESSIONS WHERE COFFEE IS PAIRED WITH LIVE MUSIC

The cafe is easy to find: just look for the black shopfront crowned with gorgeous gold lettering. The traditional exterior hints at the classic style within, which is built around the curved bottle-green bar and accented with sleek mid-century modern furniture.

Alongside good coffee, artisan pastries and sourdough sandwiches, Little Rituals is also the place to pick up houseplants and locally grown flowers.

Established
2023

Key roaster
Multiple roasteries

Brewing method
Espresso,
batch filter,
AeroPress

Machine
Victoria Arduino
Eagle One

Grinder
Mahlkonig EK43,
Victoria Arduino
MDJ

Opening hours
Mon-Sat
8.30am-4pm
Sun
9.30am-3pm

82 DARKROOM ESPRESSO

11 Faringdon Road, Swindon, Wiltshire, SN1 5AR

darkroomespresso.com | 07761 521892

f darkroomSN1 *darkroomespresso*

Photographers and baristas have a lot in common: as skilled artists, they both understand the chemistry involved in developing and creating a picture-perfect result. And that's just what Darkroom Espresso brings to Swindon's speciality scene.

Owner Stephen Jordan has worked at Darkroom since 2015, previously honing his craft at Harris + Hoole in London. Since he took the reins in 2019, the cafe has gone from strength to strength, picking up multiple Good Food Awards for the foodie offering which is treated with the same attention to detail as the coffee extraction and latte art.

TIP OVER HALF OF THE CAKES – FROM CAKESMITHS AND BUNKIE BAKES – ARE VEGAN

The cafe is especially known for its moreish grilled cheese toasties, which form the backbone of a menu that's built around comfort food and coffee, plus a wider range of hot drinks. Bath's Henny & Joe's and Teahouse Emporium bring the chai and 25 tea varieties, while Kokoa Collection's delectable hot chocolates deliver velvety winter sips.

Darkroom's two espressos and two filters are crafted using beans from Bath's Round Hill Roastery, and supplemented by guest roasts from Curve, Campbell & Syme and Skylark.

Established
2014

Key roaster
Round Hill Roastery

Brewing method
Espresso, V60, batch filter, pourover, Chemex

Machine
Victoria Arduino Eagle One

Grinder
Anfim Pratica × 2, Mahlkonig EK43

Opening hours
Mon-Fri
7.30am-5pm
Sat
9am-5pm
Sun
10am-4pm

SWINDON

83 POUR BOIS

95 Victoria Road, Swindon, Wiltshire, SN1 3BD

pourbois.com

pour_bois

Tom Smith and Corey Colar met at a coffee cupping, where they bonded over their shared preference for experimental brews. Soon after, they started travelling around the UK together to sniff out the best beans.

When the pandemic struck and they couldn't get their hands on a decent cup in their hometown of Swindon, they built a makeshift bar under the stairs at Corey's home and started serving from his front window.

TIP CHECK OUT THE HUGE RETAIL COLLECTION OF INTERNATIONAL BEANS

Once lockdown had lifted they went back to their day jobs, but the desire to add something different to Swindon's coffee scene remained. In 2022, that dream was realised when they opened Pour Bois within Oink Gallery on Victoria Road.

The gallery's vivid, eye-catching artwork is the perfect backdrop for the friends' bold coffee choices. A freezer menu of rare and interesting beans means there are usually at least ten different options available alongside the house roast from Dark Arts in London. The line-up is resolutely international, with a different country showcased each month in the guest spot – expect to encounter the likes of Friedhats, Ripsnorter and People Possession.

Established
2022

Key roaster
Dark Arts Coffee

Brewing method
Espresso,
batch filter,
pourover

Machine
Victoria Arduino
Eagle One Prima

Grinder
Mahlkonig EK43 S,
Mahlkonig E65

Opening hours
Wed-Sun
10am-4pm

SWINDON

141

DORSET & WILTSHIRE
ROASTERIES

84 READS COFFEE ROASTERS

Limekiln Farm, Thornford Road, Sherborne, Dorset, DT9 6PS

readscoffee.co.uk | 01935 481010

f readscoffee *⊙ readscoffeeroasters*

A trip to the West Coast of the USA at the height of the Seattle coffee boom led to the birth of Reads Coffee Roasters. Inspired, founders Giles and Charlotte started experimenting in rural Oxfordshire. Six years later, organic growth saw the operation move to a converted dairy in Dorset.

Over three decades, Reads has become a success story built on single origins and interesting espresso blends. The roastery's trademark Sumatra Bourbon Espresso delivers deliciously smooth cappuccinos and flat whites, while Limekiln is lighter, its African beans bringing brighter notes to the fore. The classic Neapolitan-style blend, Casa di Montagna, balances sweetness and low acidity to produce a fantastically smooth, authentic espresso.

'READS HAS BECOME A SUCCESS STORY BUILT ON SINGLE ORIGINS AND INTERESTING BLENDS'

Beans are slow-roasted on a 25kg Probat to provide a full flavour and packed in newly introduced 100 per cent recyclable bags complete with a zip and resealing tab for optimum storage. Reads also offers accessories, barista training, and machine supply and service.

Established
1999

Roaster make and size
Probat P25-2 25kg,
Ambex YM-15 10kg,
Roastilino 200g

SHERBORNE

144

85 GROUNDED COFFEE ROASTERS

14 Kingland Crescent, Poole, Dorset, BH15 1TB

groundedcoffeeroasters.com | 07572 377336

f *groundedcoffeeroasters* @ *groundedcoffeeroasters*

In 2015, husband-and-wife team Rosie and Jon Rowe launched their business by restoring a rusty old Land Rover and converting it into a coffee truck, which they named Arthur. They now have a fleet of trucks, a shop, a roastery, a team of baristas – and a three-year-old daughter called Lola.

'A 15KG TOPER TAKES THE STRAIN SO THE SMALLER MODEL CAN HANDLE SMALL-BATCH BLENDS'

In 2019, the Rowes began roasting their own coffee from their shop – a venture so successful it outgrew both its premises and the original 5kg Toper. Taking over the unit next door, in February 2024 they opened an extended roastery-cafe where a 15kg Toper takes the strain so the smaller model can handle small-batch blends and experimental roasts.

The coffee offering follows the seasons, from the summer-inspired Sweet Breeze to Winter Nights. Other options include Storm (an Indian Monsoon Malabar blend with brown spice flavours) and a Swiss water-processed Mexican decaf (a rich and bold coffee without the caffeine kick). Check out the fortnightly or monthly subscription and the online shop.

Established
2019

Roaster make and size
Toper 15kg,
Aillio Bullet 1kg

86 DUSTY APE COFFEE ROASTERS

Unit 1 Marsh Farm Industrial Estate, Hilperton, Trowbridge, Wiltshire, BA14 7PJ

dustyape.com | 01225 753838

f *dustyapecoffee* **◎** *dustyape*

Since the roastery doors opened in 2013, the Dusty Ape team have been anything but idle. Expanding their roasting capacity tenfold and enhancing the on-site cafe with cutting-edge Sanremo technology, they've curated an extensive selection of the finest small-batch-roasted beans.

Currently, Dusty Ape offers a remarkable line-up of 21 distinct coffees sourced from 12 origins, including three varieties that are a result of the team's recent expeditions to Rwanda and El Salvador. The company's commitment to fostering strong relationships with growers at origin is reflected in its long-term partnerships with farms in Brazil and Guatemala.

'THEY'VE CURATED AN EXTENSIVE SELECTION OF THE FINEST SMALL-BATCH-ROASTED BEANS'

While the roastery's success is underpinned by its wholesale arm – which includes distributing Sanremo equipment, training, and installing and servicing an expanded range of kit – domestic coffee enthusiasts aren't left out. Those eager to experience Dusty Ape first-hand can visit the Wiltshire HQ to purchase coffee and savour the daily changing selection of four different beans. For those unable to make a trip, the full offering is also available online.

Established
2013

Roaster make and size
Diedrich CR-35 35kg, Probat Probatone P12 12kg, Probat Probatino 1kg

MORE GOOD FINDS IN WILTSHIRE & DORSET

COFFEE SHOPS

RIPTIDE ESPRESSO & RECORDS - BOURNEMOUTH
204-206 Commercial Road, Bournemouth,
Dorset, BH2 5NF
riptideespresso.co.uk

RIPTIDE ESPRESSO & RECORDS - POOLE
2 Grand Parade, High Street,
Poole, Dorset, BH15 1AD
riptideespresso.co.uk

SONDER COFFEE - SALISBURY
35 High Street, Salisbury,
Wiltshire, SP1 2NJ
sondercoffee.co.uk

THE SALISBURY ORANGERY
102 Crane Street, Salisbury,
Wiltshire, SP1 2QD
thesalisburyorangery.com

ROASTERIES

CARVE COFFEE ROASTERS
Unit 16 Anvil Centre, Prospect Business
Park, Prospect Way, Swanage,
Dorset, BH19 1EJ
carvecoffee.co.uk

FINCA COFFEE ROASTERS
Unit 101, 20-22 The Grove, Dorchester,
Dorset, DT1 1ST
fincacoffee.co.uk

FOUNTAIN ROCK COFFEE
6a Albany Road, Weymouth,
Dorset, DT4 9TH
fountainrockcoffee.co.uk

GIRLS WHO GRIND COFFEE
Unit 2 Millards Farm, Upton Scudamore,
Wiltshire, BA12 0AQ
girlswhogrindcoffee.com

PEARHAUS COFFEE
Unit 5, 4-6 Abingdon Road,
Poole, Dorset, BH17 0UG
pearhauscoffee.com

GLOUCESTERSHIRE & OXFORDSHIRE
COFFEE SHOPS

⊗ CAFES

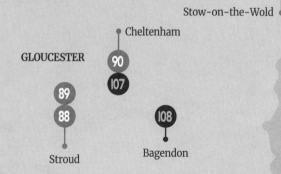

91

Stow-on-the-Wold

Cheltenham

GLOUCESTER

90

107

89

88

108

Stroud

Bagendon

87

Lydney

GLOUCESTERSHIRE

106

Yate

CITY CENTRE

Banbury

OXFORDSHIRE

OXFORD

Wheatley

Abingdon

Brightwell-cum-Sotwell

Peppard Common

Find more good coffee shops and
roasteries on page 183.

All locations are approximate

87 HIPS SOCIAL

71 Newerne Street, Lydney, Gloucestershire, GL15 5RA

hipssocial.co.uk | 01594 368628

📷 *hips_social*

Gloriously delicious food is a priority at this family-run coffee shop in the heart of historic Lydney. At the crack of dawn, its kitchens become a hive of activity as the team turn their hands to baking cakes, preparing sauces, slow-cooking meats and pickling vegetables. It's important to owners Lucy Buckingham and Tom Davies that every dish is crafted from scratch using regional ingredients. Homemade doughnuts ooze with unctuous fillings while buns are spiced with cinnamon, cardamom and orange.

TIP GRAB A TAKEAWAY COFFEE, CAKE OR TOASTIE AT HIPS SOCIAL'S LITTLE BROTHER, HIPS HARBOURSIDE

Locals arrive early for breakfasts which include bowls of porridge or yogurt; baps layered with bacon, black pudding and eggs; and sourdough topped with avocado, pickled red onion and dukkah. Lunchtime is an equally scrumptious affair featuring flavour-packed burritos, salads and toasties.

The coffee is just as carefully prepared: the house espresso was developed by Worcester's Studio Coffee Roasters, while a rotation of guest roasteries – including James Gourmet, Fire & Flow and Cuppers Choice – ensures there's always something new to try.

Established
2020

Key roaster
Studio Coffee Roasters

Brewing method
Espresso

Machine
Faema E71

Grinder
Victoria Arduino Mythos One

Opening hours
Mon, Wed
7.30am–4pm
Thu–Fri
7.30am–8.30pm
Sat
9am–8.30pm
Sun
9am–4pm

LYDNEY

152

88 ROUGH HANDS COFFEE

32 Five Valleys Shopping Centre, Stroud, Gloucestershire, GL5 1RR

roughhandscoffee.co.uk

🖸 *roughhandscoffee*

The baristas at this multi-roastery coffee shop might be working with some of the best beans in the business, but they take a 'no bullshit or bravado' approach when it comes to communicating with their customers. Everyone is welcome and curiosity is encouraged.

Founding barista Samuel Humphris slung shots in speciality cafes for a decade before establishing Rough Hands in 2021. To create the coffee shop of his dreams, Samuel selected the best bits of each of his previous workplaces and blended them with his own creativity to form a space that makes speciality accessible.

TIP NO VISIT IS COMPLETE WITHOUT CHECKING OUT THE "SATANIC" BATHROOM

The house espresso is roasted nearby by two-time UK Barista Championship finalist Callum Parsons at Fire & Flow. The El Salvadoran single origin serves up notes of chocolate, toffee and almond, making it the ultimate base for a crowd-pleasing flat white. The guest spot showcases beans from further afield such as London's Dark Arts and Wide Awake in Brussels.

Sister shop Glazed Bakehouse supplies next-level vegan doughnuts and banging baked goods, the flavours of which are updated seasonally.

Established
2021

Key roaster
Fire & Flow
Coffee Roasters

Brewing method
Espresso, V60,
AeroPress, Kalita
Wave, batch filter

Machine
La Marzocco
Linea PB

Grinder
Mahlkonig E65S
GbW, Mahlkonig
EK43, Victoria
Arduino Mythos 2

Opening hours
Mon-Sat
8am-4pm
Sun
9.30am-4pm

89 STAR ANISE CAFE

1 Gloucester Street, Stroud, Gloucestershire, GL5 1QG

staranisecafe.co.uk | 01453 840021

f *staranisestroud* *@* *staranisecafe*

Some hospitality venues come and go with the latest trends, while others ignore fads in favour of remaining true to their founding principles and enjoy a long and happy life as a result. Crafting seasonal food in a friendly environment for two decades, Star Anise is one such cafe.

The team's mission from day one has been simple: to provide delicious, nourishing food and drink to Stroud's thriving community. Friends and families gather here to sip Extract coffee, chomp plant-based pastries and tuck into wholesome dishes made with predominantly organic ingredients.

TIP TRY THE GUEST COFFEE FROM LOCAL ROASTERY NONI'S

The menu changes often, depending on what the chefs can source locally, but it's mostly veggie and vegan (except for Fish and Chip Fridays). Brunch stalwarts include eggs florentine with pickled radish and spring onion, while lunchtime welcomes vibrant salads, hearty soups and creative specials.

In spring and summer, the courtyard is the place to be. Grab a seat among the flowers and herbs, then order the house-favourite donburi bowl.

Established
2004

Key roaster
Extract Coffee Roasters

Brewing method
Espresso

Machine
La Marzocco

Grinder
Victoria Arduino Mythos One

Opening hours
Mon–Sat
8.30am–3.30pm
Sun
10am–2pm

STROUD

154

90 BOTANICA

Bramery Business Park, Cheltenham, Gloucestershire, GL51 8HE
botanicacoffeekitchen.squarespace.com | 01242 703102
f botanicacoffeekitchen ⊙ *botanica_coffee_kitchen*

An industrial estate on the outskirts of Cheltenham isn't the first place you'd expect to find a green oasis of calm, good caffeine and crazy-delicious brunch dishes, but this coffee shop and kitchen in Bramery Business Park is no mirage.

Locals and day-trippers (it's only a five-minute walk from Cheltenham Spa station) stream into this houseplant-filled space to chill out with Cotswolds-roasted coffee and chow down on seasonal staples from the creative kitchen team.

TIP CHECK OUT SISTER VENUE ARC OPPOSITE CHELTENHAM SPA TRAIN STATION

Fire & Flow provides the goods in the hopper, which the talented baristas craft into a line-up of consistently slick espresso adorned with latte art. Ask for an inverted swan – it's pretty impressive.

All-day brunch plates range from classics (next-level full English with homemade beans and sourdough toast from award-winning Peter Cooks Bread) to innovative specials such as heritage tomatoes with basil and cashew pesto, ricotta salata, capers and whipped chilli butter beans. However, if all you require is a sweet hit with your caffeine, the pastries alone (baked at the Botanica Bakery) are worth making a journey out of town for.

Established
2018

Key roaster
Fire & Flow
Coffee Roasters

Brewing method
Espresso

Machine
La Marzocco
Linea PB

Grinder
Victoria Arduino
Mythos One

Opening hours
Mon-Fri
8am-3.30pm
Sat-Sun
9am-3pm

CHELTENHAM

155

91 STOW TOWN COFFEE

2 Wells Barn, Sheep Street, Stow-on-the-Wold, Gloucestershire, GL54 1AA

stowtowncoffee.co.uk | 01451 832519

f *stowtowncoffee* ⓞ *stowtowncoffee*

Tucked under an archway in the picturesque Cotswold town of Stow-on-the-Wold, this tiny espresso bar and artisan micro-roastery is a real hidden gem.

Stow Town Coffee founders Dave and Ali Cunliffe run one of the smallest commercial roasteries in the UK from their wonderfully compact Sheep Street venue, and sell beans direct to customers at the roastery's in-house coffee shop as well as to a handful of local businesses.

The couple are passionate about speciality coffee and roast in micro-size batches to ensure there's always something super fresh and tasty for customers to sample via espresso or drip. Those keen to gen up on their coffee know-how can ask for a roasting demo to see how raw green beans are transformed into the coffee they know and love.

TIP POP IN FOR A TAKEAWAY COFFEE IF THERE'S AN AFTERNOON ROASTING SESSION IN PROGRESS

When it comes to choosing what to drink at the cafe, you don't need to worry about feeling overwhelmed by choice as Stow Town's straightforward line-up features an espresso blend, single origin and chemical-free decaf.

Established
2017

Key roaster
Stow Town Coffee

Brewing method
Espresso, pourover

Machine
Fracino Contempo

Grinder
Ceado E37S

Opening hours
Mon-Fri
7.30am-2pm
Sat
8am-12pm

STOW-ON-THE-WOLD

156

92 MISSING BEAN - BANBURY

70 High Street, Banbury, Oxfordshire, OX16 5JG
themissingbean.co.uk | 01295 367172
f themissingbean *◎ missingbeancoffeeshops*

Ride a cock horse to Banbury Cross and you'll find a cracking cup of coffee awaits. After building its reputation in Oxford, in 2021 Missing Bean became the first speciality coffee shop to make its home on Banbury High Street. It quickly gained a loyal following, thanks to a laid-back and homely vibe that draws a regular flow of customers who like to settle in and chat with the staff and each other.

Choose from a range of direct-trade espresso and rotating filter coffees, then pair your pour with a sugary treat fresh from Missing Bean's in-house bakery. To replicate the experience in your own home, pick up single-origin beans from the retail section (they can be ground to order).

TIP BUY YOUR HOME COFFEE KIT HERE, WITH A RANGE OF OPTIONS INCLUDING AEROPRESS AND V60

Grab a seat and watch the world go by as you sip and slurp, or order a flattie to-go and explore this lively market town on the River Cherwell. And if you're in town on a Thursday, don't miss the opportunity to scoff a Pippin & Co artisan doughnut with your coffee.

Established
2021

Key roaster
Missing Bean
Coffee Roasters

Brewing method
Espresso,
batch filter

Machine
La Marzocco Linea
PB ABR

Grinder
Mahlkonig EK43,
Anfim Pratica,
Mahlkonig E65 GbW

Opening hours
Mon-Sat
8am-4pm
Sun
9am-3pm

93 MISSING BEAN - BOTLEY

2 Church Way, Botley, Oxford, Ox2 9TH

themissingbean.co.uk | 01865 634536

f *themissingbean* **◎** *missingbeancoffeeshops*

This Missing Bean branch in an up-and-coming area of west Oxford is conveniently placed on the edge of a residential area and close to offices, so is always a busy hive of activity.

Meeting the needs of this clientele, the team pride themselves on their speed of service and the venue enjoys a reputation as the go-to for lunch or a cheeky pre-work breakfast. Its large outdoor seating space sees the cafe double in size during dry weather, which is especially useful on sunny Sundays when this is one of the few places open in Botley.

Everything served is delivered daily from Missing Bean's east Oxford HQ, where the coffee beans are roasted and packed in-house. Similarly, all of the food – from cakes and sweet pastries to sausage rolls and sandwiches – are prepared each morning in the bakery.

TIP BE SURE TO TRY A DOORSTEP SARNIE ON MISSING BEAN'S SIGNATURE SOURDOUGH

While Missing Bean is woven into the fabric of Oxford life, the team also consider the company's impact at a national and global level. Provenance and fair treatment are keywords here, so all coffees are sourced either direct from their grower or via like-minded green-bean importers.

Established
2021

Key roaster
Missing Bean
Coffee Roasters

Brewing method
Espresso,
batch filter

Machine
La Marzocco
Strada AV ABR

Grinder
Mahlkonig EK43,
Anfim Pratica,
Mahlkonig E80
Supreme

Opening hours
Mon-Fri
8am-4pm
Sat-Sun
9am-4pm

94 COLOMBIA COFFEE ROASTERS - SUMMERTOWN

267 Banbury Road, Summertown, Oxford, OX2 7HT

colombiacoffeeroasters.co.uk | 07738 068820

f CoffeeColombia *⊙ colombiacoffeeroasters*

Colombian coffees are famed for their lip-smacking sweet notes and smooth palate-pleasing profiles, which you'll find in abundance at this Oxford cafe. The Summertown outpost is where the CCR family serve up a dizzyingly fresh selection of own-roasted beans, all of which have been ethically sourced from different regions of Colombia.

Direct relationships with producers at origin ensure quality is top-notch and farmers are paid a fair price for their crop. Another benefit of being in regular contact is it helps the roasters stay at the forefront of growing and processing innovations, so they get their hands on the most interesting beans.

TIP *WHISPERS* SOMETIMES THE BARISTAS SERVE GUEST COFFEES FROM OTHER ORIGINS

Take your single-origin brew (crafted using your preferred method) to one of the wooden tables in the light-filled cafe and explore the all-day brunch menu. That's if you've not already been swayed by the countertop display of scrumptious bagels, sandwiches and cakes.

Don't leave without checking out the coffee goodies in the retail section and picking a bag of beans for your home hopper.

Established
2019

Key roaster
Colombia Coffee Roasters

Brewing method
Espresso, batch filter, AeroPress, drip, syphon

Machine
La Marzocco KB90

Grinder
Mahlkonig E65S, Mahlkonig EK43, Victoria Arduino Mythos 2

Opening hours
Mon-Sun
7.30am-5pm

95 BREW

75 Banbury Road, Oxford, OX2 6PE

brewoxford.co.uk

f brewoxford *⊙ brewoxford*

This Oxford speciality staple is freshening things up in 2024, relocating to a roomier spot very close to the original Banbury Road digs. The move will enable the team to broaden the cafe's food offering while also staying in the neighbourhood in which the cafe is known and loved.

Serving speciality for over a decade, Brew has grown a following of local coffee lovers who share the team's excitement for quality beans. The house espresso is roasted in Somerset by the experts at Round Hill, but the real draw are the filter coffees.

TIP IN A RUSH? THE TEAM PRIDE THEMSELVES ON THEIR SPEEDY AND EFFICIENT SERVICE

The coffee menu is split into processing methods, such as washed, anaerobic and natural, and each showcases a different coffee to sample. The roasteries providing the goods change regularly, but expect to encounter the likes of Berlin's The Barn, Leeds' North Star and Brighton's Skylark.

Brew's top-flight coffee draws a diverse crowd who pair their picks with homemade cakes and, on Thursdays, plump doughnuts from the bakers at Pippin & Co.

Established
2013

Key roaster
Round Hill Roastery

Brewing method
Espresso, V60

Machine
Elektra Sixties

Grinder
Victoria Arduino
Mythos One,
Mahlkonig EK43

Opening hours
Mon–Fri
7.30am–5pm
Sat–Sun
8.30am–5pm
(seasonal opening hours)

96 TREE ARTISAN CAFE

3 Little Clarendon Street, Oxford, OX1 2HP

01865 507431

treeartisancafe

Rabbit, parrot, bear, seahorse or even unicorn ... name an animal and there's a good chance the creative baristas at this award-winning Oxford cafe can recreate it in latte art. The Tree crew attend events and festivals around the world to show off and improve their milk-steaming skills, so it's worth putting in an unusual request when you order a flat white or latte.

It's not just about aesthetics at Tree Artisan, of course. The team are equally enthused about flavour and work with Lucid Coffee Roasters in Belfast to deliver reliably consistent espresso and whistle-clean V60 and AeroPress brews. The Brazilian house blend has a velvety, nutty and fruity composition – the perfect base for a crowd-pleasing flat white.

TIP DON'T MISS THE SEASONAL DRINKS SPECIALS SUCH AS WINTER-SPICED DARK HOT CHOCOLATE

While the baristas may be masters of their trade, the vibe is pleasingly relaxed and friendly. The team are always keen to strike up a conversation; they know most of the regulars by name and their orders off by heart.

Established
2020

Key roaster
Lucid Coffee Roasters

Brewing method
Espresso, V60, AeroPress

Machine
Slayer

Grinder
Mythos MY85

Opening hours
Mon-Fri
7.30am-6pm
Sat
8am-6pm
Sun
8.30am-6pm

97 COMMON GROUND OXFORD

37-38 Little Clarendon Street, Oxford, OX1 2HU

commongroundoxford.com

 commongroundoxford

In February 2023, Eddie Whittingham took on ownership of Common Ground and resolved to reinvent the already friendly space with a new MO: social entrepreneurship and creative enablement.

During a busy first year, Eddie and team made serious ground in their mission. The space has been transformed into a multi-purpose cafe and arts venue via a change of decor, new relationships with local suppliers and strengthened links with the community. They've also launched the Common Ground Collective, introducing a bookshop and ceramic studio within the cafe. The team are constantly tuned in to the needs of the neighbourhood, transitioning the space from cafe to evening venue for a range of events – from music gigs to comedy shows.

TIP ALL SUPPLIERS ARE LOCAL, SO PAIR YOUR COFFEE WITH A PASTRY TO SUPPORT THE COMMUNITY

The coffee offering is equally as inspiring. Oxford's Missing Bean supplies the house roast (at time of writing it was a seasonal house espresso from Finca Hamburgo in Mexico), while the guest line-up changes often (previous appearances include Routes, Curve, Skylark, Vibe With, Colonna and Bailies). There's a smorgasbord of serve styles to try out, so adventurous sippers are guaranteed to encounter something new each time they visit.

Established
2018

Key roaster
Missing Bean
Coffee Roasters

Brewing method
Espresso,
AeroPress,
batch filter, drip,
Chemex, Orea

Machine
La Marzocco
Linea Classic S

Grinder
Mahlkonig E65S

Opening hours
Mon-Fri
7.30am-5.30pm
Sat-Sun
8am-4.30pm

OXFORD

162

98 COLOMBIA COFFEE ROASTERS

106-107 The Covered Market, Oxford, OX1 3DY

colombiacoffeeroasters.co.uk

f coffeecolombia *◎ colombiacoffeeroasters*

This speciality hotspot, housed within the city's covered market alongside 50 other indie businesses, serves Colombian coffee to Oxford's caffeine fans.

Thanks to the roastery arm of this family-run coffee company, there's a kid-in-a-sweet-shop selection of fresh single-origin beans to explore. Make your choice then ask the baristas which brew style they recommend to go with it.

TIP THIS COFFEE SPOT WAS VOTED OXFORD MAIL BEST CAFE IN 2022

Beans are sourced from ethical coffee farms across Colombia; by using beans from just one country, the CCR team are able to showcase the rich diversity of flavours the terroir can offer. Don't be daunted by the lengthy menu scribbled on the wall. If you don't know whether to sample the washed-process single origin as syphon or AeroPress, the crew are on hand to help you find the perfect serve style.

Opt for a milk-based coffee to delight in the crew's impressive latte art skills – some of the baristas even craft unicorns and horses rather than hearts and swans. Need something carby? You're in luck as the kitchen specialities are bagels, sandwiches and cakes.

Established
2015

Key roaster
Colombia Coffee Roasters

Brewing method
Espresso, drip, AeroPress, syphon, batch filter

Machine
La Marzocco KB90

Grinder
Mahlkonig E65S, Mahlkonig EK43, Victoria Arduino Mythos 2

Opening hours
Mon-Thu
9am-5.30pm
Fri-Sat
9am-6pm
Sun
10am-5pm

OXFORD

99 MISSING BEAN - OXFORD

14 Turl Street, Oxford, OX1 3DQ

themissingbean.co.uk | 01865 794886

f *themissingbean* **@** *missingbeancoffeeshops*

Missing Bean on Turl Street was Oxford city centre's first speciality coffee shop when it opened in 2009 – and went on to become the parent of a family of six other cafes in the wider area.

Company co-founders Ori Halup and Vicky Troth caught the coffee bug while working in Sydney and, upon returning to the UK, found they missed the opportunity to sip well-crafted coffee in cool surroundings. Having committed to setting the matter straight by opening a cafe themselves, it was Vicky's home city that was the natural choice for their launch outlet. They clearly picked well as Turl Street has been a huge hit with workers, students and visitors alike.

TIP NEED TO COOL DOWN? MISSING BEAN LAUNCHED ITS COLD BREW CANS IN SUMMER 2023

Swing by to try the staff-favourite Ethiopian batch brew and stay for a natter with the friendly team, who know their way around everything from a single-estate macchiato to a seasonal filter.

Established
2009

Key roaster
Missing Bean
Coffee Roasters

Brewing method
Espresso,
batch filter

Machine
La Marzocco KB90

Grinder
Mahlkonig EK43,
Mahlkonig E80
Supreme,
Eureka Zenith

Opening hours
Mon–Fri
8am–4.30pm
Sat
9am–5pm
Sun
10am–4pm

OXFORD

164

100 JERICHO COFFEE TRADERS

105 High Street, Oxford, OX1 4BW
jerichocoffeetraders.com

f *jerichocoffeetraders* ⓘ *jerichocoffeetraders*

Situated in the heart of the city on Oxford's busy High Street, Jericho Coffee Traders is a buzzy little espresso bar crammed with locals and tourists who've popped in for a dose of locally roasted coffee.

It's just one arm of the Jericho Coffee Traders mini empire, run by James and Lizzie Armitage, which also includes a roastery with on-site cafe and coffee school, and a fleet of eco-friendly tuk-tuk coffee carts and bikes which turn up at events across the city.

TIP LEARN THE BREWING BASICS AT JERICHO'S COFFEE SCHOOL

Jericho's beans are sourced ethically via experienced traders from farms across the coffee-growing belt, and the range of origins can be tasted in a variety of serve styles at the bar. Regulars swear by the Burundian Mwami, a super sweet and velvety single origin featuring notes of juicy berries, citrus and caramel, with a chocolatey finish. Whatever you choose, pair your pick with a homemade wedge of cake then nab a perch (outdoors if the weather is good) to people watch.

Established
2017

Key roaster
Jericho Coffee
Traders

Brewing method
Espresso,
batch filter

Machine
La Marzocco Linea
PB AV

Grinder
Mahlkonig EK43,
Mahlkonig E65 GbW
× 2

Opening hours
Mon-Fri
8am-5.30pm
Sat
8.30am-5.30pm
Sun
10am-5pm

OXFORD

165

blendsmiths

CRAFTED FOR THE CURIOUS

101 MAYA'S CAFE BAR

121b Queen Street, Westgate, Oxford, OX1 1PB

mayascoffee.store | 07428 564052

⊙ *mayascoffeeoxford*

This popular cafe and shop is a well-loved Oxford speciality spot, yet only two years ago it was just starting out as a fledgling coffee business.

With time to think about their passions during the pandemic, brothers Edward and Charlie Harries-Jones converted an old horsebox into a mobile coffee cart. Named after their late grandmother, Maya's was a hit and, in 2022, the brothers opened their first cafe at Westgate Oxford (one of only two independent venues in the shopping complex).

TIP CHECK OUT MAYA'S OWN-BRAND CACAO BARS

The chaps are serious about showcasing local talent, so many of the beans on the menu are roasted nearby. When they do venture further afield it's done with purpose, and they work with indies that share their commitment to supporting their local communities. Examples include non-profit roastery Skylark in East Sussex and Redemption, which trains prisoners in coffee roasting skills at HMP The Mount in Hemel Hempstead.

The baristas are well versed in the coffees and their back stories, so ask about your brew's positive impact and soak up the good juju as you sip.

Established
2021

Key roaster
Skylark Coffee

Brewing method
Espresso, V60, batch filter, AeroPress

Machine
Victoria Arduino Eagle One

Grinder
Victoria Arduino Mythos MY85

Opening hours
Mon-Sun
8am-7pm

102 MOSTRO COFFEE

101 Cowley Road, Oxford, OX4 1HU

mostro.coffee | 01865 793866

f mostrocoffeeoxford | *⊙ mostrocoffee*

This coffee shop within Oxford's Truck record store received a refresh at the end of 2023, yet its focus on serving fruit-forward espresso and the city's juiciest batch brew remains the same.

Given its setting, it's no surprise that music plays a central role in the Mostro experience. A banging playlist is the backdrop for skilled baristas at the slick black bar, who fashion espresso on a La Marzocco and batch filter via Orea. Visitors may even be lucky enough to catch an impromptu free gig by a touring artist in the cafe space.

TIP PAIR YOUR BATCH WITH A SKOGEN KITCHEN KANELBULLAR (CINNAMON BUN)

The team love working with bright, clean coffees from East Africa and Central America, and source them from a variety of UK and European roasteries. There'll usually be a few options from Origin in Cornwall, as well as guests from the likes of Skylark, Round Hill, Coffee by Tate, Vibe With and Manhattan.

Artisan pastries from local bakers – try Barefoot Oxford's buttery croissants – round off the short but sweet offering.

Established
2015

Key roaster
Origin Coffee
Roasters

Brewing method
Espresso,
batch filter

Machine
La Marzocco Strada

Grinder
Mahlkonig E65S
GbW,
Mahlkonig EK43

Opening hours
Mon–Fri
8.30am–6pm
Sat
10am–6pm
Sun
10am–5pm

OXFORD

103 GREEN ROUTES

39 Magdalen Road, Oxford, OX4 1RB

routescoffee.co.uk

f *greenroutescafe* @ *greenroutescafe*

This modern meeting place on Magdalen Road is the cafe counterpart to high-flying Oxford roastery Routes. It's a community-focused spot where customers can try the latest roasts from HQ while also enjoying some of the best plant-based dishes in the region. It was even namechecked in *Vogue* as the home of 'Oxford's most exciting vegan brunch'.

Routes' roasting team are focused on supporting coffee farmers and have adopted a fully transparent, direct-source approach to ensure growers are rewarded for their graft. The team's latest collection of signature blends and single origins is available to sample as espresso or drip, while cold brew makes an appearance in warmer months.

TIP VISIT ON THURSDAY EVENINGS FOR SUPPER, NATURAL WINE AND CRAFT BEER

Seasonal and sustainable plant-forward dishes are served all day. Make a morning trip for pancakes piled with honeydew mango, granola and coconut yogurt, or visit at lunch for savoury compilations such as toasted sourdough sarnies stuffed with tofu pastrami, gherkins, sauerkraut, onion strings and russian dressing.

Established
2019

Key roaster
Routes Coffee Roasters

Brewing method
Espresso, drip, cold brew

Machine
La Marzocco Linea PB

Grinder
Mahlkonig E65S GbW, Victoria Arduino Mythos One, Mahlkonig EK43

Opening hours
Mon–Wed, Fri
8am–4pm
Thu
8am–10pm
Sat–Sun
9am–4pm

OXFORD

169

104 MISSING BEAN - ROASTERY CAFE

1 Newtec Place, Magdalen Road, Oxford, OX4 1RE

themissingbean.co.uk | 01865 492828

f themissingbean *missingbeancoffeeshops*

Having established an artisan coffee roastery in east Oxford in 2014, it was a natural progression for the Missing Bean crew to offer their followers the opportunity to sip on-site. The resulting laid-back cafe space within the original roastery is a powerhouse: everything on sale has been roasted or baked within its four walls.

For visitors popping in to pick up beans to brew at home, friendly baristas are on hand to share expert advice on grinding and brewing in a range of serve styles. Those settling in for a coffee in-house can sample the latest roasts via batch filter or espresso, with a flourish of accomplished latte art.

TIP BRING CONTAINERS FROM HOME TO STOCK UP ON FRESH COFFEE BEANS AT THE REFILL STATION

This is the perfect environment in which to chill out, so grab a bite to eat (sweet or savoury, courtesy of the in-house bakery) and watch beans bronzing in the Giesen machine as you slurp and munch. On dry days, park yourself in the outside seating area, or bring a reusable cup to bag a discount on takeaway drinks and take a stroll along the river.

Established
2014

Key roaster
Missing Bean Coffee Roasters

Brewing method
Espresso, batch filter

Machine
La Marzocco KB90

Grinder
Mahlkonig EK43, Mahlkonig E80S, Anfim Pratica

Opening hours
Mon-Fri
8am-4pm
Sat-Sun
9am-4pm

105 MISSING BEAN – ABINGDON

1 Stert Street, Abingdon, Oxfordshire, OX14 3JF

themissingbean.co.uk | 01235 538936

f themissingbean *◎ missingbeancoffeeshops*

Part of Oxfordshire's Missing Bean collective of speciality coffee shops, the Abingdon branch – in what's claimed to be England's oldest town – offers a slice of the city in a more tranquil location. This Missing Bean is also a pooch-friendly pit stop, thanks to its beautiful surroundings, including Abbey Gardens and the nearby riverside track along the Thames.

Let the knowledgeable staff guide you through a menu which includes a seasonal house espresso and signature single origins (both roasted at the Missing Bean roastery), then watch as they craft the perfect brew from your pick of the list. In their quest for ethical and sustainable excellence, the roasters always select beans for espresso from farmers with whom they have direct trade relationships. Other coffees are sourced from importers with similar values.

TIP FOR A MISSING BEAN EXPERIENCE CHEZ VOUS, GRAB BREWING EQUIPMENT AND BEANS IN STORE

Breakfast, brunch and lunch options hail from the Missing Bean bakery at the east Oxford roastery. Customers are kindly reminded that, despite Abingdon's 250-year tradition of bun throwing, the sweet treats are for eating only.

Established
2021

Key roaster
Missing Bean
Coffee Roasters

Brewing method
Espresso,
batch filter

Machine
La Marzocco Linea
PB ABR

Grinder
Mahlkonig EK43,
Mahlkonig E80
Supreme,
Anfim Pratica

Opening hours
Mon–Fri
8am–4pm
Sat–Sun
9am–4pm

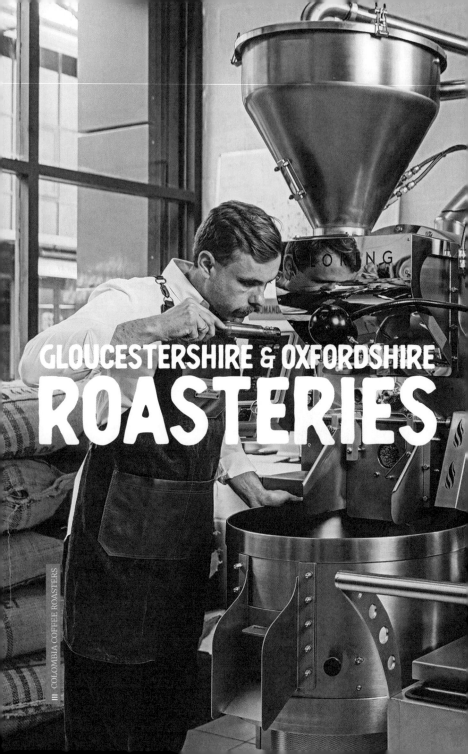

GLOUCESTERSHIRE & OXFORDSHIRE
ROASTERIES

106 COLONNA COFFEE

Unit 5 Apollo Park, Armstrong Way, Yate, Gloucestershire, BS37 5AH

colonnacoffee.com

f *colonnacoffee* @ *colonnacoffee*

Six years after launching Bath speciality coffee shop Colonna & Small's, founder Maxwell Colonna-Dashwood established this roastery to supply both his shop and discerning home brewers.

Innovation is Maxwell's driving force: not only has he won the UK Barista Championship three times, he's also published several books on speciality coffee, co-developed a specialist water-filtration jug and co-authored scientific papers on the subject. The same drive prevails at the roastery, where some of the world's finest and rarest coffees are roasted to exacting standards.

The core range is divided into four categories: Foundation, Discovery, Rare and Gesha. The genres represent the seasonality and flavour range of each coffee and help customers whittle down the vast selection of beans. Colonna was one of the innovators of speciality-grade capsule coffee, so those who favour convenience but don't want to compromise on quality can order fully recyclable pods to their door.

'THE WORLD'S RAREST COFFEES ROASTED TO EXACTING STANDARDS'

The latest addition to the Colonna brand is a new London coffee shop on Farringdon's Leather Lane. Visit to sample the roastery's experimental beans prepared by expert baristas.

Established
2015

Roaster make and size
Diedrich CR-70 70kg,
Diedrich CR-35 35kg,
Diedrich IR-12 12kg

YATE

174

107 RITUAL COFFEE ROASTERS

Units 31-32 Lansdown Ind Est, Gloucester Road, Cheltenham, Gloucestershire, GL51 8PL

ritualcoffee.org | 07341 843535

f ritualcoffeeroasters ⊙ ritualroasters

The philosophy at Ritual? If you do one thing, do it well. The team at this Cheltenham roastery go the extra mile to make their coffee the best it can be, nurturing long-lasting and sustainable relationships with farmers at origin and ensuring their wholesale partners know how to transform the beans into memorable flat whites.

'We're more than just a roaster; we're a partner in coffee,' says director Courtney Conroy. This partnership goes beyond supplying top-notch speciality beans and extends to barista training, equipment supply and set up, and being on-hand for advice and technical support.

'COFFEE FANS CAN VISIT THE ROASTERY TO SIP THE LATEST BLENDS'

The brand doesn't only satisfy wholesale customers, however, as coffee fans can visit the on-site brew bar to sample the signature House Blend flat white – a butterscotch, plum and cashew delight – alongside new blends and single origins. They can also tuck into brunch at The Ritual Kitchen where dishes such as braised beef-shin hash can be paired with a rich filter brew.

Established
2019

Roaster make and size
Samiac 20kg

108 FIRE & FLOW COFFEE ROASTERS

Unit 2a Tall Trees Estate, Bagendon, Cirencester, Gloucestershire, GL7 7JE

fireandflowcoffee.co.uk

f *fireandflowcoffee* ⊙ *fireandflowcoffee*

It's all go at this innovative Cotswolds roastery. Founders Callum Parsons and Charlotte and Phil Adams are always planning their next move and, in 2023, this included opening a plant-based cafe within the roastery and launching their first fruit-macerated coffee (a honey-processed Colombian with added wine yeast and orange infusion).

Collaborating with other local indies is a key element of the Fire & Flow philosophy. The team recently worked with Cotswold Lakes Brew Co. to craft a delish cold-brew coffee stout using their signature house blend Aurora. They also have an exciting Lion's Mane coffee (a collab with Slad Valley Mushrooms) in the pipeline – the mushrooms are thought to have health benefits such as regulating blood sugar and reducing blood pressure.

'COLLABORATING WITH OTHER LOCAL INDIES IS A KEY ELEMENT OF THE FIRE & FLOW PHILOSOPHY'

This synergistic approach extends to the roastery's wholesale partners too, who get 360-degree support. Going above and beyond simply supplying speciality beans, the F&F crew provide barista training, coffee education, menu innovation, service-flow consultancy, and machine servicing and maintenance.

Established
2020

Roaster make and size
Joper BSR KIT 15kg

109 JERICHO COFFEE TRADERS

Unit 2 Oxford Eco Centre, Osney Mead, Oxford, OX2 0ES

jerichocoffeetraders.com

f *jerichocoffeetraders* **◎** *jerichocoffeetraders*

James and Lizzie Armitage head up this ever-expanding speciality empire which has evolved from a mobile espresso bar to two coffee shops, a roastery and a coffee school.

Those with an interest in top-notch coffee but who lack the skills to brew it like a pro can book onto Jericho's Coffee Enthusiast Experience. The three-hour workshop covers the bean basics and how to grind, cup and brew at home. If that sounds too taxing, why not simply chill in the roastery-cafe and sample the goods as you watch the expert team in action?

'A GREAT WAY TO BROADEN THE PALATE AND SAMPLE BEANS YOU MIGHT NOT OTHERWISE TRY'

Beans for Jericho's clutch of coffee shops are sourced from Brazil, Colombia, Ecuador, Ethiopia, Rwanda and Kenya, and carefully bronzed on a Giesen W15A by head roaster Stretch.

There are a number of subscription options to get Jericho beans delivered to your door. Adventurous sippers will like the Surprise Package which drops a different speciality coffee each month. It's a great way to broaden the palate and sample beans you might not otherwise try.

Established
2015

Roaster make and size
Giesen W15A 15kg

110 MISSING BEAN COFFEE ROASTERS

Unit 1 Newtec Place, Magdalen Road, Oxford, OX4 1RE

themissingbean.co.uk | 01865 236650

f themissingbean | *@ missingbeancoffeeroasters*

The Missing Bean story began on Oxford's Turl Street in 2009, where founder Ori Halup opened his first coffee shop. Ori and team provided the coffee for a university college ball a year later, and in 2014 opened their own roastery. They've since added an on-site cafe, plus three further coffee shops in Botley, Banbury and Abingdon. The latest development is an in-house bakery which supplies the cafes with baked goodies.

Established
2014

Roaster make and size
Giesen W15A 15kg, IKAWA

'ADVENTUROUS COFFEE FANS CAN DROP INTO ONE OF THE REGULAR CUPPING NIGHTS'

Direct trade is at the heart of the business and on a scale unusual for a roaster of this size. To ensure their offer is ethical, the team strive to source single-origin coffees straight from farmers in Colombia, Kenya, Peru and Thailand and have recently sourced from Mexico and Nicaragua too. Beans from particularly remote locations are bought from independent importers who value close partnerships with farmers. Missing Bean's eco ambitions are achieved through fully compostable packaging, electric delivery vans and a local cycle courier.

Adventurous coffee fans can drop into one of the regular cupping nights or sign up to the subscription service to get a regular bean delivery.

||| COLOMBIA COFFEE ROASTERS

30 Wheatley Business Park, Old London Road, Wheatley, Oxfordshire, OX33 1XW

colombiacoffeeroasters.co.uk

f *CoffeeColombia* 📷 *colombiacoffeeroasters*

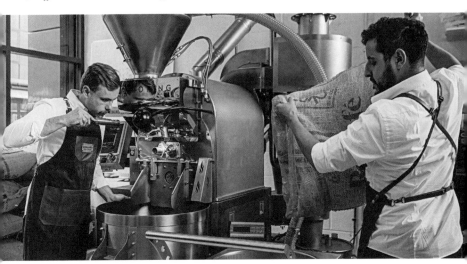

The team at this family-run roastery are passionate about Colombian coffee and share their enthusiasm for it with the people of Oxford via two city-centre coffee shops and a popular online subscription service.

They source, roast and brew their pick of the Colombian crop to showcase the incredible range of tasting notes that beans from the region have to offer. By maintaining direct relationships with producers, they exchange feedback with farmers and explore innovative growing and processing techniques. However, while Colombia is the main source of beans for this roastery, they do feature guest coffees from other origins to use in their blends.

'AN ENERGY-EFFICIENT LORING FALCON S15 IS USED TO ROAST THE COFFEE'

Sustainability is front of mind at CCR and the team are committed to contributing to Oxford's 2040 zero-carbon goal. An energy-efficient Loring Falcon S15 is used to roast the coffee before being packaged in recyclable aluminium-free bags.

The team recently opened the doors of the Wheatley roastery to the public. Join them for a deep dive into coffee roasting and pick up a bag of freshly roasted single-origin beans at the same time.

Established
2012

Roaster make and size
Loring Falcon S15
15kg

112 DARK HORSE ROASTERY

Highlands Farm, Brightwell-cum-Sotwell, Wallingford, Oxfordshire, OX10 0QX

darkhorseroastery.co.uk | 07887 656114

f *darkhorseroastery* **⊙** *darkhorseroastery*

As befitting a coffee business by the name of Dark Horse, this roastery can be found on a farm in rural Oxfordshire. Owner Emily Stewart spent two decades working in speciality coffee in London but, in 2018, was drawn back to her countryside home with a plan to establish and nurture a demand for ethical and sustainable coffee in this part of the world.

'LOOK OUT FOR EXPERIMENTAL MICRO-LOTS FROM THE VINHAL ESTATE IN BRAZIL'

Emily converted her childhood horsebox into a mobile coffee shop, dubbed The Horsebox Coffee Co. The set-up was so successful it spawned a diminutive partner on wheels, the Deux Chevaux. However, Emily's dream was always to build a roastery and education centre, something she realised in 2018. She named it Dark Horse in memory of an old friend and identified her ethos as 'teamwork, partnership and passion – from farmer to barista'.

The house signature blend uses beans from Fairtrade organic co-operatives in Guatemala and Honduras, sourced direct with the help of Algrano. Look out for experimental micro-lots from the Vinhal Estate in Brazil, which feature alongside the core collection of seasonal single-estate beans. A newer addition hails from the rural highlands of Timor-Leste and is sourced by Kar Yee and Stewart of Karst Organics.

Established
2018

Roaster make and size
Diedrich
IR-12 12kg,
Aillio Bullet 1kg

113 ANONYMOUS COFFEE CO.

Unit 16 Manor Farm, Peppard Common, Henley-on-Thames, Oxfordshire, RG9 5LA

anonymouscoffee.co.uk | 01491 756470

f *anonymouscoffeeco* **◎** *anonymouscoffeeco*

There's nothing anonymous about this Oxfordshire roastery. In fact, owner Phil Carter has an open-door policy at his Peppard Common enterprise, so curious caffeine fans can drop by for a brew at the coffee bar and have a nosey at his Genio roaster.

Established
2018

Roaster make and size
Genio 6kg

'OUR GOAL IS TO MAKE GREAT TASTING, SUSTAINABLY PRODUCED COFFEE'

Phil has worked in the speciality industry since 2008 and started roasting coffee in 2020, but it was when he got the keys to his own roastery in 2023 that Anonymous really roared into life. Sustainability and responsibility are the brand's guiding principles and, as well as paying over market value for coffee, using sustainable packaging and being a Living Wage employer, Phil is also working towards B Corp certification.

'Our goal is to make great tasting, sustainably produced coffee that's easy for people to discover and enjoy,' he says.

Those who can't make it to the roastery to sample the goods can order them online (local postcodes get free delivery). Explore the two house blends (Fernwood and No Name) as well as a raft of seasonal single origins from Africa and the Americas.

114 JERICHO COFFEE TRADERS

Unit 2 Oxford Eco Centre, Osney Mead, Oxford, OX2 0ES

jerichocoffeetraders.com

f *jerichocoffeetraders* @ *jerichocoffeetraders*

Want to hone your brewing skills at a roastery that shuns unnecessary jargon in favour of fun interactive courses? Jericho Coffee Traders' relaxed home-barista sessions fit the bill.

The coffee school was launched at the central Oxford roastery at the end of 2021 and has already polished the skills of hundreds of budding coffeesmiths.

The three-hour Coffee Enthusiast Experience is where speciality fans can learn about the bean-to-cup process. If you've ever wondered how and where high-grade coffee is made, and how to use cupping to taste the differences between regional coffees and various roast profiles, this hands-on course has the answers. Students can also learn how coffee flavours vary with different ratios, recipes and brewing methods (including V60, AeroPress and espresso).

'THE COFFEE SCHOOL HAS ALREADY POLISHED THE SKILLS OF HUNDREDS OF BUDDING COFFEESMITHS'

Tutees get the chance to nosey around the JCT engine room and roastery, and the complimentary coffee and pastries make this experience a great gift for coffee-loving friends. Bespoke training for aspiring baristas and cafes is available too.

Established
2021

OXFORD

182

MORE GOOD FINDS IN GLOUCESTERSHIRE & OXFORDSHIRE

COFFEE SHOPS

ANONYMOUS COFFEE CO.
Unit 16 Manor Farm, Peppard Common,
Henley-on-Thames, Oxfordshire, RG9 5LA
anonymouscoffee.co.uk

BRUIN CAFE
87a High Street, Wheatley,
Oxford, OX33 1XP

GLAZED BAKEHOUSE
13a Bedford Street, Stroud,
Gloucestershire, GL5 1AY
glazedbakehouse.com

HORSEBOX COFFEE COMPANY
Oxford University Museum of Natural
History, Parks Road, Oxford, OX1 3PW
horseboxcoffeeco.com

JIM BEANS
51 St Martin's Street, Wallingford,
Oxfordshire, OX10 0AJ

NEW ENGLAND COFFEE HOUSE
1 Digbeth Street, Stow-on-the-Wold,
Gloucestershire, GL54 1BN
newenglandcoffeehouse.com

NO.25 BENSON
25 High Street, Benson, Wallingford,
Oxfordshire, OX10 6RP
no25benson.co.uk

SORREL
2 Great Norwood Street, Cheltenham,
Gloucestershire, GL50 2AN
sorrel-stores.co.uk

THE OX SHED
5 Ratcliffe Court, Cholsey,
Oxfordshire, OX10 9QF
oxshed.co.uk

THE PAPER BOAT CAFE
The Old Toll House, Folly Bridge,
Oxford, OX1 4LB
the-paper-boat-cafe.business.site

UE COFFEE ROASTERY CAFE & KITCHEN
11a Windrush Industrial Park,
Linkwood Road, Witney,
Oxfordshire, OX29 7HA
uecoffeeroasters.com

ROASTERIES

NONI'S COFFEE ROASTERS
C5 Phoenix Trading Estate, London Road,
Stroud, Gloucestershire, GL5 2BX
noniscoffeeroasters.com

UE COFFEE ROASTERS
11a Windrush Industrial Park,
Linkwood Road, Witney,
Oxfordshire, OX29 7HA
uecoffeeroasters.com

BERKSHIRE, HAMPSHIRE & ISLE OF WIGHT
COFFEE SHOPS

✖ CAFES

✖ ROASTERIES

Find more good coffee shops and roasteries on page 203.

All locations are approximate

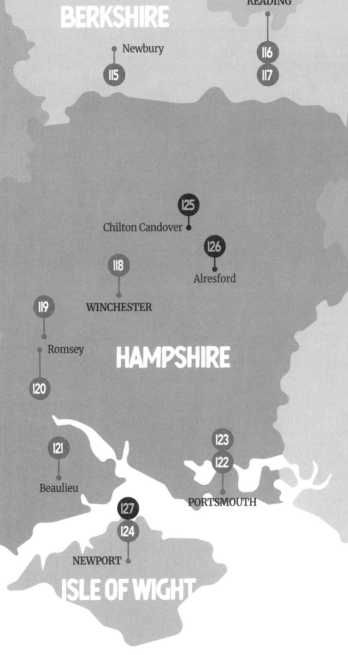

BERKSHIRE

READING

Newbury

116

115

117

125

Chilton Candover

126

118

Alresford

119

WINCHESTER

Romsey

HAMPSHIRE

120

121

123

Beaulieu

122

PORTSMOUTH

127

124

NEWPORT

ISLE OF WIGHT

115 MILK & BEAN

32 Northbrook Street, Newbury, Berkshire, RG14 1DJ
milkandbeancoffee.co.uk | 07960 087286
f *milkandbeancoffee* ⓞ *milkandbeancoffee*

Brewing top-notch coffee began as a hobby for Chris Chaplin and Freya Lynch. In 2021, the young couple bought a secondhand coffee machine (Bertha) and horsebox (Herbert) and put them together to serve flat whites and homemade cakes at local festivals and markets. When Chris lost his job at the end of that year, they read it as a sign to turn their shared passion into a career.

Milk & Bean's permanent site opened on Newbury's Northbrook Street in August 2023. The duo completely transformed a former chocolate shop and turned it into a bright, contemporary cafe accented with their signature navy-blue colour – even the custom La Marzocco is on brand.

TIP VISIT FOR COFFEE; STICK AROUND FOR CHEF FREYA'S FRIDAY BRUNCH MENU

From Milk & Bean's counter, the barista crafts silky espresso using Cast Iron's Unity house roast. There's also a Colombian sugarcane decaf from the Chichester roastery – which delivers flavours of chocolate brownie, Biscoff and plum – plus a rotating guest single origin available as V60 or batch.

Established
2023

Key roaster
Cast Iron
Coffee Roasters

Brewing method
Espresso,
batch filter, V60

Machine
La Marzocco
Linea PB X,
La Marzocco
Linea Mini

Grinder
Mahlkonig
E65S GbW,
Mazzer Robur E

Opening hours
Tue-Fri
7.30am–4pm
Sat
8am–4pm
Sun
9am–3pm

116 COFFEE UNDER PRESSURE - ST MARY'S BUTTS

53 St Mary's Butts, Reading, Berkshire, RG1 2LG
coffeeunderpressure.co.uk | 01189 503699
f coffeeunderpressure *@ coffeeundrpressure*

Tucked away in a peaceful spot in the heart of the city, next to the historic Reading Minster, Coffee Under Pressure's flagship cafe on St Mary's Butts is where locals and caffeine-savvy visitors convene to kick back with a cracking cup of coffee.

While this original shop has since been joined by two sister venues (one on Reading's Blagrave Street, the other in Bristol), the team have ensured quality remains top priority. Coffee is sourced from Missing Bean in Oxford and the baristas are trained to extract every drop of flavour from each dose.

TIP SUCKER FOR A MOCHA? TRY THE INDULGENT DARK CHOCOLATE VERSION

Two single-origin options for both espresso and filter guarantee a host of flavours, styles and processes to choose from. There are a further six single origins available in the retail section, allowing home brewers to continue their coffee explorations in their own kitchens.

The cafe's contemporary coffee offerings are complemented by a small selection of traditional Greek foods such as spinach and feta pie, as well as cakes and other carby treats.

Established
2015

Key roaster
Missing Bean
Coffee Roasters

Brewing method
Espresso, V60,
AeroPress

Machine
La Marzocco
Linea PB ABR

Grinder
Victoria Arduino
Mythos One × 2,
Mahlkonig EK43

Opening hours
Mon-Sun
10am-5pm

117 COFFEE UNDER PRESSURE - BLAGRAVE STREET

7 Blagrave Street, Reading, Berkshire, RG1 1PJ

coffeeunderpressure.co.uk | 01189 503699

f *coffeeunderpressure* ⊙ *coffeeundrpressure*

Railway station coffee is usually below par, so those hopping on or off the train at Reading are advised to detour just 100 metres from the station to this popular indie coffee shop.

Given its location, Coffee Under Pressure is usually a hive of activity at commuter o'clock, but from around 10am visitors can find a peaceful setting in which to sample a well-honed cup of speciality. Grab one of the stools or benches and pair your coffee with something tasty from the small consignment of cakes and pastries (including Greek custard pies).

TIP CAFE FULL TO THE BRIM? HEAD TO THE SISTER SITE ON ST MARY'S BUTTS

Beans, roasted in Oxford by the Missing Bean team, are strictly of the single-origin variety and are prepared as espresso, V60 or AeroPress. A rotating selection of four roasts gives customers the opportunity to try something fresh each time and to follow the coffee harvests around the globe. Or, for the ultimate in indulgence, order the house speciality: a white, milk or dark chocolate mocha.

Established
2018

Key roaster
Missing Bean
Coffee Roasters

Brewing method
Espresso, V60,
AeroPress

Machine
La Marzocco
Linea Classic

Grinder
Victoria Arduino
Mythos One × 2

Opening hours
Mon-Fri
8am-3pm
Sat-Sun
10am-4pm

READING

118 CABINET ROOMS

1-2 De Lunn Buildings, Jewry Street, Winchester, Hampshire, SO23 8SA

cabinetrooms.com | 01962 866480

f cabinetroomswinchester *ⓞ cabinetrooms*

Eschewing contemporary trends in favour of their own mix of 1930s glamour and Bloomsbury-Group chic, Cabinet Rooms founders Gary Whiter and Marcus Roe have fashioned a one-of-a-kind venue for the discerning coffee drinkers of Winchester.

Whether dropping in to read the papers with a guest filter brew, catching up with friends over coffee cocktails or taking part in one of the regular clubs or events, visitors are made to feel at ease at this grown-up cafe-bar. Gary, Marcus and team have put huge effort into making the space inclusive and say: *'We wanted to create a haven for the creative and thoughtful who are looking for a place to meet like-minded people.'*

TIP TOO EARLY FOR A TIPPLE? PICK UP ONE OF THE PREMIXED COCKTAILS FOR LATER

Hearty breakfasts are served until midday followed by lunch until 2pm, where you'll find crowd-pleasers such as fresh soup, cheese and chutney toasties, and grab-and-go sandwiches for those with no time to linger. In the evening, it's all about cheeseboards, sharing platters, nuts, olives and bar snacks.

The house espresso blend from Extract in Bristol makes a cracking flat white but, arguably, the best way to sample it is in one of the slick cocktails. Try the dairy-free Flat White Ukrainian or the Cabinet Room's riff on a classic Espresso Martini.

Established
2017

Key roaster
Extract Coffee
Roasters

Brewing method
Espresso,
Chemex, V60

Machine
Sanremo Zoe

Grinder
Sanremo SR50

Opening hours
Tue
10am–4pm
Wed
9am–9pm
Thu
9am–10pm
Fri–Sat
9am–11pm
Sun
10am–8pm

WINCHESTER

119 LEMON AND JINJA

Unit 11 Belbins Business Park, Cupernham Lane, Romsey, Hampshire, SO51 7JF

lemonandjinja.uk | 07375 557016

f lemonandjinja *ⓞ lemonandjinja*

A huge expansion in early 2023 enabled this award-winning eco shop and cafe to triple in size and broaden its range of sustainable refill products. Since 2019 Lemon and Jinja has made minimal-waste shopping easy for the people of Romsey, and now, thanks to the extra space, customers can also chill out with a coffee once they've restocked their pantries.

In line with the shop's sustainable ethos visitors are encouraged to sit in and enjoy a Hampshire-roasted coffee or, if they're on the move, take it away in a reusable cup (those caught on the hop can borrow one from the cup library). The team at River Coffee roast two blends for the shop cafe, Flow and La Laja, and are also working with the Lemon and Jinja crew to create a bespoke coffee to serve and sell in-store with profits going to charity.

TIP THE EVENTS SPACE UPSTAIRS HOSTS REGULAR WORKSHOPS SUCH AS CERAMICS AND MACRAMÉ

It's a plant-based set-up, so the local coffee is paired with oat milk as standard (other alt options are also available) in white serves. Vegan lunch plates, flapjacks, cinnamon buns, cookies and more are available and make sticking around even more tempting.

Established
2019

Key roaster
River Coffee

Brewing method
Espresso, drip

Machine
Conti CC202

Grinder
HeyCafé HC-600 2.0 ODG, HeyCafé HC-880 LAB, Mazzer Super Jolly

Opening hours
Mon-Sat
9am-5pm
Sun
10am-4pm

ROMSEY

120 FIG & FOX

42-44 The Hundred, Romsey, Hampshire, SO51 8BX

figandfox.co.uk | 01794 501119

𝑓 *figandfoxdesign* ⊚ *figandfoxdesign*

Sipping coffee and nibbling cake amid a cornucopia of gorgeous homewares and lifestyle products is a satisfying experience for all the senses. It's one Helen and James Mitchell like to offer shoppers at their Romsey gift shop in the form of espresso drinks and a counter laden with goodies baked a few miles away at Hoxton Bakehouse in Southampton.

Moonshot is the popular house blend, a balanced sip roasted by Winchester's Moon Roast. Its notes of milk chocolate biscuits, stone fruits and toasted nuts appeal to coffee geeks and speciality newbies alike.

TIP ASK FOR A SCOOP OF BLACK VANILLA ICE CREAM IN YOUR ESPRESSO

Order a brew when you first arrive and savour it while browsing the houseplants, cosmetics, jewellery, cards, gourmet foods and bags of coffee beans. The delightful curation of gifts from local artisan makers has been carefully selected by Helen and James.

Like everything else in the shop, coffee is sourced with sustainability in mind because the couple believe that every little gesture – such as donating used grounds – makes a difference. Guest coffees are roasted within a 30-mile radius of the shop and include beans from Bournemouth's Bad Hand and Southampton's Blue Hour.

Established
2022

Key roaster
Moon Roast

Brewing method
Espresso

Machine
Victoria Arduino
Eagle One

Grinder
Fiorenzato F64

Opening hours
Mon–Fri
9am–4.30pm
Sat
9am–5pm
Sun
10am–4pm

121 PALLETS TEA & COFFEE HOUSE

High Street, Beaulieu, Hampshire, SO42 7YA

palletscoffeehouse.co.uk | 01590 612409

f palletscoffeehouse

It was in 2017 that the coffee lovers of Beaulieu welcomed Pallets to the High Street, although the building has a much earlier connection to the owner's family. Thirty years ago, it belonged to Pallets owner Dom Ide's grandma Brenda, who ran a floral-themed gift shop where he now serves speciality coffee. Dom's affinity for the building is palpable in the decor: he built the furniture from upcycled wooden pallets to create a quaint and cosy corner in the picturesque town.

TIP YOU'LL FIND PALLETS' SISTER SITE, THE BEAULIEU BAKEHOUSE, A FEW DOORS DOWN

Dom and his team of baristas work their magic using Moon Roast beans. Its popular Moon Shot blend is a permanent fixture, delivering smooth nutty notes that are enhanced by Pallets' full complement of extraction methods – ranging from espresso to V60 and cold brew. Blue Hour Coffee does the honours on the guest front, and provides two seasonal single origins each month.

Don't forget to order a slice of chocolatey crumb cake, made to Dom's great-grandma's secret recipe, with a scoop of New Forest Ice Cream. Old-school entertainment comes in the form of puzzles, board games and playing cards.

Established
2017

Key roaster
Moon Roast

Brewing method
Espresso, V60,
AeroPress,
Clever Dripper,
cold brew,
batch filter

Machine
La Marzocco
Linea PB

Grinder
Fiorenzato F64

Opening hours
Mon-Sun
8.30am-4.30pm

122 HIDEOUT COFFEE COMPANY

8 Charter House, Lord Montgomery Way, Portsmouth, Hampshire, PO1 2SB

hideoutcoffeecompany.com | 02392 839916

f hideoutcoffeecompany *⊙ hideoutcoffeecompany*

There's an exciting sense of anarchy at this coffee and doughnut shop which has been proudly 'going against the grain since 2018'. Hideout Coffee Co.'s ground floor takes its creative cues from old-school tattoo parlours and skate shops and marries them with sleek Scandi design. In contrast, downstairs feels very Wes Anderson thanks to its brightly coloured walls and eclectic decor.

The cool interiors may entice customers through the door but it's the first-rate coffee and rotating line-up of lip-smackingly good doughnuts that keep them returning for more. The La Marzocco buzzes from morning till late afternoon, cranking out endless cups of the River Coffee house roast. It's joined by regular guest appearances from roasteries including Cuppers Choice, Dark Arts, Penelope, 17 Grams and Cast Iron.

TIP HIDEOUT HAS WON AWARDS FOR ITS DISTINCTIVE BRANDING SO CHECK OUT THE MERCH

It would be remiss not to pair your coffee with one of Hideout's famous doughnuts. The Homer (a fluffy dough ring stuffed with strawberry jam and topped with strawberry icing and iconic multicoloured sprinkles) is a consistent crowd-pleaser on a menu that's updated regularly and includes vegan-friendly options.

Established
2018

Key roaster
River Coffee

Brewing method
Espresso, cold brew, batch filter

Machine
La Marzocco
Linea Classic S

Grinder
Victoria Arduino
Mythos One × 3,
Heycafé HC-880
LAB

Opening hours
Mon–Fri
8am–4pm
Sat
9am–4pm
Sun
9.30am–3.30pm

123 HUNTER GATHERER

249 Albert Road, Southsea, Portsmouth, Hampshire, PO4 0JR

huntergatherer.coffee | 02392 610791

f *huntergatherercoffee* @ *huntergatherercoffee*

A colourful brew bar complemented by a mint green VA Eagle machine and a stream of vibrant dishes flying out of the kitchen hint at the deliciousness to be discovered at Hunter Gatherer.

This upbeat foodie cafe specialises in plant-based eats, with breakfast and brunch dishes being the kitchen team's forte. Hero compilations include stuffed bagels, homemade toasted brioche piled with seasonal toppings, and soul-warming dal served with warm tortillas. Everything is crafted from scratch using ultra-fresh local produce.

TIP PLANNING AN EVENT? HUNTER GATHERER CREATES BESPOKE CAKES AND HAS A CATERING SERVICE

Coffee receives the same TLC and the main Mythos hopper is stocked with Craft House Coffee's trusty Industrial blend, which delivers a sumptuous chocolatey espresso. A second grinder is used for flavour-popping guest roasts from the likes of Curve, Kiss the Hippo, PLOT and Obadiah.

Gorgeous homemade bakes are switched up every day, although cheesecakes, plump cinnamon buns, and soft-serve ice cream (in the warmer months) are house favourites.

Established
2016

Key roaster
Craft House Coffee

Brewing method
Espresso, V60,
cold brew

Machine
Victoria Arduino
Eagle One

Grinder
Victoria Arduino
Mythos One × 2

Opening hours
Mon–Sun
8.30am–3pm

124 CAFFE ISOLA & THE CHAPEL ST ROASTERY

85a St James Street, Newport, Isle of Wight, PO30 1LG

caffe-isola.co.uk | 01983 524800

f Caffe Isola *© caffeisola*

Caffe Isola in Newport town centre is the I.O.W Espresso Co.'s flagship retail cafe. From humble beginnings in Watchbell Lane in 2006, it's now breathing life into the historic Beavis building and Congregational Church lecture hall in Nodehill – an area buzzing with indie retailers.

Roasting began at Caffe Isola in 2010. When the roasters' requirements outgrew the space, the operation was moved to dedicated premises and the first floor of the cafe was turned into a profiling roastery. Now, the roasters have room to experiment with small batches while customers can watch the process from start to finish.

TIP WHY NOT BOOK CAFFE ISOLA FOR YOUR NEXT PARTY?

Downstairs, the cafe offers simple, quality food with an Italian twist, with everything made using fresh ingredients and available to eat in or take away. The best part? It's accompanied by the company's own Island Roasted coffee.

The cafe also sells the best of the island's food, drink and craft produce, plus an extensive range of tea and coffee gear. Keyboard warriors will love the hot-desking space and small conference room available for hire.

In the evenings, Caffe Isola morphs into a licensed venue which hosts quizzes, music nights and themed dinner events.

Established
2006

Key roaster
Island Roasted

Brewing method
Espresso,
batch filter,
Clever Dripper

Machine
Astoria Storm

Grinder
Fiorenzato F83 E × 2,
Fiorenzato F64 EVO

Opening hours
Mon-Sat
8am-6pm
Sun
9am-5pm

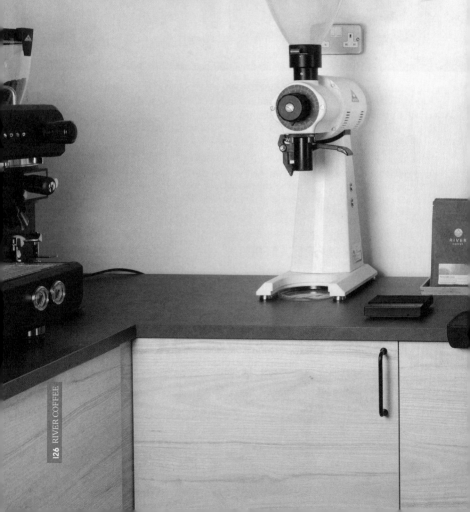

BERKSHIRE, HAMPSHIRE & ISLE OF WIGHT
ROASTERIES

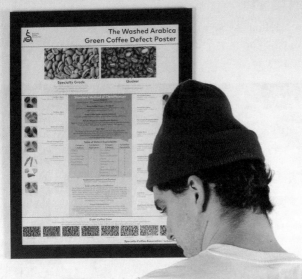

125 MOON ROAST

Chilton Manor Farm, Chilton Candover, Alresford, Hampshire, SO24 9TX

moonroast.co.uk | 01256 389996

f *moonroast* ⊙ *moonroastcoffee*

Four generations of Bradshaws worked in the coffee and tea industry prior to Francis Bradshaw taking on the mantle of the family trade in 2012. Roasting on a Probat P12 from a small barn in his backyard, Francis moonlighted as a coffeesmith until the operation grew large enough that he quit his day job and upped sticks to a Grade II-listed renovated barn on a local working farm.

While the roastery's roots are historic, its approach is thoroughly modern. A team of nine use the latest tech to roast small batches each day and recently invested in a state-of-the-art sustainable Loring roaster. Rigorous post-roast cupping ensures consistency and uncovers the most flavoursome profiles.

'THE TEAM RECENTLY INVESTED IN A STATE-OF-THE-ART SUSTAINABLE LORING ROASTER'

Washed and natural greens are sourced from across the globe and, in a bid to forge closer links with producers, in 2023 the team visited suppliers in Uganda and Peru.

The Moon Roast catalogue includes 14 Great Taste award winners and the beans are grouped into two collections: Core and Explore. The former features versatile omni-serve blends and single origins, while the latter offers a broader choice of flavour profiles.

Established
2012

Roaster make and size
Loring Kestrel 35kg,
Probat P25 25kg,
IKAWA

126 RIVER COFFEE

Ranscombe Farm, Barnetts Wood Lane, Alresford, Hampshire, SO24 9SF

rivercoffeeroasters.com | 01962 773810

f *rivercoffeeuk* ⊙ *rivercoffeeuk*

Will Harrigan travelled around Latin America's coffee-growing regions for a year before returning home to establish his own roastery in Hampshire. He spent time working on farms and in washing stations, establishing connections with producers. His travels have resulted in fruitful direct-trade relationships: nearly all the coffees roasted by the team at River HQ are sourced from farms he has visited.

'OUR AIM IS TO DELIVER A GLOBAL COLLABORATION OF EXPRESSIVE FLAVOUR'

Since 2018, he has worked closely with the Montero family in Costa Rica to produce a honey-processed single origin, while the Flow house blend features beans from the Rio Brilhante (Bright River) farm in Brazil which he only discovered recently.

'Our aim is to deliver a global collaboration of expressive flavour – a sustainable journey from bean to cup produced with scientific care,' says Will.

To keep up with growing demand, Hannah Scott was recently appointed as operations manager and the team have set to work on developing a training room in which they'll host workshops for wholesale partners and classes for home brewers.

Established
2018

Roaster make and size
Coffed SR30 30kg,
Diedrich IR-12 12kg

127 ISLAND ROASTED

Blackhouse Roastery, Blackhouse Quays, Little London, Isle of Wight, PO30 5YH

islandroasted.co.uk | 01983 857670

f islandroasted *⊙ islandroasted*

The Island Roasted story began over 20 years ago, when owners Dan and Viviana Burgess launched an event-catering business and discovered a gap in the market for speciality coffee support. So they founded the I.O.W Espresso Co. to import quality coffee and machines from Italy, and are now the Isle of Wight's leading supplier of commercial espresso machines, barista training and hand-roasted artisan coffee – they process nearly 40 tonnes each year.

Island Roasted's first in-shop roaster was installed in 2010 at Newport's Caffe Isola, then in 2013 the team opened a dedicated roastery on the banks of the River Medina. The first floor of Caffe Isola is now a profiling roastery, focusing on small batches and developing new coffees.

'THE ISLE OF WIGHT'S LEADING SUPPLIER OF HAND-ROASTED ARTISAN COFFEE - THEY PROCESS NEARLY 40 TONNES EACH YEAR'

A recent rebrand has resulted in colourful new packaging artwork (created by head of coffee Kurtis Leighton) for single-origin beans, featuring animals from the country in which they were grown. Domestic coffee fans can source them from the subscription service which sees beans roasted each Thursday and posted that evening (or hand-delivered on the Isle of Wight the next day).

Established
2008

Roaster make and size
Vittoria VT15 20kg,
Diedrich IR-12 12kg

MORE GOOD FINDS IN BERKSHIRE & HAMPSHIRE

COFFEE SHOPS

OPEN HOUSE DELI
4a Middle Brook Street, Winchester,
Hampshire, SO23 8AQ
openhousedeli.co.uk

PODIUM PLACE
31a Bone Lane, Newbury,
Berkshire, RG14 5SH
podiumplace.co.uk

SOUTHSEA COFFEE
63 Osborne Road, Southsea,
Portsmouth, Hampshire, PO5 3LS
southseacoffee.co.uk

THE PADDLE IN THE FOREST
76 Brookley Road, Brockenhurst,
Hampshire, SO42 7RA
thepaddleintheforest.co.uk

THE PADDLE ON THE GREEN
4 Church Hill, Milford on Sea,
Hampshire, SO41 0QH
thepaddleonthegreen.com

THE ROASTING PARTY - PARTY AT THE MILL
Station Mill, Station Road, Alresford,
Hampshire, SO24 9JQ
roastingparty.co.uk

THE YARD
Chilton Manor Farm, Alresford,
Hampshire, SO24 9TX
theyardhampshire.co.uk

WINCHESTER COFFEE ROASTERS
Unit 7a Sun Valley Business Park, Winnall,
Winchester, Hampshire, SO23 0LB
winchestercoffeeroasters.co.uk

ROASTERIES

BIG HAND LITTLE HAND COFFEE
Down's Park Avenue, Totton, Southampton,
Hampshire, SO40 9GY
bighand-littlehandcoffee.com

FULL BLOOM COFFEE ROASTERS
Barton on Sea, New Forest, Hampshire
fullbloomcoffee.co.uk

PEABERRY COFFEE ROASTERS
Unit 66 Basepoint Business & Innovation
Centre, Caxton Close, Andover,
Hampshire, SP10 3FG
peaberrycoffee.co.uk

PER'LA SPECIALITY ROASTERS
31 Bone Lane, Newbury,
Berkshire, RG14 5SH
drinkperla.co.uk

THE ROASTING PARTY
Unit 4 Sun Valley Business Park, Winnall,
Winchester, Hampshire, SO23 0LB
roastingparty.co.uk

WINCHESTER COFFEE ROASTERS
Unit 7a Sun Valley Business Park, Winnall,
Winchester, Hampshire, SO23 0LB
winchestercoffeeroasters.co.uk

EAST & WEST SUSSEX
COFFEE SHOPS

COFFEE&

FILTER/BLACK COFFEE	2.7	ICED COFFEE	3.2
LK COFFEE	3	FRAPPE	4
OCHA	3.5	FREDDO CAPPUCCINO	4
CHAI LATTE	3.4		
HOT CHOCOLATE	4	SMOOTHIES	5
TURMERIC LATTE	3.2	FRESH ORANGE JUICE	4.5

ALMOND, SOYA, COCONUT MILK
O EXTRA COST (TAKEAWAY ONLY)

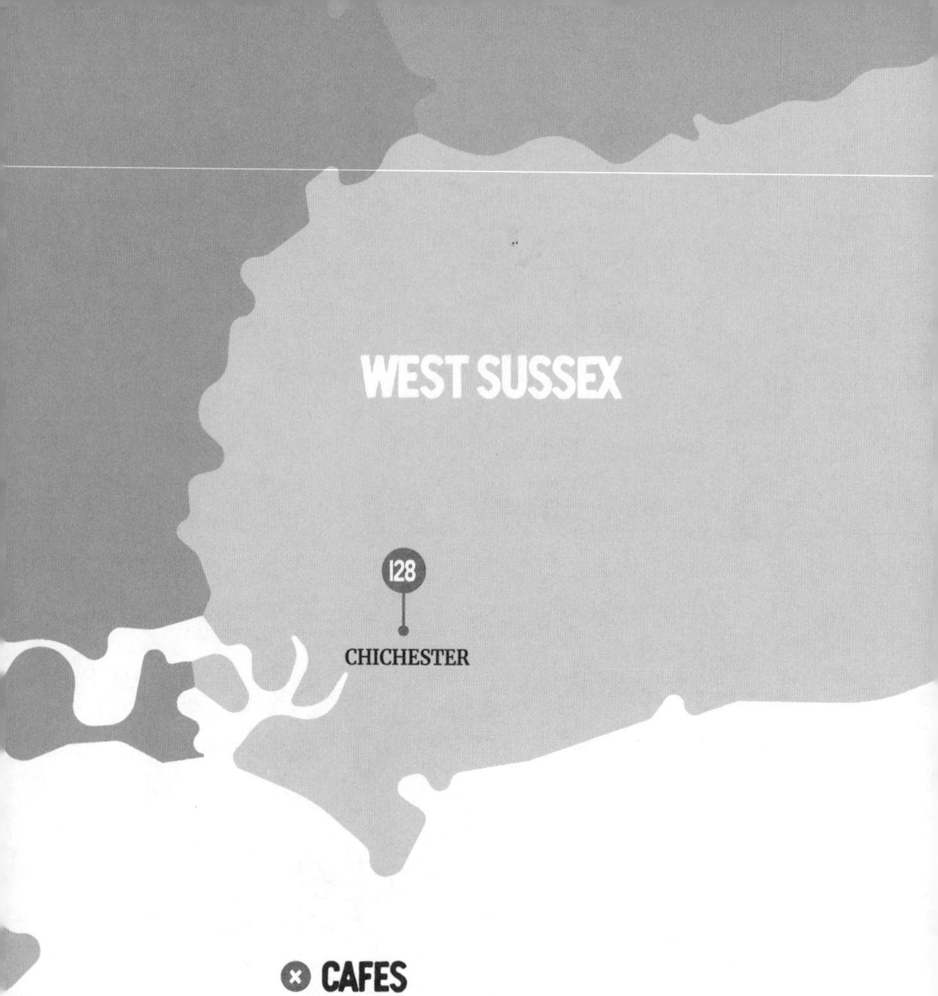

WEST SUSSEX

128

CHICHESTER

✕ CAFES

Ditchling Common

EAST SUSSEX

LEWES

Hove Brighton

Eastbourne

⊗ ROASTERIES

137 Back Yard Coffee
138 PHARMACIE Coffee Roasters

Find more good coffee shops and
roasteries on page 223.

All locations are approximate

128 COMMON GROUNDS COFFEE

3a Little London, Chichester, West Sussex, PO19 1PH

wearecommongrounds.square.site | 01243 697980

wearecommongrounds

There's no questioning what this tiny shop on Little London sells, thanks to the giant coffee-plant mural that climbs its exterior.

For half a decade, the Common Grounds team have fuelled the people of Chichester with speciality-grade coffee from their pint-size cafe in a quiet lane off the high street. The space may be small (there are just four tables inside and a single bench out front), yet the consistently good brews and friendly service have had a big impact on the local community.

TIP CHECK OUT THE ESPRESSO SOFT-SERVE AND FORTNIGHTLY TREATS FROM ACE DOUGHNUTS

Clifton Coffee has supplied the house espresso since the doors opened in 2018, and it's accompanied by a selection of seasonal roasts for V60 and Clever Dripper. Beans from roasteries such as Red Bank, New Ground and Craft House supplement the core collection, and if you enjoy what's in your cup you can pick up bags of beans in-store or order them for delivery to your door.

Seasonal specials keep the experience fresh and the baristas on their toes, and are joined by a short but sweet bill of pastries, savouries and bakes (including gluten-free and vegan options).

Established
2018

Key roaster
Clifton Coffee Roasters

Brewing method
Espresso, V60, Clever Dripper

Machine
La Marzocco Linea PB

Grinder
Mahlkonig E65s GbW, Victoria Arduino Mythos One, Mahlkonig EK43

Opening hours
Mon-Fri
8.30am-3.30pm
Sat
9am-4pm

129 FIKA - HOVE

1 Norton Road, Hove, East Sussex, BN3 3BE
fikasussex.co.uk | 07496 068420
🅞 *fikasussex*

Brighton isn't short of people with sore heads come Sunday morning, and this Hove coffee shop has been answering their prayers since 2019. Stacked fried-egg sandwiches and seriously good coffee is the FIKA team's tried-and-tested hangover cure, available at their flagship venue all week long for both the suffering and the smugly sober.

Coffee is roasted in town at the house roastery, Back Yard, and doled out in a variety of espresso-based serves. Those on the Biscoff bandwagon can have the spiced biscuit blended in a Biscoff latte – a buttery alternative to the classic dirty chai.

TIP CHECK OUT THE NEW SISTER SITE AT BRIGHTON'S SEA LANES

The accompanying food menu revolves around the fried-egg sandwich staple, elevated by the FIKA chefs with a menagerie of accompaniments. For example, the Pig in Blue pairs lacy fried eggs with streaky bacon, blue cheese, caramelised onion and maple mayo. Those requiring something a little heartier to banish the beer fear will find it in a line-up of brunch burgers.

Established
2019

Key roaster
Back Yard Coffee

Brewing method
Espresso

Machine
Iberital
Expression Pro

Grinder
Victoria Arduino
Mythos One,
Fiorenzato F64 EVO

Opening hours
Mon-Sun
8am-3pm

130 TRIPLE POINT COFFEE

53 Gardner Street, Brighton, East Sussex, BN1 1UN

◎ *triplepoint_coffee*

A new addition to the Brighton speciality scene, this minimalist espresso and brew bar on Gardner Street will appeal to experimental coffee drinkers who like to switch up their order and sample the latest beans from the south coast's best roasteries.

Espresso is the holy grail at Triple Point and, at any time, there are at least five types to choose from. A custom Conti Monte Carlo with a transparent back panel allows customers to watch the inner workings of the machine as the barista pulls their pick of the menu. Batch, AeroPress and pourover serves are also available for those who prefer a lighter brew style.

TIP ALL COFFEES ON THE MENU ARE ALSO AVAILABLE TO BUY AS BEANS TO BREW AT HOME

The criteria for roasteries looking to get their beans in the hoppers at Triple Point is simple: be local, independent and roast speciality. Parallel, Craft House, Taith and Coffee@33 feature regularly, while Skylark has a permanent spot thanks to its top-flight coffees and charitable work in the local community.

This espresso bar only opened in June 2023, but it's already tagged on a house bakery to supply its counter with artisan bakes and pastries. Don't leave without browsing the comprehensive retail selection of brewing gear.

Established
2023

Key roaster
Multiple roasteries

Brewing method
Espresso,
AeroPress,
pourover,
batch filter

Machine
Conti Monte Carlo

Grinder
Mahlkonig EK43 S,
Mythos MYG75

Opening hours
Mon-Fri
8.30am-4pm
Sat-Sun
10am-5pm

131 LOST IN THE LANES

10 Nile Street, Brighton, East Sussex, BN1 1HW

lostinthelanes.com | 01273 525444

f *lostinthelanes* @ *lostinthelanes*

Losing your bearings in Brighton's meandering Lanes is part of the fun when visiting the seaside city. And whether it's a planned pursuit or chance encounter, stopping for coffee and a bite at this all-day eatery is an experience worth getting lost for.

Established in 2017 as a chef-led cafe, Lost in the Lanes is first and foremost a place to eat. However, the team wanted to serve a coffee that matched the quality of the food so enlisted local roastery PHARMACIE to craft them a bespoke single origin from Costa Rica. The Sloth, which delivers notes of plum, tamarind and dark choc, is served as espresso. A monthly guest filter from roasteries such as Chichester's Murmuration also features on the menu.

TIP VISIT ON SATURDAY EVENINGS FOR ELEVATED DISHES SUCH AS SLOW-BRAISED LAMB BELLY

In 2022, the cafe doubled in size by taking over the unit next door, and now the open-plan kitchen overlooks a spacious dining room. There's also a dedicated coffee bar for takeaway orders.

Carve out an hour to sit in and order an all-day brunch featuring the likes of slow-braised beef cheek with pomme puree, potato crisp and horseradish crème fraîche, and smoked haddock chowder with crisp pancetta and soft egg.

Established
2017

Key roaster
PHARMACIE Coffee Roasters

Brewing method
Espresso, batch filter

Machine
Slayer

Grinder
Mythos, Mahlkonig EK43

Opening hours
Mon-Fri, Sun
9am-5pm
Sat
6pm-11pm

132 FIKA - SEA LANES

300 Madeira Drive, Unit 5a Sea Lanes, Brighton, East Sussex, BN2 1BX

fikasussex.co.uk | 07496 068420

🅾 *fikasussex*

The bread and butter of this new Brighton Beach hangout is 'filthy fried-egg sandwiches and damn good coffee.'

A pebble's throw from the city's new oceanside Olympic pool, FIKA's Sea Lanes outpost (find the original in Hove) is the ideal spot to refresh and refuel after an invigorating outdoor dip.

TIP KEEP 'EM PEELED FOR A THIRD FIKA SITE OPENING IN 2024

Start with a caffeine kick courtesy of Back Yard Coffee, then follow your espresso or filter brew with an all-natural protein smoothie pick-me-up.

The house-special fried-egg sandos are just the kind of fodder you want to get your chops around while the chill of the Atlantic is still in your bones. The Hide & Squeak (farmhouse bread, grilled halloumi, fried egg, smashed avo, harissa aioli and pickles) is guaranteed to warm you from the inside out.

Stick around to soak up the chilled seaside vibe and order a coffee chaser as you further explore the list of house-roasted beans – many of them are also available to buy for your home hopper.

Established
2023

Key roaster
Back Yard Coffee

Brewing method
Espresso,
batch filter

Machine
La Marzocco Linea

Grinder
Victoria Arduino
Mythos One,
Fiorenzato F64
EVO × 2

Opening hours
Mon-Sun
7am-5pm

133 NELSON COFFEE

15 Station Parade, Eastbourne, East Sussex, BN21 1BE
nelsoncoffee.co.uk | 01323 7000718
f *nelsoncoffeeco* **◎** *nelsoncoffeeco*

There's something especially gratifying about drinking a coffee that was roasted mere metres from your table – and even more so when you get to witness the roasting magic while you sip. It's this roaster-to-cup experience that bean-geek locals and caffeine-seeking Eastbourne visitors can enjoy at Nelson Coffee.

The house roast, Bear Blend, is a 70/30 split of Brazilian and Rwandan beans, resulting in chocolate, caramel and red-plum flavours. In the cafe the preference is to add milk, but for those who prefer their coffee black the team offer an evolving array of carefully selected single origins to suit any serve style. Like what you taste? Sign up for a Nelson subscription to get its freshly roasted speciality beans delivered to your door.

TIP TAKE YOUR PUP TO THIS POOCH-FRIENDLY SPOT

Accompanying the brews is a smorgasbord of house-baked pastries and cakes, plus a seasonally changing brunch menu with Aussie leanings. Feast on the likes of courgette fritters with grilled halloumi, minted yogurt, smashed avo, harissa relish, dukkah and mixed leaves in a parmesan dressing. Got something to celebrate? Round up the troops for Nelson's Bottomless Brunch (available every Saturday) and enjoy any dish with unlimited Mimosas and Bellinis.

Established
2014

Key roaster
Nelson Coffee Roasters

Brewing method
Espresso, batch filter

Machine
La Marzocco Linea PB ABR

Grinder
Victoria Arduino Mythos One, Mahlkonig EK43

Opening hours
Mon-Fri
8am-4pm
Sat-Sun
9am-4pm

EASTBOURNE

134 FOUNDRY COFFEE

Eastbourne Railway Station, Terminus Road, Eastbourne, East Sussex, BN21 3QJ

foundry.coffee | 01323 417585

f *foundrycoffeecompany* **⊙** *foundrycoffeecompany*

Eastbourne locals and visitors no longer need to divert their route to the station to pick up a quality coffee for the train, as this venue is dishing it out on-site from the former ticket office.

First-class coffee served swiftly is the MO at Foundry. Commuters dashing in to pick up a flattie for their journey can enjoy a seasonal house blend from Murmuration Coffee Co., which reveals notes of chocolate, toffee, raspberry and orange. Those with more time to spare should explore the diverse selection of single origins available at the brew bar, and indecisive visitors can plump for the coffee flight to try one coffee prepared three ways.

TIP A NEW, ROOMIER SISTER SITE IS DUE TO OPEN SOON

Breakfast on the go is sorted thanks to a speedy menu of classic baps (sausage or bacon), hearty porridge bowls and healthy granola and yogurt pots, all of which are made in-house each morning. Avocado toast and pancake stacks are must-tries for those whose schedule allows time to kick back and relax a little longer in the industrial-chic cafe space.

Established
2022

Key roaster
Murmuration
Coffee Co.

Brewing method
Espresso,
AeroPress, V60,
cold brew, pourover

Machine
La Marzocco KB90

Grinder
Victoria Arduino
Mythos One × 3,
Mahlkonig EK43

Opening hours
Mon-Fri
7am-6pm
Sat
7.30am-6pm
Sun
8.30am-6pm

135 URBAN GROUND - BOLTON ROAD

2a Bolton Road, Eastbourne, East Sussex, BN21 3JX

urbanground.co.uk | 01323 410751

f *UrbanGroundEB* ⊙ *urbangroundeb*

In 2011, finding a quality cup of speciality coffee outside the big cities was almost impossible. Having worked in London where flat whites and artisan sandwiches had become the norm, Andy and Michelle Spirou thought there was an opportunity to recreate the experience in Eastbourne.

After six months of searching, they found the perfect site on Bolton Road and eight weeks later Urban Ground opened its doors. Even though it's surrounded by the ubiquitous chain coffee shops, the indie hub is still going strong after 13 years – thanks to its quality offering that gives speciality-conscious sippers a place to relax, enjoy a high-end brew and support a local business.

TIP CAFE PACKED OUT? ORDER COFFEES AND SARNIES TO-GO AND HEAD TO THE BEACH

On dry days, the alfresco seating area hums with activity. Square Mile flat whites and batch filters fuel busy chatter and are accompanied by superfood lattes, colourful fruit smoothies, speciality teas, homemade cakes and stacked sandwiches.

A rotation of guest roasteries offers alt coffee options, as does the mix of serve styles which includes AeroPress, cold brew and flash brew. Ask the baristas for the latest line-up and tasting notes.

Established
2011

Key roaster
Square Mile
Coffee Roasters

Brewing method
Espresso,
AeroPress,
batch filter,
cold brew,
flash brew

Machine
La Marzocco
Linea Classic

Grinder
Victoria Arduino
Mythos One

Opening hours
Fri-Sat
8.30am-4.30pm
Sun-Thu
9am-4pm

EASTBOURNE

215

136 URBAN GROUND - SOUTH STREET

56 South Street, Eastbourne, East Sussex, BN21 4XB
urbanground.co.uk | 01323 398221
f *UrbanGroundEB* @ *urbangroundeb*

The reassuring mantra of 'Saving good people from bad coffee' communicates succinctly the mission of this contemporary community cafe in the heart of Eastbourne. Andy and Michelle Spirou started Urban Ground over a decade ago – their original cafe on Bolton Street was one of the first venues to serve speciality coffee in the seaside town. This sister site followed on the successful heels of the first.

The roomy South Street venue is a great spot for brunch, which is available all day and centres on dishes such as turkish eggs, chorizo hash and eton-mess french toast.

TIP PICK UP BAGS OF FRESHLY ROASTED SQUARE MILE BEANS TO BREW AT HOME

Andy and Michelle have worked with Square Mile since 2014, and the London roastery supplies both cafes with top-notch beans. Red Brick, the house espresso, changes throughout the year to reflect the coffee harvest but is always a smooth and mellow sip with tonnes of chocolate, nut and red-fruit flavours. It's accompanied by a menu of guest filter coffees which can be prepared in a variety of soft-brew methods.

Established
2017

Key roaster
Square Mile
Coffee Roasters

Brewing method
Espresso,
AeroPress,
batch filter,
flash brew

Machine
La Marzocco Linea
PB ABR

Grinder
Victoria Arduino
Mythos One

Opening hours
Mon–Thu
8am–3pm
Fri–Sat
8am–4pm
Sun
9am–3pm

EAST & WEST SUSSEX
ROASTERIES

137 BACK YARD COFFEE

SM Tidy Ind Est, Building OPQ, Unit M, Ditchling Common, East Sussex, BN6 8SG

backyardcoffee.co.uk | 01444 616670

f *backyardcoffeeroast* @ *backyard.coffee*

Established
2016

**Roaster make
and size**
Typhoon 20kg

Every roaster has a signature house blend or single origin which becomes the crown jewel of the roastery's collection. For Back Yard founder Elliott, it's his Foundation blend.

The Great Taste award-winning coffee has been on Back Yard's books since Elliott started roasting in 2016. It's made from ethically procured beans from two farms: one in Uganda's Rwenzori Mountains National Park (Elliott has worked with them for five years and visited in 2023) and the other a family-run farm in Brazil. The result is a delicious all-rounder which delivers notes of dark chocolate, praline, cherry, blackcurrant and citrus.

'A LEADING-EDGE HYBRID ROASTER REGENERATES ITS OWN HEAT SOURCE, REDUCING EMISSIONS'

Sustainability is woven into the fibre of this Ditchling Common roastery; the company's carbon footprint is considered at every step. An agreement with the Brazilian farm ensures a tree is planted in the Amazon for every sack of beans purchased, while a leading-edge hybrid roaster regenerates its own heat source to reduce emissions. All the packaging is fully recyclable too.

Next on the agenda for the team is a new roastery with a takeaway hatch. Keep an eye on Instagram for launch details.

138 PHARMACIE COFFEE ROASTERS

Unit 11 Cliffe Industrial Estate, Lewes, East Sussex, BN8 6JL

pharmacie.coffee | 07475 083619

f *pharmacie.coffee.roasters* ⊙ *pharmacie_coffee_roasters*

The hosts of the SCA UK Roasters Championships 2023 have coffee chemistry cracked. After years spent running cafes in Brighton, founder Rick Curtis decided to dive into roasting by converting an old mechanic's shop down a cobbled mews in Hove. PHARMACIE quickly became a cult favourite with those in the know, who would make a detour to get their hands on locally roasted beans.

'AN ADJOINING ESPRESSO BAR, OPEN ALL WEEK, IS A DESTINATION FOR BEAN GEEKS'

Now the roastery is housed in a cool industrial unit on the River Ouse in Lewes, where head roaster Carola Mapp can be found at the helm of a Giesen W30. An adjoining espresso bar – open all week and available to hire as a venue – is a destination for bean geeks, cyclists, hikers, office workers and families keen to sample a global menu of single origins hailing from Burundi to Yemen.

The roastery's micro-lot approach means there's always something exciting on offer – perhaps a geisha from Colombia or an unusual yeast-fermented Ugandan. PHARMACIE also provides slot roasting and labelling services for its partners plus home subscriptions for domestic customers.

Established
2012

Roaster make and size
Giesen W30 30kg

MORE GOOD FINDS IN EAST & WEST SUSSEX

COFFEE SHOPS

BLACK RAIN COFFEE CO.
136 Lewes Road, Brighton,
East Sussex, BN2 3LG
blackrain.coffee

BOND ST. COFFEE
15 Bond Street, Brighton,
East Sussex, BN1 1RD

DHARMA COFFEE
20 Western Road, Hove,
East Sussex, BN3 1AE
dharmacoffee.co.uk

FLAT OUT
59 Church Road, Hove,
East Sussex, BN3 2BD
flatoutcoffee.com

FOUNDRY COFFEE
49 Grove Road, Eastbourne,
East Sussex, BN21 4TX
foundry.coffee

KOMODO COFFEE
19a Brighton Square, Brighton,
East Sussex, BN1 1HD
komodo.coffee

LOAM COFFEE & STORE
111 Gloucester Road, Brighton,
East Sussex, BN1 4AF

MINCKA
41 Perrymount Road, Haywards Heath,
West Sussex, RH16 3XE
minckacoffee.com

STOOGE COFFEE
4 Trinity Street, Hastings,
East Sussex, TN34 1HG
stoogecoffee.com

ROASTERIES

CAST IRON COFFEE ROASTERS
Units 11–12 The Mill, Stane Street,
Chichester, West Sussex, PO18 0FF
castironroasters.com

HILLSIDE COFFEE
14 Hillside, East Dean, Eastbourne,
East Sussex, BN20 0HE
hillsidecoffee.co.uk

HORSHAM COFFEE ROASTER
Unit 5 1a William Way, Burgess Hill,
West Sussex, RH15 9AG
horshamcoffeeroaster.co.uk

SKYLARK COFFEE ROASTERS
Unit 1 Fairway Business Centre,
Westgate Road, Brighton,
East Sussex, BN2 4JZ
skylark.coffee

KENT & ESSEX
COFFEE SHOPS

✪ CAFES

✪ ROASTERIES

Find more good coffee shops and
roasteries on pages 245.

All locations are approximate

152 Saffron Walden

ESSEX

151
145
CHELMSFORD

150
144
Southend-on-Sea

148
Whitstable

149
Margate

146
Sevenoaks

MAIDSTONE

CANTERBURY

142
143

KENT

139
Staplehurst

140
Tenterden

Warehorne

141
Hythe

147

139 KIN COFFEE

3 Milestone Buildings, High Street, Staplehurst, Tonbridge, Kent, TN12 0AB
kincoffee.co.uk | 01580 893235
f *kincoffeeuk* ⊙ *kincoffeeuk*

When you combine passion with hard graft, an idea can quickly snowball into reality. That's what happened when Kin founders Kate Frost and Greg Salmon established a coffee shop in Staplehurst to complement their roastery (located in a refurbed potting shed).

TIP ORDER A SLICE OF TOASTED BANANA BREAD SMOTHERED IN LOCAL FARMHOUSE BUTTER

The Kin team specialise in naturally processed coffees: the headliner is Earlybird, a smooth all-rounder delivering a malty, chocolate-biscuit aroma and flavours of caramel and toasted nuts. The beans are sourced from the award-winning Fazenda Bom Jesus in Brazil, a farm with which the roasters have had a direct relationship since 2021 – they even visited in 2023. Those who favour flavours that are a little more funky should try Kin's boozy and fruity extended-fermentation micro-lots via filter, or the alt guest espresso as a flat white.

While coffee is undoubtedly the star of the show, it's ably supported by delicious locally sourced food. Milk comes from a local dairy, cakes from a baker in the village and the thick streaky bacon from pigs reared down the road.

Established
2022

Key roaster
Kin Coffee

Brewing method
Espresso,
batch filter

Machine
La Marzocco
Linea PB

Grinder
Victoria Arduino
Mythos 2

Opening hours
Mon-Sat
8am-3pm
Sun
10am-2pm

STAPLEHURST

140 THE NUTMEG DELI & COFFEE SHOP

3 Sayers Lane, Tenterden, Kent, TN30 6BW

07899 651119

f thenutmegdeli *◎ nutmegdeli3*

Once you clock that this cosy cafe and deli is run by the team behind Coldblow Coffee – one of the best roasteries in the South East – it inspires confidence that it's going to deliver the goods.

Tucked away on Sayers Lane, The Nutmeg has a small footprint and big ideas. This is founder Grant Robinson's third artisan enterprise – he started with a mobile espresso van on Hythe Beach followed, seven years later, by the roastery – and is where he curates his speciality coffees alongside fabulous local produce.

TIP ASK THE TEAM TO GRIND YOUR COLDBLOW BEANS TO SUIT YOUR HOME-BREW SET-UP

Peruse the deli counter crammed with exceptional cheeses, olives, charcuterie, salads and the kind of baked goods you'd make a detour for, all of which can be sampled in-house alongside one of The Nutmeg's famous toasties. Accompany the fine food with a cup of Coldblow's crowd-pleasing and reliably delicious Frameworks Espresso Blend (beans from Brazil, Colombia and Ethiopia) or the Peruvian Sugarcane Decaf. If you're into single origins, you can pick up a bag from the house roastery to brew at home.

By popular demand, The Nutmeg is now open daily for impromptu coffee dates and last-minute gourmet emergencies.

Established
2010

Key roaster
Coldblow Coffee

Brewing method
Espresso

Machine
La Marzocco Linea Classic S

Grinder
Mazzer Major VP

Opening hours
Mon-Fri
8.30am-5pm
Sat
9.30am-5pm
Sun
9am-3.30pm

141 MIT MILCH COFFEE

2 Corner House Buildings, Red Lion Square, Hythe, Kent, CT21 5BD

07540 609376

 mitmilchhythe

Mit Milch is German for 'with milk', a fitting name for this small but perfectly formed speciality coffee shop that serves some of the finest brews on the south Kent coast with impeccable latte art.

Unlike most cafes, the team here don't source their beans from a specific roastery. Instead, they showcase a roll call of roasteries including PHARMACIE, New Ground, Craft House, We Are Here, Chimney Fire, Sanctuary, Penelope and others. Owner Luke Reene is passionate about sniffing out the best beans from across the UK and Europe, and he mixes things up regularly to entice customers to come back to taste what's new.

TIP ARRIVE EARLY TO BAG A FLAKY CRUFFIN – THEY SELL OUT QUICKLY

Mit Milch has recently upgraded to a VA Eagle as its main espresso machine, which has opened up the variety of espresso drinks on offer. The real draw, however, is the filter coffee: three roasts from different origins, processed using different methods, run at the same time and switched up each month.

More than just a coffee house, Mit Milch prides itself on being a mental health hub too, where customers can take time out of their day and have a chat as they wait for their order.

Established
2015

Key roaster
Multiple roasteries

Brewing method
Espresso, drip

Machine
Victoria Arduino Eagle One

Grinder
Compak E8

Opening hours
Mon–Fri
8am–3pm
Sat
8am–4pm
Sun
9am–3pm

142 LOST SHEEP COFFEE AND KITCHEN

14-15 Sun Street, Canterbury, Kent, CT1 2HX

lostsheepcoffee.com | 01227 230444

f *lostsheepcoffee* ⊙ *lost_sheep_coffee*

Shepherding locals and visitors towards top-notch caffeine since 2012, the Lost Sheep team are pioneers of the Kent coffee scene. This cosy hangout on Sun Street is the newest member of the flock, joining the popular pod on St George's Lane and the roastery HQ in Whitstable.

Inspired by Melbourne's vibrant coffee culture, Stu and Sarah Wilson made it their mission to create the perfect Aussie-style flat white in Kent. Over a decade since they started slinging shots from the back of a coffee cart, their focus on pouring flawless flatties continues but is now accomplished using own-roasted beans.

TIP CHECK OUT THE BREKKIE MENU OF EGGS, FRENCH TOAST AND PANCAKES

The shop blend, Get to the Hopper, is a homage to the coffees they experienced in Oz – and their appreciation of classic Schwarzenegger movies. It's a smooth Colombian/Brazilian mix, delivering an indulgent choc-caramel hit. Alternatively, try The Filter One which, alongside Get to the Hopper, picked up a silver gong at the Great British Food Awards 2022.

Stuffed toasties and stacked sarnies make sticking around to enjoy the chilled vibe a tempting prospect.

Established
2021

Key roaster
Lost Sheep Coffee

Brewing method
Espresso,
batch filter

Machine
La Marzocco
Linea PB

Grinder
Compak E8

Opening hours
Mon-Fri
8.30am-4.30pm
Sat
8.30am-5pm
Sun
10am-4pm

143 LOST SHEEP COFFEE POD

St George's Lane, Canterbury, Kent, CT1 2SY

lostsheepcoffee.com | 01227 230444

f *lostsheepcoffee* 🄰 *lost_sheep_coffee*

This Lost Sheep hub in the heart of Canterbury has evolved in three phases since Sarah and Stuart Wilson started serving Aussie-style espresso in 2012. First, they upgraded their original three-wheeled van to a static pod and then found their current home in a converted shipping container.

It's hard to miss this incarnation of the takeaway coffee shop: the chipboard-bedecked container is located at the top of the high street next to the busy bus station. From early doors, the baristas serve house-roasted espresso drinks to commuters who want to start their day with a hit of quality caffeine.

TIP GOT A NESPRESSO MACHINE? GET LOST SHEEP SPECIALITY-GRADE PODS DELIVERED TO YOUR DOOR

Choose between the bestselling Get to the Hopper house blend (a South American mix rich in chocolate notes and caramel sweetness) and the guest espresso – usually a single origin or something equally special. Whatever you go for, it'll have been roasted at Lost Sheep's HQ in Whitstable.

Those grabbing a flattie to-go on their way to catch a bus can also pick up coffee beans and Nespresso-compatible pods to ensure the good coffee vibes continue at their final destination.

Established
2012

Key roaster
Lost Sheep Coffee

Brewing method
Espresso

Machine
La Marzocco Linea

Grinder
Compak E8

Opening hours
Mon–Sat
7.30am–5.30pm

CANTERBURY

144 CULT COFFEE AND TATTOOS

112 Leigh Road, Leigh-on-Sea, Essex, SS9 1BU

@ *cultcoffeeandtattoos*

Covered head to toe in an intricate array of inked designs, Cult's Andy Yates is a walking, talking advertisement for this tattoo parlour and coffee shop in Leigh-on-Sea. The former heating engineer wanted to break into the speciality industry so, in 2019, teamed up with his tattoo-artist friend to launch this one-of-a-kind coffee shop.

Befitting its name, the venue has garnered cult status for its consistently good brews and cool vibe. Needle-phobes needn't fear visiting for a coffee as the ink artistry takes place in a private studio. And with pop-art-adorned walls and a swathe of leafy plants, the cafe's ambience is very much home-from-home.

TIP GOT A MATE WHO LOVES COFFEE? TREAT THEM TO A CULT GIFT CARD

Allpress Espresso supplies the coffee which is pulled through a sleek La Marzocco machine as a raft of espresso drinks, accompanied by single-origin filters and cold brew. Pair your pick with a slab of freshly baked cake or a homemade protein ball from the enticing countertop display.

It's not just tattoos and caffeine that Andy is passionate about: he's invested in his local community and recently gave away coffees all day in exchange for donations to a local children's charity.

Established
2019

Key roaster
Allpress Espresso

Brewing method
Espresso, V60,
batch filter,
cold brew

Machine
La Marzocco
Linea PB

Grinder
Victoria Arduino
Mythos One,
Mahlkonig EK43

Opening hours
Mon
7am-2pm
Tue-Fri
7am-4pm
Sat
8am-4pm
Sun
9am-1pm

Want to buy green coffee that drives maximum impact through every cup?

MAXIMUM IMPACT COFFEE · 100% OF PROFITS TO PRODUCERS ·

100%

Great.

We are a green coffee importer that gives 100% of profits back to the producers we represent.

rawmaterial.coffee

RAW MATERIAL

145 DRIINK COFFEE CLUB

39b Baddow Road, Chelmsford, Essex, CM2 0DD

driinkcoffeeclub.co.uk

f *driinkcoffeeclub* ⓘ *driinkcoffeeclub*

When a coffee shop has been killing it for a few years and built a reputation for serving some of the best brews for miles, there are two options if it wants to expand: open a second venue or sidestep into roasting. The team behind this Chelmsford fave chose the latter.

Established in 2018 by tattoo artists Jason Butcher and Lianne Moule, Driink Coffee Club has always been a hub of rare and interesting beans where local speciality fans gather to sample the latest arrivals. In 2019, things got even more exciting when head of coffee Joel Rivers joined the team and played a leading role in the venue's migration to roastery-cafe.

TIP CHECK OUT THE SLICK LA MARZOCCO LEVA X: A SUPER-RARE ESPRESSO MACHINE

The prime spots on the menu are now filled with distinctive, high-scoring coffees (90+), which are roasted in-house in an Aillio Bullet. They're supplemented by a range of more accessible – but equally thrilling – single origins from leading roasteries such as Sweven, Wood St and Hot Numbers.

While the coffee is top-drawer, the vibe is pleasingly casual. The baristas are knowledgeable without being preachy, and very happy to talk the uninitiated through the bill of brews.

Established
2018

Key roaster
Driink Coffee Club

Brewing method
Espresso, V60,
Chemex,
batch filter

Machine
La Marzocco Leva X

Grinder
Ceado E37T,
Ceado E8D

Opening hours
Mon-Fri
8am-3pm
Sat-Sun
9am-3pm

CHELMSFORD

235

KENT & ESSEX ROASTERIES

146 CORBAN COFFEE ROASTERS

Unit C3 Chart Farm, Styants Bottom Road, Sevenoaks, Kent, TN15 0ES

corbancoffee.co.uk | 07917 576881

f *corbancoffee* **⊚** *corban_coffee*

Bucolic countryside envelopes this specialist roastery in a leafy farmyard on the outskirts of Sevenoaks. Owner Denver Anderson set up the enterprise in 2017 after spending years bronzing his own beans at home.

Built from upcycled and recycled materials, the rustic roastery is home to one of the UK's first Loring S7s – a sleek, eco-friendly small-batch roaster. The Loring is put to good use cranking out the house blend and seasonal single origins from Colombia, Uganda, Kenya and Costa Rica.

'CUSTOMERS CAN VISIT THE ROASTERY AND BLIND-TASTE THE RANGE TO IDENTIFY FLAVOUR PROFILES'

Education is a fundamental part of the Corban Coffee experience and Denver's customers get to learn all about where the beans come from, and the supply chain involved in getting it from plant to cup. He does this by hosting regular taste-test workshops where customers can visit the roastery and blind-taste the range to identify flavour profiles and their preferences.

New for 2024 is a rolling subscription service, where customers can opt for espresso or filter and then get the latest seasonal beans delivered to their door.

Established
2017

Roaster make and size
Loring S7 7kg, IKAWA

147 COLDBLOW COFFEE

Spot House Farm, Warehorne, Kent, TN26 2EP

coldblowcoffee.co.uk | 07899 651119

f *coldblowcoffee* ⊙ *coldblowcoffee*

Formerly an arborist, Coldblow founder Grant Robinson swapped a reverence for one kind of plant for another when he set off on a journey of discovery into traceable, expertly roasted coffee.

'THE OPENING OF THE ROASTERY WAS A CULMINATION OF YEARS OF LEARNING THROUGH DOING'

It was in New Zealand that Grant discovered speciality cafe culture. He was so inspired that, on returning to the UK, he began slinging shots from a tiny Piaggio Ape on Hythe Beach. After a while he retired the mobile espresso bar to set up The Nutmeg Deli & Coffee Shop in Tenterden. Then, in 2017, he launched Coldblow Coffee.

The roastery was a culmination of years of learning through doing, and its popularity soon blossomed. To keep up with wholesale demand Grant recently installed a 15kg Giesen, and has also introduced recyclable Sugarflex packaging to align with his sustainability goals. All of Coldblow's beans are traceable, World Coffee Research-approved and sourced from ethical importers who work directly with farmers from Brazil to Uganda. Visit the online shop for the latest blends, single origins and decafs.

Established
2017

Roaster make and size
Giesen 15kg

148 LOST SHEEP COFFEE ROASTERY

Unit 8 Oyster Bay, St Augustine's Business Park, Whitstable, Kent, CT5 2FF

shop.lostsheepcoffee.com | 01227 230444

f *lostsheepcoffee* ⓘ *lost_sheep_coffee*

When Stu and Sarah Wilson visited Melbourne in 2011, their minds were blown by the city's coffee culture. It was such an experience that, in 2012, they were inspired to launch a three-wheeled coffee van to introduce Aussie-style coffee to the people of Kent. Today, they have a shop and a pod in Canterbury, plus their own roastery in Whitstable.

Bestselling and award-winning blend Get to the Hopper combines directly traded Brazilian and Colombian beans for a super-smooth chocolate-caramel profile. It's perfect for flat whites and lattes to satisfy any coffee lover – antipodean or otherwise.

The 86+ Black Edition range highlights the best single-origin coffees, all fully traceable, fairly traded and hand-roasted in small batches to ensure consistency of quality. Each is guaranteed to score above 86 on the cupping table.

'THE 86+ BLACK EDITION RANGE HIGHLIGHTS THE BEST SINGLE-ORIGIN COFFEES'

There's also a range of micro-lots, rare varietals and unique processes which are part of a portfolio that helped Lost Sheep bag two silver gongs in the 2023 Great British Food Awards.

Established
2017

Roaster make and size
Giesen W15 15kg

149 WE ARE HERE

Unit 1 Fullers Yard, Victoria Road, Margate, Kent, CT9 1NA

weareherecoffee.com | 07841 539593

f *weareherecoffee* **⊙** *weareherecoffee*

We Are Here is a queer-owned roastery with a conscience. Proudly putting people and planet first, they donate 10p from every bag of coffee to charities such as Missing People.

The team are on a mission to make good coffee that's accessible to all, yet each bag is carefully designed to meet a specific brew method and taste preference. THIS ONE is a bold, classic and confident roast which works well as espresso – with or without milk. Alternatively, those who want to go off-piste and sample a fruity filter should plump for THE OTHER ONE.

'ON A MISSION TO MAKE GOOD COFFEE THAT'S ACCESSIBLE TO ALL'

The OG range comes in distinctive neon packaging, but you can also buy the same coffee with THE QUEER ONE branding, from which a donation goes to trans education charity Gendered Intelligence.

Alongside supporting underrepresented communities, the roastery champions sustainability. Surplus beans go to the ambulance post next door, coffee grounds and chaff are given to a local fashion designer who uses them to make coffee leather, and sacks and pallets are shared with locals who employ them in various projects. We Are Here also has a selection of branded merch for sale, made by local suppliers.

Established
2020

Roaster make and size
Loring S7
Nighthawk 7kg

MARGATE

241

150 LITTLE FIN COFFEE ROASTERY

19 Farriers Way, Southend-on-Sea, Essex, SS2 5RY

littlefinroastery.com | 07879 816920

f littlefincoffeeroastery *⊙ little_fin_coffee_roastery*

L ittle Fin was founded in 2018 by Charlotte and Ian Patterson, a couple with a penchant for fresh and flavoursome filter coffee. Armed with only a Gene Cafe countertop roaster and an AeroPress, they dedicated hour after hour to perfecting Finbari, their first single-origin coffee.

Over the past five years the business has scaled up considerably. Beans are now bronzed in a 10kg Toper and the roastery recently moved to bigger premises. The new HQ is a base for all roasting operations and includes a coffee bar with elevated seating, so visitors can watch the process below as they sip.

'A LITTLE FIN FAVOURITE IS THE COLOMBIAN SUAREZ'

Established coffee trader DRWakefield supplies most of the speciality beans used by Little Fin and sources them from farms in Colombia, Guatemala, Ethiopia, Kenya, Brazil and Honduras. A current Little Fin favourite is the Colombian Suarez, which is available as a single origin as well as being combined with the smooth Guatemalan El Fogan to make the bestselling Black Gold blend.

Pick up a bag of each from the roastery's retail shelves or order online through the Coffee Club subscription service.

Established
2018

Roaster make and size
Toper TKM-SX 10
10kg

151 DRIINK COFFEE CLUB

39b Baddow Road, Chelmsford, Essex, CM2 0DD

driinkcoffeeclub.co.uk

f *driinkcoffeeclub* ⓘ *driinkcoffeeclub*

When you sip a Driink coffee you can count yourself part of an exclusive club of speciality fans who've tasted that particular roast. That's because, from an Aillio Bullet installed in their Chelmsford cafe, the team roast the highest-grade beans they can get their hands on (usually 90+) in uber-small batches.

Head of coffee Joel Rivers loves sniffing out rare and complex examples from single farms, often choosing those with experimental processing or mind-bending flavour notes. And, thanks to his experience as a roaster and barista, he's usually mulling over the ideal serve style before the beans even reach the roaster.

'HEAD OF COFFEE JOEL RIVERS LOVES SNIFFING OUT RARE AND COMPLEX EXAMPLES FROM SINGLE FARMS'

The best place to enjoy this dynamic offering is at its Baddow Road coffee shop. A variety of styles is on offer, including V60, Chemex and Moccamaster, although arguably the most exciting way to sample the goods is to watch the baristas pull espresso through the La Marzocco Leva X (one of just a handful in the UK).

Whatever you sample is also available to buy from the retail section, while those eager to refine their home-brewing skills can book a barista workshop with the Driink crew.

Established
2022

Roaster make and size
Aillio Bullet 1kg

152 NINTH COFFEE ROASTERS

Unit 4 Saffron Business Centre, Elizabeth Close, Saffron Walden, Essex, CB10 2NL

ninthcoffeeroasters.com

ninthcoffeeroasters

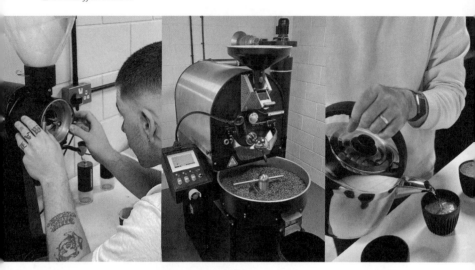

If you've always thought being a coffee roaster sounds like a sweet-as job, roadtest the idea by hanging out with the crew at Ninth Coffee in Saffron Walden.

Co-founder Arron Voice opens up the roasting space on Fridays (9am-2pm) so visiting and local coffee fans can chill out with the team, chat about beans and sample the latest roasts.

'THE DUO ARE KEEN TO SHARE WHAT THEY'VE LEARNT SO OPERATE AN OPEN-DOOR POLICY'

Arron started out in the service wing of the coffee industry before sidestepping into roasting in 2020. Experiments at home progressed to slot roasting for his previous employer then, in 2022, he took the leap and invested in a Probat P5, launching Ninth with friend Callum Riley. The duo are keen to share what they've learnt so operate an open-door policy all week, welcoming those who want to find out more about roasting.

Bom Jesus, Ninth's flagship espresso, is imported by Cal's Coffee which has family links with the farm that grows it in Alta Mogiana, Brazil. The fully traceable natural-process coffee is a mashup of chocolate and hazelnut-praline flavours which taste great with or without milk.

Established
2022

Roaster make and size
Probat P5 5kg,
IKAWA Pro V2

MORE GOOD FINDS IN KENT & ESSEX

COFFEE SHOPS

CLIFFS
172 Northdown Road,
Margate, Kent, CT9 2QN
cliffsmargate.com

FORTS CAFE - BROADSTAIRS
1 Chandos Road, Broadstairs, Kent, CT10 1QP

FORTS CAFE - MARGATE
8 Cliff Terrace, Margate, Kent, CT9 1RU

FRINGE + GINGE
72 Northgate, Canterbury, Kent, CT1 1BB

HILL ST.
7 Hill Street, Saffron Walden,
Essex, CB10 1EH
hill.st

LIFE ON HIGH
140 High Street, Sevenoaks, Kent, TN13 1XE
lifeonhigh.co.uk

OAST
68 Northdown Road,
Margate, Kent, CT9 2RL
oastmargate.co.uk

ORCHARD LANE COFFEE HOUSE
80 Sandgate High Street, Sandgate,
Folkestone, Kent, CT20 3BX
orchardlanecoffeehouse.co.uk

SIXTY FIVE MM COFFEE
Gilbert House, River Walk,
Tonbridge, Kent, TN9 1DT
65mmcoffee.co.uk

TABLE
90 High Street, Earls Colne,
Essex, CO6 2QX
tablecafe.uk

ROASTERIES

CURVE COFFEE ROASTERS
Unit 14 Copperleaf Business Park, Dane
Valley Road, Broadstairs, Kent, CT10 3AT
curveroasters.co.uk

GARAGE COFFEE ROASTERS
Southview, Maypole Lane, Hoath,
Canterbury, Kent, CT3 4LL
garageroasted.co.uk

KIN COFFEE
3 Milestone Buildings, High Street,
Staplehurst, Kent, TN12 0AB
kincoffee.co.uk

WOOD ST COFFEE ROASTERS
Unit 44 Shire Hill, Saffron Walden,
Essex, CB11 3AQ
woodstcoffee.co.uk

NOTES

SOMEWHERE TO KEEP A RECORD OF EXCEPTIONAL BEANS AND BREWS YOU'VE DISCOVERED ON YOUR COFFEE ADVENTURES

NOTES

SOMEWHERE TO KEEP A RECORD OF EXCEPTIONAL BEANS AND BREWS YOU'VE DISCOVERED ON YOUR COFFEE ADVENTURES

INDEX

FOR BREW FREAKS, BEAN GEEKS

THE COTTAGE

PAULA HILLMAN

Paula Hillman

BLOODHOUND
— BOOKS —

www.bloodhoundbooks.com

Print ISBN: 978-1-5040-8628-8

Also by Paula Hillman

Seaview House

Chapter One

The gentle dip of paddles, the swish of icy-clean water; these sounds are working with my fatigue, and my eyes close for a moment. The canoe pushes forward, rising and falling through the golden shimmer of the afternoon. My breath moves with it. Up from my stomach and out across the surface of the lake. There is a gather of warmth inside my layers of fleece and Gore-Tex, an enticing softness. But I mustn't fall under its spell.

'Evie.'

A spray of water on my face.

'Evie. Everyone else is turning for shore. Are we?'

Ian Turnbull has stopped paddling. He rounds on me, cheeks pink and raw and flaky.

I blink into the cold. 'Yep. Heavy on your side.' A nod of my head. 'And less on yours, Danni.'

'Yeah, *Danni*. Ease off.' Then, under his breath, 'Idiot.'

'Leave her alone, and just do your bit,' I say. It's taken almost the full two weeks for me to be this relaxed with him. He gives a loud snort, then brings us around with his paddling. Danni waits; she'll do nothing without clear instructions.

'Good girl, Danni,' I call. 'As soon as we're pointing straight to the shore, you start your paddling again.'

A nod of her small head and I know she's heard. A week ago, taking the Canadian canoes out with these two would have been impossible. Ian would only follow his own rules. And Danni – her fear of the world doesn't even allow her to choose her own breakfast cereal.

For a moment, the only sound is the dip-and-shimmer of water. But Ian can't keep his mouth shut for long.

'Oi,' he shouts across to another canoe, coming at us from around the frosted headland. 'Beno. We've beaten ya, dickhead.' A flick of his paddle. Danni groans.

The others call back. 'Turnip, you idiot. Fuck off.'

My colleague, Pip, has two boys with her in another boat, all acne and lip-sneers. They're not as tricky as Ian, but they've had their moments. One of them is gesturing at us. We are near enough to the shore that we can allow some horseplay.

'Evie,' Pip shouts above their heads. Her bobble hat is pulled so far down that I wonder how she can even see me. 'Frost Camps or not, last one back is going in.'

This is code for some splashing about at the water's edge. Something that groups of teenagers don't do anymore. Something called having fun.

Most of the group had looked at us with undisguised contempt when we'd told them they couldn't bring their mobile phones out onto the water.

Ian had vocalised his feelings in a way that made his tutor snap out of torpor and try to reprimand him. I'd slung an arm around the boy's shoulder and given a cutting challenge. It was taken up. If he managed to get across Windermere and back, and it wasn't too cold, he could attempt to throw me in. There had been a kind of smile, after this. Something the tutor had never seen before, and thought was a snarl. But I knew different.

Boys like Ian are easy. A few nips of razor-sharp wit, and a flash of superpower – mine is scampering up rock faces with minimal roping – and he had rolled over. In his own way. And that was the point of outdoor centres like ours. Challenge the body and the brain is forced to find new pathways. Old habits fall away, or most of them do: Ian has held onto his love of the *f-word*.

I kneel forward and match the rhythm of my paddle to Ian and Danni's. A crowd has gathered on the shore, a wall of fluorescent orange and multicoloured headgear. There are shouts of encouragement and some jeering, especially when Ian's chalet-mates realise it's him.

'Go, Turnip.'

'Bury Beno.'

'Don't let the fuckers win.'

Nobody mentions Danni. She is head down and paddling hard, but completely overlooked.

'Danni. Champion of the World,' I call, lifting my paddle to wave at the shore. Pip is pulling her boat alongside us. A scrape of metal and she's there, holding on, beaming at me from under her hat.

Danni moves her paddle forward and pushes against the gunwale of the other boat. Pip has no choice but to let go, and they do a quarter turn, springing away from us. Danni lets out the tiniest of cheers. Spontaneous. Coming from a part of her I haven't yet seen. I suspect that Pip would have let us win, regardless; she was backpaddling earlier.

'You've got me there, Danni.' Pip's voice is drowned out by splashing and the loud growls coming from Ian's mouth. I've never seen him so engaged.

Our boat is almost at the shore. I can feel the silty lake-bottom with my paddle. As the water runs out and we slide to victory, Danni and Ian throw up their arms. There is a symmetry to the moment. A perfect symmetry. This is why I work here, for moments like this, the coming together of human spirit.

'What a fucking win.' Ian has jumped out of the boat and is dragging it forwards. Staking his victory. Danni and I fall back, shaking our paddles, joining his claim. To the side of us, Pip and her boat hit the shore. Then somehow, we are all in the water, kicking and splashing, and scooping handfuls at one another. The cold has stopped hurting. Instead, it stands like an embarrassing friend, tolerable but awkward, with a brash face and icicle lips.

I can see my boss, waiting on the jetty, arms folded across his wide chest. His head is tilted slightly, jaw jutting, and he's thumbing over his shoulder, eyes locked with Pip's.

'Come on, guys,' I say. 'We can't stay wet for long. Not in this weather.'

A chorus of groans. Ian's is loudest.

'But what a brilliant day. Shout out for team Apollonius.' I jump up and down, punching the air.

The last canoe has come in with Rob and three more teens. They are as high as the others. Soon, we are all jumping about and chanting the name of the school, crunching fragments of shingle and slate beneath our wellies. When the energy finally falls away, there is a quiet moment. It binds us together as strongly as if we were circled with a rope and lassoed.

I am ready to call time on the fun, to start giving out orders for dealing with the wet canoes and paddles and buoyancy aids. Then Ian lunges towards me and throws his arms around my shoulders. He is taller than me, and much heavier. I can do nothing but accept the embrace. It is crushing, and just a little too familiar.

A slow handclap starts up. He half-releases me, turning to the applauding crowd. A raised fist punches upwards, and I jump at the realisation that he is somehow claiming me as a prize. I must flip this, and quickly. My boss isn't clapping; there is a dark expression across his face.

'Let's hear it for Ian Turnbull.' My voice is rising to the top of its range. 'He's proved me wrong, today. I said he was too scared. But the boy did good.' I pull myself out of his grasp and strengthen the clapping. Not everyone joins in. Danni is standing by herself, kicking up the shingle with aggressive repetition.

'And now.' I pause. 'It's time for Clean Up.'

The joy escapes from the scene. It is exhaled and sent scuttling away across the lake, then disappears into the fading light of the afternoon. We start to collect equipment and lift the boats on to their stand.

'Quick now, kids,' my boss commands, above us all. 'You need to get out of your wets and into the refectory. Chips tonight.'

A tired cheer goes up.

'I just want my bed,' mutters Pip, pulling her hat upwards by the bobble. Her long braid falls out and snakes down to her waist. 'And Apollonius House safely on its way back to Stratford.'

'You've enjoyed it, really. You know you have.' I understand what she means. These kids have gained so much from their fortnight, and we have been sucked dry. That is how this place works. We donate our metaphorical blood so that others can be saved.

'I have. But I'm done in, Evie. I really am.'

'Getting too old?' Rob. He has come up behind us. Looming. A solid presence, but there's no warmth. He doesn't like children, or teens, prefers the corporate groups, the *team-builders*: they do as they are told.

'Some of it is the cold,' Pip says. 'I'm sure human beings have an inbuilt hibernation gene. We fight, but it's always there.' Her lips are purple, and trembling.

5

'Let's finish up here and call it for the night. The evening team are already inside,' I say.

Our charges begin to wander away, heading to their chalets. Ian is the last of them. He lingers on the edge of my vision, calling out my name and flinging random pieces of equipment about.

'You get going, kiddo. Take off those wet clothes.' I step towards him. 'Come on.'

'You offering to help me?'

Now I see where this is going. What the hanging around has been all about. Here is a boy who hates the world, but he's learnt to like me. I must tread carefully.

'Nope. I'm not going to help you; not your mother, am I?'

His lips twist upwards, like he's smelt something unpleasant, but he doesn't answer.

'Now get going. I'll see you later.' I don't wait for any more of a response; he's on the path to reconciling himself with life, and that's my job done.

My own chalet sits higher up, in an area of private woodland. It belongs to the outdoor company I work for, but I think of it as home. And I'd never be able to afford to buy my own place, not within the boundary of the National Park, anyway. The life suits me, for now. As my mother often reminds me, I wasted my time at university by studying a useless subject. Sports science. What kind of job would that lead to? And yet, here I am.

A muddy path takes me up between thickets of trees, planted especially for screening the staff living area. The woodland floor is littered with copper-and-gold. Ghostly trunks of silver birch stand alongside gnarly red cedars. The light is greenish and fading fast. It's another world: soothing and private, and so different from the atmosphere of the camp. I let boisterous and bolshy Evie slide off my shoulders, become myself again. A quiet nature-lover. Who'd have thought it? Pip, maybe: she knows me quite well.

But not Rob. When I'd failed to join in with the musical-beds he and the other camp staff played, he'd accused me of saving myself for the top spot. The number one. Not that I'd be against climbing my way up to the higher echelons of camp command, but I'd never sleep my way there. That he thought I would has given our relationship a barbed texture; we don't do well when we work together.

I unzip the pocket of my waterproof and pull out the door key. Then let myself in and scrape the heels of my boots on the step to pull them off. Every staff chalet has a drying area with its own electric heater. Mine is behind a cedarwood door next to the kitchen. Through the winter, when White Platts Camp goes into recess, and our personal hikes and activities are curtailed by ice and snow, I like to sit in my drying room, and read, even though it smells like burning rubber and wintergreen oil.

I sling my waterproofs over the rails that hang from the ceiling and lay my boots and socks on one of the benches. Everything else goes in the laundry bag.

I shuffle back across the hall in my underwear, and step straight into my shower room. It isn't much bigger than the average coat cupboard in a normal house. The toilet and sink are shoe-horned in on either side of a very slim shower cubicle, but the water is always scorching. It needs to be. I can live rough as well as the next person, but I must be able to have a scalding shower and wash my hair. Unless we're on an overnight bivvy. And I like those less and less.

After the shower, I towel myself dry and find a sweatshirt and joggers from the tiny wardrobe in my bedroom, then step back into the kitchen area to make myself some food. This is caravan life at its most luxurious. I have a fridge and a cooker and even a portable television. The signal isn't good, but I can pick up the BBC news and weather if I need to.

My lasagne takes an hour to cook, but by that time, the chalet is warm, and I've hunkered down for the night. I listen to a radio broadcast as I eat, and enjoy the way my face burns with the remnants of energy from a day well spent. My eyes fog with fatigue and I allow myself to drift, just for a moment. Then comes a knock on my front door. I jolt back to reality and look at my watch. Eight o'clock. There's never anyone up here at this time.

'Who is it?' I call. No reply. I pull open the door. There's no risk, living where we do. We don't exist, as far as the world is concerned. Yet here is Ian Turnbull, bold as you like, standing on my doorstep. All hoody and glinting eyes.

'Me,' he says.

'Ian. What are you doing here?' I look over his shoulder into the darkness.

'You said to see you later. Well, here I am.'

I stretch my eyes. 'That's just an expression. I didn't mean you should come and find me. You need to go.' I pause. 'Where do the evening staff think you are?'

'They won't even miss me. Too busy glugging wine from the camp beakers.'

'I doubt that,' I say. But it's not the point. I need to get rid of him. 'I'll just get my coat, then I'll walk you back down.'

'Don't bother.' The words escape from his lips with a spray of spittle and heat. Then he strides away into the darkness.

I have two choices. If I follow him back to camp, then I'm going to leave myself vulnerable. Ian Turnbull is the size of a fully grown man, even if his brain hasn't caught up yet. Would he attack me? I'd like to think he wouldn't, but I can't be sure. So, I take the other choice. I pick up my mobile phone and try to ring Pip. No signal. That's always the way, between craggy rock faces and woodland.

When I've let enough time pass, I decide to walk down to camp and have a chat to the evening staff. It's not sitting right with me, this visit from Ian Turnbull. He might not have even got back.

As I am slipping my coat on, there is a loud knock on the door. My stomach flips over. This kid isn't going to give up. But I find Malcom Fairley, my boss, standing on the step instead of Ian.

'I need to talk to you, Evie,' he says. 'All right if I come in?'

'Course.' I pull back the door. He steps past me, grim-faced and hunched down in his parka. With him comes the scent of a typical camp evening, woodsmoke and burned sugar.

'Have you had that lad, Ian Turnbull, up here? The one from Apollonius?'

His tone surprises me.

'I haven't *had* him up here, as you call it. He decided to walk here all by himself.'

'Don't be flippant,' Malcom spits. 'We just spent the last half hour trying to find him. And he's saying you asked him to come to your chalet.'

'Oh, for goodness' sake.' I turn away for a moment and rub my hands across my face. 'Why are we even having this conversation?'

'What's made him say it, Evie?' A sneer twists at Malcom's lips. It makes me wonder what is really going on.

I decide to rein in my words, to stop them coming from a place of confused anger. 'Why do teenage lads say anything? There'll be some agenda which adults can't understand. There always is.'

'Did you tell Ian Turnbull to come to your chalet, Evie. Yes, or no?'

'You have to ask?'

'All I know is that there's a kid down at camp who's in

trouble for wandering off, and who's showing signs of distress. I must respond to that.'

'You respond to it, then,' I mutter. 'But when you do get around to finding out the truth, let me know. I'll be waiting here, trying to rest after a stressful day, working for you and our organisation. Don't mind me.'

I stomp towards the chalet door and yank it open, then wait while Malcom makes his way outside.

'Sorry I've kept you up so late,' I snarl.

Chapter Two

I t is a brittle, powder-white morning. I tug at the zip of my fleece jacket so that the bottom half of my face is covered. Through the night, I'd been wide awake and worrying. I tried to send a message to Pip, to ask her what she thought I should do. To ask for her support. But the phone signal didn't improve, and I gave up in the end.

The woods are hush-quiet. Not even birdsong this morning. My boots on the mud-and-bark pathway crunch so loudly that it's like I'm intruding. The privacy of trees, their quiet strength, gives them a sentient quality. They've become my family, somehow. And they've precious little competition for the role.

As the main camp building comes into view, my boss is standing on the veranda, along with one of the staff members from Apollonius House, a grim-faced woman, with a hairline that is receding as much as any weight on her body. They are staring up at me as I walk.

'Morning,' I call, waving my hand. 'You're about early.'

The joviality isn't returned; their faces remain hard, jagged.

'I need a word, Evie.' My boss steps off the veranda and

takes hold of my elbow. His grasp gives me no options. 'My office, I think.'

I already know what this is about.

He pushes open the doorway of a chalet-building that contains some office space and a staffroom. I step in behind him, catching a whiff of coffee and cigarettes. We have a *no-smoking* policy on our site, and that smell makes me feel uneasy.

'Come in, please.' Malcom's voice has an edge to it. A sharpness that he shouldn't be using with me. I am one of his senior staff, the course convenor, and have even deputised for him, on occasion.

I exhale, deliberately noisy, sit down on the chair facing his desk. 'I'm guessing this is about Ian Turnbull. Did you not manage to get the truth out of him?'

Malcom rests his elbow on the desk and looks at me. 'It's moved on a bit since then,' he says, brows furrowed.

'Oh?'

'We didn't know it, but last night, once we'd got everyone settled, he sent a text message to his parents. Where the hell he got the phone from, I don't know.'

I shoot up from my seat. 'A text message?'

'Yes. Repeating his allegation that you asked him to your chalet. He told them you backed out, but he got into trouble for it. They're not happy, as you can imagine.'

My breath catches in my throat, and I can't say anything else. The room swims. I've been thrown into the lake, am suddenly surrounded by a watery and muted light. Malcom's words are swallowed up by my drowning.

Then Rob is standing there. Holding my arms, sitting me back down again. 'Man up, Cooper. You need to listen to this.'

'Don't tell me to *man up*.' I am surfacing, slowly. 'Have you heard what this lad is saying about me?'

'Ian Turnbull is just a child, and he was in a right state last night, fifteen years old or not.' Malcom's hands are flat on the desk, and he's leaning towards me. 'When I watched you with him yesterday afternoon, I could see something was going on between you. It looked like flirting, Evie.'

I shake my head. Gently at first, but it becomes more forceful. 'Oh, no. No. No. Absolutely not. He's been very challenging, and we formed a good relationship. But that's all.'

'You were hugging him.' Malcom's eyes are narrow, scornful. 'That wasn't on, Evie.'

'Oh, come off it. Those sorts of things happen all the time. If you got out with the pack a bit more, you'd realise it.' As soon as I say this, I know what is going on here. A boss should support his staff, especially where children are concerned. But I'm not his staff, am I? I'm a rival. 'And why is Rob here?' I turn to face my colleague. His skin has a pink tinge. 'I suppose you believe Ian Turnbull, too?'

'It's not a question of belief,' Rob says. Patronising. 'Malcom asked me in here so that everything we say can be witnessed. We don't think you would have knowingly asked a teen back to your chalet, but we have to gather up the facts.'

'Facts,' I say, coldly. 'That *boy* came to my chalet. I sent him packing. Those are the only facts.'

Malcom peers up at me. Grey eyes, flinty. 'Can you talk me through everything? I just need to write down your version of events. Let's try and keep this calm. If there needs to be a full investigation, I can't take sides.'

'Sides,' I spit. 'There are no sides. For Christ's sake, Malcom. Too much is being made from this. A testosterone-fuelled kid being cheered on by the pack. That's all it was.'

Both men lean back in their chairs. I have to keep a hold of the situation, but it's sliding away from me as surely as if I were grasping it with wet hands.

Rob turns his gaze on me. 'Did you say anything that might have encouraged him? I know he was messing around at the end of the canoeing, yesterday.'

'Look,' I say, 'I'm not being funny, but why are you trying to interview me? You're not a bloody policeman.' I'm not helping myself. I know this. But the sight of Rob Bardwell, sitting there, quizzing me as though he's a senior colleague. It's irritating me almost as much as Malcom and his fearful condescension. 'No. Ian's just been another difficult teenager who's responded to the way we do things here.'

Malcom rakes his nails across his scalp. 'Why the hell didn't you report him coming to your chalet the moment he did?'

'I was worried.' I lift my shoulder but lower my tone. 'That he was lurking in the woods or something. He's a big lad. I didn't want to put either of us at risk.'

'All the more reason why you should have told someone straight away,' Malcom snaps back at me.

'I did try to phone Pip Joy but the signal was weak, so I gave up.' There is no proof of this. Everything is pointing to me trying to cover something up. 'What else could I do?' My hands are outstretched. They are trembling. 'Then you turned up anyway. Problem solved.'

'Problem not solved,' Malcom is saying. Where I've only ever seen the distance between a boss and his staff, I now see disdain. 'You won't like it.' He draws in a deep breath. 'But I think you should go home for a few days. Just so it looks like I'm doing something. You're due some days off, anyway.'

I open my mouth to argue, but he interrupts.

'I want you out of the way until Apollonius have gone back to Stratford. And keep your fingers crossed the parents realise this was just a stupid prank.'

Home. What is he talking about? White Platts is my home. 'So, that's it?' My words catch like a fly in the throat. 'No support, no taking my side, just sling me off-site. In other words, I'm guilty as hell.'

I don't look at him or Rob. My chair scrapes back, then I am gone. Out of the office and into the brittleness of the

14

morning. A few members of staff are hanging about, steaming mugs in hands and untidy morning hair. The lake is a glassy bronze, and it hits me that I won't be slicing through that surface today. Or breathing in its sweet-water smell. My legs become numb beneath me.

I stagger back to my chalet, and find Pip, leaning against the front door. 'Evie. I've been trying to get hold of you.'

'Too late.' I push past her to stick my key in the lock. 'And now I'm leaving.'

She follows me inside. 'That kid from Apollonius has caused a load of trouble, I've heard. All the others are talking about it.'

'I bet they are.'

'Hey. Don't bite my head off. It'll all blow over. Just got to sit tight.'

'It seems I haven't to *sit tight*. The opposite, in fact. I've to get off-site. And fast.'

In my bedroom, I pull open the wardrobe and drag out my largest rucksack, the one I use for taking kids on all-nighters. That thought causes the tears to flow, finally.

Pip takes the sack from my hand and leads me to the bed, then sits me down. 'It's all just crap,' she murmurs, kneeling in front of me. 'Everyone in the group saw what that kid was like and how you managed to tame him. We'll all vouch for you. This will soon be relegated to one of those camp gaffes we all laugh at, if a little uncomfortably. Just wait and see.'

Camp gaffes... I hope so, hope the whole episode will become like many of the other low-level things that happen when working with children and adolescents. Rob Bardwell fell on a kid whilst they were rock climbing, one time, and though the parents were angry, they agreed that it had been a simple, unplanned-for, accident, no damage done. We have laughed about it since. But I don't feel like laughing now. I try to speak but no words come.

'Trust Malcom to do the right thing,' Pip is saying. 'I do. That's why he's the boss.' She strokes my hand. 'But if he's said you need to go home for a while, then you should. It'll be for show, that's all. So he can tell the Turnbull parents.'

I rest my head on her shoulder and cry for a little while. Or that's what it looks like. But really, I am weighing up what to do next. This *home* that they all keep mentioning, would be my mother's house. And I'm sure she'd be happy to let me stay for a few days. Any more than this, and our relationship would start to crumble. Barrow is only an hour away. I could telephone ahead. Then let Pip do the defending of my reputation.

'I'll telephone my mum,' I say. 'And then go. But Pip—'

She rocks back on her heels. 'What?'

'You will go to Malcom and explain everything, won't you. I tried, but he seemed determined to believe the worst. He can't do that, can he?'

She shakes her head. 'No. And I don't think he does. He's just tired. You know. After last night.'

'Why? What else happened last night?'

'Ian Turnbull had the evening staff fussing around him for hours, apparently. No one got to bed until after two. Malcom didn't sleep at all. So he said this morning.'

I have been an idiot. I should have followed Ian back down to camp. Tried to sort things out there and then. 'I should have gone after him,' I say. 'But I was a bit rattled, if I'm honest. So I stayed put.' I move past Pip and stand up. 'And I'll take the rap for that. But nothing else. As if I'd have designs on a fifteen-year-old boy. It's disgusting.' I wipe the corner of my mouth with one knuckle.

Pip raises her eyebrows and watches as I shake open my rucksack and start piling in the few sets of clothes that I have: warm tops, base layers, T-shirts and canvas trousers. There are personal items in the chalet, but nothing worth stealing whilst I'm away. And it won't be for long.

'I'm here for you, Evie.' Pip hugs me. 'Give me a call when you get to Barrow. As soon as I can talk to Malcom, I'll give you a heads-up.' She follows me as I stomp out into the chilly morning. 'I hope the proverbial book gets thrown at this Turnbull character.'

Chapter Three

On the drive home, my expansive anger turns to something more claustrophobic. Although the journey is only thirty miles, I stop the car three times, so that I can clamber out and stretch away some of my worry.

The last of these stops is Greenodd, a village on the edge of the Leven estuary. In the lay-by, I look across the mudflats to Mearness Point and the woods beyond. There is a briny smell in the cold air, and it makes me think of home, where my mother will be waiting, with my bed made up and a plate full of judgments to serve me. But those thoughts don't trouble me as much as the one where Ian Turnbull's story, whatever it amounts to, is believed. And I'm relegated to a list where disgraced teachers and instructors languish because of their foolish actions around children. Would that happen? On the word of a teenage boy? I have worked at White Platts for almost ten years, with never a bad mark against my name. Surely that counts for something.

But I worry that Malcom Fairley could do with an excuse to get rid of me. Since my promotion to a more senior position, his attitude towards me has changed. Not in a way that I could ever vocalise, but I feel it, nonetheless. Which gives me a twist of fear, deep in my stomach. I am probably not as strong as I think.

A glance at my watch tells me that it will be break-time at White Platts. There will be thermal containers of coffee, and chunks of warm shortbread, made by Chris, the resident chef and most revered person on the site. I'm missing the place already. It's in my blood. The mornings in summer when the light is so soft it blurs the surface of the water. And dark winter walks up slate-grey escarpments. Without those things, there is no me.

As I drive away from Greenodd, the landscape starts to change. The pasture is less green. Walls are sandstone or red brick; no Lakeland slate here. My hometown is a relic from the Victorian age, an eclectic mix of Gothic and modern buildings, housing estates and the domineering presence of the aeronautical industry. But there is a coastline, and low fells, and even some decent historical sites for walking and exploring, so I'll keep myself busy for a couple of days. Until Ian Turnbull and his petty little vendetta are chased along the road back to the Midlands.

The housing estate where my mother lives is right next to the town's general hospital, and is packed full of bungalows, each with a hedge and low-maintenance garden. Hers is exactly like this, though she thinks it is superior. It has *Blengdale* inscribed on a wooden plaque just to the left of her front door. A tribute to her love, like mine, of Lakeland forests. She has lived here for as long as I can remember, it being *convenient* for her work as a nurse. My mother loves convenience, and though she's retired now, it's still her buzzword.

I barely remember my dad. Except that he seemed to be unwell a lot of the time, with what she often refers to as *his nerves.* Right at this moment, I understand how that works. Mine are being shredded on the jagged edges of a picture that won't let itself be erased from the dark recesses of my mind. It's Ian Turnbull's sick fantasy, brought to life in glorious technicolour. I'll just have to hope no one else can see it.

When I pull my car onto my mother's driveway, she is immediately at the door, all sharp-cut hair and dove-grey sweater. Well-groomed is how I'd describe her, though she doesn't think the same about me. I'm right. Within a minute of stepping into the house and accepting hugs, she's telling me that I'm too thin and offering to make an appointment for me at her hairdresser's.

'David could do wonders with that mop,' she's saying, 'and he's got so many contacts. I bet it'd be a scream if you went out with him and a group of his friends.'

Never mind that he's more than fifty years old and into Motown. And scooters.

'Leave it, Mum, will you,' I say. 'I'll only be here for a couple of days. No time to get my hair done.'

She eyes my rucksack, then leads me towards my old room. It's at the back of the bungalow and looks out across swathes of faded green and twiggy borders. Most likely, she has only just made up the bed and opened the window a little. The duvet is freshly plumped, the smell cold, overlayed with dust. For a moment, I become dizzy with the realisation that this isn't home anymore. And I wonder what it must be like to have no place to lay your head. The thought jolts me and I shiver.

'I'll close the window.' My mother pulls at the white plastic handle. 'Freshen up, and we'll have some lunch.'

It doesn't take me long to change my clothes. I drag out an old pair of jeans and a bottle-green sweater that are still hanging in my wardrobe from the last time I was here. Jeans are not allowed at the camp. Malcom thinks they are scruffy.

And dangerous. I agree with him. The first thing we do when a new intake arrives, is to insist they only ever wear tracksuits or proper outdoor trousers for our sessions. The moans that follow this announcement can be dampened down with our stories: two hikers who almost froze to death because of soaking-wet denim, and a sinking kayaker whose wet jeans weighed as much as he did. So, today, I choose my Levi's.

Lunch is full of questions, and minestrone soup in white china bowls. My mother wants answers to many of the things I've asked myself. My words are guarded. She can't have access to my deepest thoughts, mainly because I never know how she'll repeat them to other people. And then she frames her favourite question.

'Is there anyone, you know, close? Who can support you?' Her head is dipped towards a spoonful of soup, but her eyes meet mine. 'A man, perhaps?'

'Or a woman?' I say, just to watch her squirm. 'No. There's nobody special, but I have some good friends at the camp. They'll stick up for me, I know they will.'

'Have you heard anything from Alex?' She reaches for another hunk of bread. But that doesn't fool me.

'No. Why?'

She shrugs. 'No reason. Just thought, if you needed legal help, he'd be the one.'

Alex and I grew up together. His family live next door to *Blengdale*. Well, his mother does. His father has been dead for many years. Almost as many as my own, something else Alex and I were able to share. I love the guy dearly. He's the brother I would have wanted, though our school lives didn't collide until we were older. We exchange Christmas and birthday cards. Sometimes even meet up.

But we could never be anything more than that, despite his suitability in my mother's eyes at least, as a husband. He runs a successful solicitor's practice in the town centre, is a sharp dresser and has an equally blade-like sense of humour. And he's gay, which my mother doesn't recognise as part of the human condition, and something that precludes him from being my husband.

'I won't need legal help,' I say. 'What is it that you think I've done? And anyway, once Malcom Fairley has the chance to look at what happened, he'll call me back to camp. And that will be that.'

'It wouldn't hurt to catch up with Alex while you're home though, would it?'

'If I see him, I see him.' I lift my shoulders. 'But he lives over on the island now, so I'm unlikely to bump into him.'

She opens her mouth to give me further instruction, but I interrupt. 'The soup was lovely, by the way. I'll help you wash up then I'm going for a walk. Got to keep my fitness levels up.'

An expression slides down her face, then disappears into the neckline of her cashmere. She's good at this: disdain transformed into caring. I hope she's not going to suggest we walk out together. I need to feel the burn. Not possible with an accompanying fifty-something. She's very fit, but dislikes perspiration. Except, I suspect, on the brows of men.

'Don't worry about the washing up,' she says. 'You go and get your exercise, darling. Before it gets too dark. I'll put us a casserole in, for supper.'

Supper, as she calls it, is usually a plastic beaker full of cocoa and a slice of Chris's latest traybake, at nine o'clock in the evening, after we've put our latest camp intake to bed for the night. Tea is what we call our evening meal, and the earlier it is, the better. Working in the open air polishes up the appetite as much as enhancing well-being, but I could never wait until seven o'clock in the evening for my main meal. Something else that my mother and I disagree on.

I pull back my chair. It scrapes across the floor tiles. She gives a small huff and then covers it with a smile.

'Where will you walk to?' she asks, stacking bowls and scraping crumbs.

'Not sure. But I'll only be a couple of hours. Hopefully, Malcom or Pip will have telephoned by then.'

In my bedroom, I pull a waterproof jacket from my rucksack, then take a pair of old trainers from a tub in the corner. It's full of sandals and plimsolls and slippers, squashed and tatty, and completely unusable at camp. But there is still a bit of life in them, so I could never bring myself to throw them away. And I've warned my mother not to, though she hates the sight of untidy things.

'I'll see you later,' I call to her, slipping my phone into my pocket. Then it's down the hall and out into the chill of early afternoon.

Five minutes takes me to the edge of the estate, away from the squat, hedged-in bungalows and up to the main road. I weave between lorries laden with gravel from a nearby quarry, and private cars. A side road slopes away underneath an arch of red sandstone, then I am in a different world.

Thick grey tree trunks and spiky bushes loom up beside me. They are hung with crumpled copper-and-red berries turned to black. The gradient causes me to break into a slow jog. Thin slices of afternoon light break through the ancient canopy.

Road-sounds fade away and I am alone, save for two squared-off sandstone cottages. One has a closed-up look about it, but the other is well-groomed, with smooth lawns at the front and a softly-tinkling fountain. I slow my pace a little and take gulps of the earthy air. A few more steps will see me into the centre of this valley.

I know what's coming, but it still hits me, like an unexpected stomach-punch. The Ruin. The great Abbey of Furness. It sprawls across soft green lawns in a faded, fragmented way, all pink and a patchwork of bright lichen. I stop for a moment and curl my cold hands around its protective railings.

A sound builds. Low and heavy at first, then the slide of metal running over itself. A train is coming. The line runs behind the ruin, through a road tunnel, then onwards to the town centre. The tranquillity of the place is suddenly torn apart by loud blasts of a horn, and the rush of two silver-and-purple carriages. Then it is over, and the quiet settles again.

Through the trees, I follow a track carved out between arcs of dying bramble and ground ivy. I kick at the litter of beech nut shells and leaf decay. There is a dog barking, somewhere out of sight. I stride along, knowing that soon the track will take me to the edge of the railway line. Then I will have to use the crossing, let myself through its kissing gate, and run like mad. To my left, through clumps of overgrown hazel and ash trees, is the open mouth of the railway tunnel. And directly in front of me, just across the line, is the rugged sandstone gable of a house.

I make my way across and stand in front of the place. It is so quiet. The dark windows are covered with a film of grit, and the garden is surrounded by a rusted fence. The bird feeders are empty, and looming evergreens have gained the upper hand. Even the roof slates have slipped slightly. A plastic sign hangs from the front gatepost.

To Let: Tunnel Cottage.

And a telephone number and a high street estate agent's name. One that I know very well. Rosina Kerr. As different to me as water is to steam, but we were inseparable at school. That bond was stretched when we went to university, but if we do meet, the flow is still there. Momentarily, I wonder why Tunnel Cottage is empty. And then my phone rings.

Malcom. A jolt of my heart. Finally, it's over.

'Hi, Malcom,' I say, relief flooding through me.

'Hello, Evie. Look, before you get too enthusiastic, I have to tell you the news is not good.'

What does that mean? 'Oh?' I step forward, towards a metal gate. The entrance to a wide meadow.

'It's Ian Turnbull's parents, I'm afraid. They want to take this thing right to the wire.'

'What wire? What are you talking about?' The words are choking me. The way he says *this thing.*

'They want a full investigation. A court case and a pay-off, by the sound of it. They were pretty difficult. Their son has told them all sorts.'

'I don't get it, Malcom. Ian had such a good couple of weeks. We didn't fall out, or anything. We had a good laugh, along with all the other kids. I thought he liked me.'

Malcom clears his throat. 'That's part of the problem, I think. Teenage boys aren't driven by their rational brain, Evie. We've spoken about this before.'

I'm in the meadow now, stomping through thick bleached-out grass. 'You're not saying you think there's anything in these accusations, are you?' I wait. 'Because if you are—'

'Evie… watch your words, now. I know you're angry, but this lad's parents have already taken legal advice. I don't want to hear anything from you I shouldn't.'

'There's nothing to hear. I swear to you, Malcom, the lad came to my chalet, uninvited. I got rid of him. That's it. No case to answer.'

I run my eyes along the edge of the meadow. A narrow beck runs parallel to the railway line. Its surface is almost level with the top of the banking. There would be a watery chaos if the line and the beck were to collide, somehow.

'I believe you, Evie. But I must do this by the book. I've taken advice myself, and I have to tell you to stay away from work until further notice. Sorry, but my hands are tied.'

I dare not speak. Words sit on my tongue, but they're a mix

I don't trust. If I set them free, Malcom will take them, I'm sure. Use them. And I don't want to give him anything, any scrap of me at the moment. My chin trembles.

'Evie. Did you hear what I said? Stay put for now. It could be a few months. And speak to your union. They'll have some pointers for you.'

I cut off the call. I don't have a union, never seemed much point, when the camp insured us against loss and liability while we were engaged in our jobs. Surely, Malcom would hire a solicitor or something, to represent me. But I need to speak to Pip. There must be a reason why the situation with Ian Turnbull has cut loose, when it should have been firmly closed in that *camp gaffes* box.

Pip isn't answering her phone, which makes sense. She will be working, out on the lake or up the side of a fell. Exactly where I should be. All I can do is leave her a message. She'll ring when she can, I know she will.

My head is full of noise, despite the peace of the meadow and the crystalline notes of water over rock. I inhale deeply, tasting the tang of red clay and decaying bracken. Someone is walking towards me along the far side of the beck. This is the last thing I want. Small talk. But I know my hometown. Strangers have the place in common, and that is enough. I turn away before my ignorance can be mistaken for lack of northern manners. Then I begin to run.

Jay

That someone is in the meadow on a freezing cold Saturday afternoon makes Jay dip his head and push his hands deep into his pockets. This is his place. There's no dog involved, so at least that's something: he can't bear it when people see an open

26

field as a place for pets to let fly. To slow his pace, he pretends to be looking at the beck, though he already knows every one of its aspects: the catch of light when spring sunshine touches the surface, the slicing flow after a spell of rain. And its deceitful beauty in high summer.

Whoever it is, they are shouting into a mobile telephone; a thing he doesn't possess. Why anyone would want to be at the beck and call of another person, he can't comprehend. But deep in his heart is the knowledge that there is no one who'd want him anyway.

It's the figure of a woman, from what he can see out of the corner of his eye; and now she's turning to run in the opposite direction. To escape from here, she'll have to negotiate the gate and the track. And the tunnel. Then there's his cottage: she'll run past the place, and she won't even notice. Though it's not really his. As long as a time never comes when anyone else calls it *theirs*, he can cope.

As he walks back across the meadow, Jay lifts his face to the sun again. There is no warmth to be had; it's the end of autumn, after all, winter really: air that bites, is granite cold, and days so short, the darkness presses against his window mid-afternoon and he can hardly get his work done. Home is where he should be, but his aunt's house has never felt like that. What makes a home, he wonders? The time when he had one already seems like a hundred years ago. It flashes across his memory as a series of sensations: cool shade in the heat of the day; the end of an endless journey; strong arms to keep the bullies at bay.

A pair of woodpigeons flap across in front of him, startled, no doubt, from their warm roosting in the thick boughs of the beech trees that populate this area. He loves the way they stick their heads forward as they fly, like they're on a mission. All that's missing are tiny leather helmets and goggles. Some feathers fall softly to the ground, and he bends to pick them up;

these are small and silver-grey. Nothing like the scatter in the aftermath of a sparrowhawk attack. But they'll go in his collection, and he'll probably draw them later. Every moment of this beautiful place will be captured on paper somehow. It's for survival: his own as much as anything else.

Chapter Four

There is no jogging, this time. I break into a full-scale, elbow-jab of a sprint, past Tunnel Cottage, across the railway line, ignoring the ruin, and back through the squat bungalows, to my car. I am determined to make the return journey to camp, and throttle Malcom Fairley. I don't, though, in the end. Mainly because my mother is in the front garden of *Blengdale* when I get back, chatting to Alex Swarbrick.

'Evie. You're here,' she croons, catching my eye. Alex is in his Saturday best: leather jacket, ragged jeans and an arm decoration that looks suspiciously like a crash helmet. The strawberry-gleam of a motorcycle triangulates my understanding. He's been splashing out.

'Hello, all.' I grimace. 'Al. You've become a biker.'

He holds up his hands. 'I don't think so. Haven't got the hair for it, have I?' He runs a hand through short blond locks. 'It was Paul's idea. To get a bike, I mean. We've had great fun. I passed my test about six months ago.'

'And you're still alive.' I hug him. 'Who's Paul?'

'My partner.' A wink signals his translucent use of language, but in jumps my mother, rabbit-ears alert.

'They've merged their practices in town,' she tells me. 'Two solicitors: Swarbrick and Murray. Very *poe-wsh.*' The way she elongates that word... I could scream.

'Partners then?' I whisper, and she shoots me another look.

Alex smells of Kouros and the cold. His cheek against mine causes a memory: saying goodbye on the grim platform of the town's railway station, a gigantic full stop hanging over our heads, waiting to formalise the ending of our teens together. Not realising that life became more intense as you got older, not less.

'Your mum's been telling me what happened at your work,' he says, innocent as a baby.

'Has she now.'

'We can have a chat about it if you like. I'm not in any hurry.' A flounce.

I want to berate him. Tell him I'm not one of his case-loads, to be fitted in to a free Saturday. But I know Alex. That I'm a charity case won't have crossed his mind; the righting of wrongs is what turns him on, though we have often disagreed on semantics. He's a straight good-versus-bad kind of guy, whereas I'm all *shades of grey*.

'Sure. That'd be good,' I say, then louder, 'Things have progressed from what Mum knows anyway.'

High alert, again. She cranes towards us. 'Come on in, then. I'll make coffee.'

'No,' I snap. 'Thanks. But I'd rather walk for a bit. Is that okay with you, Al?'

He nods towards the motorbike. 'I've a spare helmet in the top-box. We could have a zoom along the Coast Road or something. Have a chat.'

I stretch my eyes. 'Really?'

He jangles his keys, making my mother squint. 'Got a thicker coat?' he asks. 'Or another sweater?'

Within minutes, I'm tucked in behind him, trying not to

inhale the rancid-sebum smell of the spare helmet. The bungalows slide past again, and suddenly we're thundering onto the main road, zipping between cars, blades of cold slicing my jeans. There is no room for thinking. The drive is the purpose. Buildings fall away and the landscape becomes stark, with sky and strips of pasture. Then greyish-blue, and we're at the sea. I lift my visor and let in the salt-soaked air, stare across the tan-coloured desert towards the silver horizon. Alex has slowed the bike down. We judder along, while the engine coughs and gnaws at his restraining hand. He pulls onto a thin strip of tarmac and lets the revs run away to nothing, then puts his feet down to steady us both. With a tug of his helmet, he turns to look over his shoulder.

'Good fun, eh?'

I fumble under my chin, and slide my helmet upwards, try to agree with him, but instead, choke on my words and begin to cry.

'God, Evie.' He slips his arms around me. 'This isn't like you. It's anger, I guess. Frustration. You never even cried when your dog died.'

That comment makes me smile, despite myself. 'Yes, I bloody did.'

'As I remember it, you went around handing out tissues to our mothers, and making cups of tea.'

'We were ten years old, Al,' I say. 'Dying didn't mean anything. And my mother got me another dog the next day. Never hangs around, does she.'

'She certainly doesn't.' Alex crosses his eyes, a gesture we have always used to make one another laugh.

'But, seriously,' he says after a moment. 'You shouldn't let yourself get upset about a little blip at work. It'll blow over. These things always do.'

I sigh. 'I'm not being funny, but this suddenly feels very much more than a little blip. I've just spoken to my boss, and he's told me to stay away from work for a while because the parents of this terribly mistreated kid want to bring a case against me.'

Alex fixes a concerned expression on his face and adds a hand to his chest for good measure, but I'm struggling to believe he understands how worried I am. 'What sort of a case?' he asks. 'There's no case to answer, as far as I can make out. From what Fiona's told me, anyway.'

'She only knows what I've allowed her to,' I reply. 'But Ian Turnbull – that's the kid – has convinced his parents that I invited him back to my chalet. Though what my intentions were is anybody's guess. He's fifteen years old, for God's sake.'

Alex takes my hand, and we step carefully down between gigantic boulders of limestone that have been placed along the edge of the road, level with the sand. I feel suddenly cold. It creeps along my shoulders inside my jacket, and I get a sense of being raw, exposed somehow. Other people have caused this. Ian Turnbull and his parents, yes, but I can't help feeling that Malcom Fairley and Rob Bardwell are enjoying a surf on this particular wave of misunderstanding, too.

Chapter Five

I blink myself awake.

A grey dawn is sneaking underneath the window blind, bleak and unwelcoming. The bungalow is silent. I listen for my mother, moving around, clinking cups or turning on taps, but there is nothing. It's probably earlier than I think. I lift my phone from the white MDF bedside table. Not quite six o'clock. With a roll of my shoulders, I sit up and try to ease away the pain at the base of my neck.

Yesterday, at the beach with Alex, I'd found the open shoreline so disorientating after my life in the hills that the world had tilted and the tears, tucked away behind my eyes, had fallen forwards. I don't feel much better now.

Alex had been very understanding once he knew the full story, and had fed me with ideas about where I could go next with this ridiculous allegation, but nothing really sunk in until Pip finally returned my call. She'd spoken to Malcom and tried to fight my corner, but his response had mirrored the one I'd been given: prepare for a long fight.

I'd made a few decisions in the early hours of the morning.

If I was to stay away from work, then I'd insist on full pay and spend the money on a rental somewhere in town – Alex's suggestion – so I didn't accrue any money in my bank account, should the worst happen. It would save the last shreds of my sanity, too, not having to constantly explain myself to a worried parent.

Alex also offered to represent me, if there was to be a court case, though he believed things wouldn't get that far, despite the grinding bureaucracy of the system. Give it six months, he'd said, just to be on the safe side. That's when I'd resorted to getting cross with him while he smirked and sat on his hands. Until I'd collapsed in a hysterical heap, laughter coming from a place right alongside my misery. Ian Turnbull's parents could drag up whatever they liked. Keep me in limbo for as long as they liked. In the end, the truth would show itself, would swing from the trees on lengths of blue nylon rope as surely as their lying son had done.

I lift my legs from under the duvet and move into the bedroom's chill. My feet slide across the laminate floor. I pull yesterday's sweater over my pyjamas and tiptoe out into the hallway.

'Evie? Is that you?' My mother never was a deep sleeper.

'Just going to make myself a drink,' I say with a sigh. 'Do you want one?'

But she's out of her bedroom before I can say anything else, fuzzy-haired and face softly bare. 'I'm up now, anyway. I'll get us some breakfast.'

'You don't need to. I was just going to get a cup of tea then do some emails.'

Her expression slides.

'I'll have some toast, if that's all right,' I say, wanting to keep the peace. 'Too early for anything else.'

She follows me across the hall and into the kitchen, where we stand shoulder-to-shoulder while she fills the kettle and puts thick slices of white bread under the grill to toast.

'Pull the table out,' she says, 'and we can sit in here. Then you can tell me what Alex said.'

This is one of the reasons why I can't stay with her while I'm away from White Platts. Nothing in my life is private, as far as she's concerned. I will always be fourteen years old and in need of a parent's guiding, interfering hand.

'Same old table, same old conversations,' I mutter.

'Don't be like that, love. It helps to talk; I've told you that before.'

Told you. A favourite phrase of hers.

I slide my hands along the rough edges of the beechwood table that has graced the corner of the kitchen forever, then give it a tug. It scrapes forward enough that we can sit on the tucked chairs if we want to. But I'd rather not.

'You sit down,' I tell her. 'I'll make the brews and toast. Then I want to go and email Rosina Kerr.'

'Oh?' Curiosity rises from her like a helium-filled balloon. Silvery and light, and impossible to restrain.

'Alex thinks I should find a place to rent, if I'm staying in town for a few months.' Alex has his uses. Adding his name certifies the idea as feasible, at the very least.

She looks at me for a moment, all head-tilt and clutching at the neck of her dressing gown. 'I suppose he knows what he's talking about. But you're welcome to stay here. I wouldn't want you to think–'

I jump in. 'No one's doing any *thinking*, Mother. If it comes to me losing my job, Alex says it would be better for me to not have a large amount of money in my bank account. Nor any assets. That's all.'

An expression of undisguised shock crosses her face. 'Lose your job? Why in the world would that happen? You haven't done anything.'

At least she's with me on that point. 'I know that. You know that. But Alex has told me all about what he calls *sugar-seekers*.

People who get a whiff of compensation and it gets their blood up.'

She shudders. 'Even when the scent is based on lies?'

'Even then. And from what Malcom Fairley told me, my accuser's parents have their eyes firmly fixed on me. Not the well-being of their son.'

Behind me, the kettle steams. I switch off the grill and flip slices of toast onto the plates my mother has laid out.

'Well,' she says with a groan. 'It's a bloody good job you've got Alex on your side, isn't it?'

'Yep.' *Because I could never manage to do anything on my own*, I don't say.

'He's a good lad. Shame you two never made a go of things.'

This, again. But I refuse to waste any more words on the subject. Alex being gay holds no meaning for my mother.

'I'll see you later,' I say, lifting my cup and plate. I feel her eyes on my back as I shuffle off.

On Alex's advice, I send a formal email to Malcom. In it, I state the facts exactly as they happened, with timings and details that cannot be construed as opinion. Then I ask for a date and time for claiming my belongings and give him the name and address of my representing solicitor. Which feels weird. Malcom was my colleague until a couple of days ago, and I thought we had some sort of friendship. Perhaps not. Either way, the tone of the email isn't something I'm happy with. But I must look out for myself now, apparently.

Something else is nibbling away at the edges of my consciousness. It's the way Pip had been, on the phone yesterday evening: aloof, like she hardly knew me. I've explained this away as the added stress she'll be feeling having to cover my duties, but I'm not managing to convince myself.

I also send an email to the contact page on Rosina Kerr's website, asking for details of short-term, and cheap, rentals in the area. It makes sense to stay out of the National Park now, both financially and for the sake of my mental health. Seeing Windermere and the fells on a daily basis would just be rubbing my nose in it.

I am surprised when later, after I have showered and had an apologetic coffee-and-Sunday-newspapers session with my mother, I find a return email from Kerr's estate agency. Attached to it are listings for ten properties, ranging from bungalows on the estate where I am now, to small Victorian terraces in the heart of the town, and even a sandstone tenement flat near the docks. All within my price range. And as I scroll through the listings, right at the bottom of the page is Tunnel Cottage, and a clipped-on note from Rosina, calling the place a *wild card.*

It is a cold and raw afternoon, but it fizzes with possibilities. I break into a breathy trot as I make my way down into the wooded valley where Tunnel Cottage is sited. Rosina Kerr has agreed to meet me at the place, despite it being Sunday, and for that I am grateful. To be shown the cottage, as much as to have the chance to talk to someone about something other than my predicament. Though I'm sure she'll ask. The Rosina that I remember has no filters. And now that there's a few years of gossip to catch up on, she'll want what's due.

She is waiting for me in the ramshackle car park attached to the Furness Abbey ruin. Clad with pizzazz, as always, and leaning against a bright red Mini. 'Hiya,' she says with a wave. 'I wasn't sure if I'd recognise you.'

Her trademark fifties styling still looks good. In the first flush of our experimental years, I had opted for jeans and oversized sweaters, while she chose vintage frocks made for tiny waists, and fat, lacquered rolls of hair. But a love of nature united us. I liked to study it and walk in it, she wanted to paint it. I admired her work and she leaned on my outdoor strength. Now, she is holding out her arms and balancing on peep-toed shoes.

'Hello.' I dip into her embrace and recognise Chanel. 'Stylish as always.'

'I was so excited when you emailed me,' she says, giddy as ever. 'The old team, back together again. You haven't changed at all.'

I want to tell her to grow up, to stop using words like *excited* because they make me feel like we're eight-year-olds giggling about a birthday party. But there isn't a mean bone in Rosina's body, as I remember, and I'm sure she was put on this Earth to force everyone's spirits out of their boots and into the air.

'Thanks for meeting me. On a Sunday, too. You must be dedicated.'

She slips a frock-coated arm through mine and tugs me towards the main road. 'I adore my job. Coupling up people with homes. It's fabulous,' she says. 'And you're going to love this cute little cottage.'

I'm not sure I can stand this overload of frivolity.

'There's a track just along from here.' I nod towards the thicket of nude hawthorn bushes. 'Rather than walk up the hill and over the tunnel.'

'Not in these shoes, darling.' She twists up her ankle. 'We'll have to do it the conventional way.'

We walk together along the blistery tarmac road. There is no pavement, just an edging of clotted leaf rot. Rosina continues to cling to me, and I relax into her company. Above us, the knotted boughs of ancient trees make it feel like we are in a rustic cathedral. Then we reach the top of the railway tunnel. Some of the brambles and hedgerow have been cleared, and it is possible to look down on the cottage. I lean against a rusting safety rail and try to get a feel for the place. The house itself is a small, asymmetrical building, pink sandstone competing with deep grey gables. But the gardens are extensive, filled with mismatched outbuildings and huge conifers. The garden path leads straight onto the railway crossing, and the meadow I remember from my previous walk stretches away for more than a mile, chasing the length of the beck. Today, it is dotted with heather-grey sheep.

'Why hasn't anyone bought the place?' I ask. 'It's nothing like the rest of the rentals on your books, is it?'

Rosina doesn't answer for a moment. She stares down at Tunnel Cottage and inhales deeply, pressing her scarlet lips together. 'It needs a bit of work, to be honest. But the owner won't pay out for modernisations. It's never sold, so I've been asked to find a tenant.' She turns to me. 'It's in your price range only because of that. I hope you don't mind me saying so.'

'I like the look of it,' I tell her. 'I saw it the other day, while I was out walking. I didn't know, at that point, that I'd be wanting somewhere to stay.'

She fakes a little shudder. 'It's awful what happened to you. If there's ever need for a character witness, I'll be there for you, hun.'

Hun? What is she talking about? I'm nobody's hun. That word doesn't belong to my world. We might have had a connection when we were eighteen, but we've built our adult selves in very different ways. These thoughts make me feel snobbish. I must try harder.

'Thanks. I don't think it'll come to that. But I'll need a bit of time, and I couldn't see myself living with my mother for any longer than necessary.'

Rosina shrugs up her shoulders and puts her fingertips against her cheeks. 'Your mum's lovely,' she breathes. 'Don't be too hard on her.' Then I remember that she doesn't have hers, that her mum died while we were together at sixth-form college.

'And I'm a grown-up,' I say. 'I'm used to living by myself. That's all.'

'Oh. I have Poppy to keep me company, now. I hated living by myself.'

And when I raise my eyebrows, she tells me that Poppy is her bichon frisé, the white candyfloss love of her life.

'Where is she now?' I ask.

'She hates mud and wet leaves. At this minute in time, she'll be snuggled up in her basket, dreaming about lunch.' A lift of her sleeve and she's looking at her watch. Slim and gold and the type of thing I haven't seen since I used to rummage through my gran's jewellery box when I was a kid. 'Come on. Let's go and see Tunnel Cottage.'

When we reach the top of the cottage's long drive, I pause to look over the view. Low fells of bleached grassland lean away from the valley floor. Some are sprinkled with sheep, others lie empty. All are marked out with grey hedge-lines or pink sandstone. And across the railway track I can see the ruin itself, silent and strong. There is something about this place: it's bleak and beguiling all at once, and I know that I will say yes to Rosina's offer regardless of what the cottage looks like inside. Which is just as well, because when I cast my eyes over the dusty fireplaces and basic kitchen, I am half-tempted to change my mind. But I don't. It needs cleaning, and a few days of warming up, that's all. It's no more basic than my chalet.

'What do you think?' Rosina peers at me, nostrils flaring and a smile that only works on the bottom half of her face.

'I really want to live here,' I tell her. 'I hope I'll be allowed to spruce the place up a bit.'

'Oh? Most of the people who've shown an interest usually fall at the first hurdle.'

'What does that mean?'

'Nothing, really.' She rolls her eyes. 'But with only the abbey as your neighbour, and the crumbly state of the place, they don't want to know. I haven't had it on my books for long, and there's been minimal interest.'

'Well, I like it,' I laugh, 'especially the rental price. So, what do I do now?'

'Do you know what, Evie? As it's you, I can leave the keys.' She beams and holds them up. 'Drop into the office tomorrow, and we can work out contracts and the like. Do you want a lift back home?' Then she's out of the front door and onto the steep driveway.

'I'll have more of a poke around if you don't mind?'

She's looking at her wristwatch again. 'That's fine. Now. I've got to get back to Poppy. See you in the morning for coffee?'

'You will.' I pause. 'Rosina?'

She's already tottering away. 'Yes?'

'Thanks so much.'

'Welcome, hun.' A kiss of her fingertips, blown towards me, then she's gone.

I step back into the tiny hallway of the cottage. There is a loose telephone wire poking from the skirting board, and poorly-laid carpet tiles cover the floor. A coat rack hangs just behind the door, looped around with sets of keys on dirty strings. I pluck at a yellowed paper label attached to one of them, try to unroll it, but it crumbles between my fingers. There are names written on the others: *kitchen, pantry, tool-shed.* Someone cared enough to try and impose order on the place. I like that. It feels homely.

The lounge is probably the best-looking room. There is a brick fireplace with a thick wooden mantel, a set of scrubbed pine bookshelves to one side and a tall cabinet on the other. Cream-and-rose carpet reaches to all the walls, and looks clean, though there's a darker area near the hearth. Apart from a large and solid-looking wooden rocking chair and a small sofa, there is no furniture in the room.

It's cold though, probably due to a pair of old-style French windows. They take up almost a whole wall and have metal frames, not in keeping with the rest of the place. Opening them would take you nowhere. They don't have any view except for the thick trunks of a leylandii hedge; one that looks at least thirty years old, by the size and girth of it. I briefly wonder if it's damaged the house in some way: I remember how some of the trees at White Platts had roots which forced their way into the structure of the prefabricated buildings, lifting floors and causing a creep of damp. I push against the dirty brass handles, but the doors are locked and there isn't a key.

There is another window that, by my reckoning, should look out over the front garden. It is obscured by a pair of thick curtains hanging from a dark-wood pole. They are clean enough, and I push them back slightly so that I can check I'm right. A flash of blue catches my eye. Someone is out there. And it's not Rosina.

Jay

He is doing it again. Spying.

And he'll keep doing it, whenever there's a threat. This time, it's two women, one bright as a peacock on a summer's day, the other small and mouse-brown; they've found their way inside the cottage.

He'd been dozing in his den when there was a gaggle of

voices, and a jangle of keys. Spending the night here was the right decision after all, though it was fuelled by something other than protecting the place.

One of the women doesn't stay inside for very long. He watches her tottering up the steep driveway, poking a finger at the screen of a mobile telephone.

Leaving just one woman inside.

Inside.

That's a place he dares not linger, though he has a secret way to get in when need gets the better of him. Then, he'll wander the rooms, silence pressing against his eardrums, looking for things that are no longer there: coloured plastic buckets and spades in the cupboard under the stairs, the oilcloth that covered the kitchen table, with a pattern of pineapples that he wanted to lick in search of juice. And the tiny upstairs bedroom that was his and his alone, with a view so beguiling it used to make him cry.

So why is there a woman inside his cottage? And why isn't she coming out?

Jay decides to knock on the lounge window. Just once. Something like the game he used to watch others playing, when he lived in a street with no gardens, only stone front steps polished until they shone. Perhaps that'll be enough to put her off the place.

As he's about to lift his hand to the glass, the curtains are pulled back and he has to dart away. In the shadows at the side of the cottage, he waits.

A moment passes, then he hears the front door open and soft footsteps on the path. He hates himself all over again, but he must keep people away. It crosses his mind that one day he'll fail and have to watch another family move in: one with smiling parents and soft-haired children. That's a thought for another day though, because the woman is in the front garden and calling into the cold grey of the afternoon.

'Anyone there,' she is saying. 'Hello?'

Mousey is not a good description of her, Jay thinks. Her features are sharply pretty, her hair golden brown. But she looks strong and wiry and like she's not about to run away any time soon. He stays where he is. There isn't time to get to the tunnel, his best hiding place, but one he loathes.

The woman puts her hands in the pockets of her anorak, and plants booted feet firmly on his lawn. Not that it's much of one, anymore. Over the years, he's seen men wearing utility trousers and ear defenders come and keep it shorn, but it's never enough. Every winter sees it as high as the meadow, then it falls in on itself. And now the woman is stomping towards him with no knowledge that he is there. With a crane of her neck, she peers into the dark place where trees grow thickly, and the rubbish bins are kept. But she doesn't see him and has no sense that she is being watched.

He holds tight to his breath. There is a moment when she seems to be looking right at him, then she huffs to herself and makes her way back towards the front door.

What exactly is happening, he's not quite sure.

Chapter Six

O n the walk home from Tunnel Cottage, I wonder about the person I caught lurking in the garden. Well, didn't catch them, and now I'm starting to think there never was anyone. It's not like me to be so jumpy and I have no option but to blame it on Ian Turnbull. For more than ten years, I have lived quite happily, by myself, in a chalet in the middle of the woods. In the evenings, the quiet was a thing of perfection, the darkness so thick you could cut it with a knife; slice it and serve it up with a midnight cup of coffee. That's part of the appeal of renting the cottage, anyway. There's a silence to the valley, a sense of timeless green tranquillity, and I want to be part of it.

At the bungalow, I find my mother waiting, with a face full of questions and a collection of afternoon tea things spread across the kitchen table. The lilac cashmere and matching eyeshadow give me a hint that she wasn't expecting me to be alone.

'Oh. Hello, darling,' she says, peering past. 'I thought you might have brought Rosina home with you. Didn't she show up?'

'She did, but she's gone back to her life now. I've taken Tunnel Cottage, though. In case you're interested.'

She lifts her brows. 'Stop being so spiky and come and have some tea. I just thought it'd be nice to get to know her again. Especially if you're going to settle here. You'll need a few friends, won't you? And Rosina was always so nice.'

I sigh and drag out one of the kitchen chairs. 'I'm already settled, Mum. I've never been anything but settled. But you're missing the point. I'm not here to make friends. My job's under threat and I'm waiting for an investigation into my conduct. Have you got any idea how that feels?'

'Things happen for a reason.' She lifts the teapot. 'I always thought you could do better for yourself than working in that *rough* environment. You were really clever at school.'

I want to scream. The Ian Turnbull incident a blessing? How dangerous is this woman? She's my mother, yet she has no idea what my job has entailed: the thrill of skimming rockfaces, the glow of pride when people conquer their fears on my watch, the gruelling fitness and skill involved. And she thinks I'm not *clever*? Now she is wittering on about Alex.

'I still think you should keep in with him,' she is saying. 'The two of you were always a match. And he's done so well for himself.'

I slam away from the table. 'He's gay, Mother. And in a relationship. What part of that do you not understand?'

I don't wait for her answer. What I'd hoped for were some suggestions of items I could take to the cottage to make it feel a little more homely. Some offers of food to fill the fridge. Instead, I am being made to feel like a juvenile delinquent who is going through a phase.

I spend the rest of the day in my bedroom, setting up meetings with Rosina and Alex, and my bank. Monday is going to be a busy day. And it is my intention to get into Tunnel

Cottage as quickly as I can, so that my relationship with my mother can go back to one of dutiful politeness and regard; the only one that works.

The next morning, I decide to walk into the town centre. The sky is a palette of soft greys, the chill of yesterday chased away by a low pressure dragged in with the tide. I have eaten breakfast with my mother, and she has waved a white flag in the form of boil-washed sheets and a stack of other household linens that might be useful in my new home. And I am grateful for her offer. If only it hadn't been delivered with a comment about my lack of a *bottom drawer*. It was pretty clear what she'd meant. But I'd bitten down any snappy retort and smiled graciously.

It has been many years since I walked the two-mile route. It takes me through the Victorian gentrified outskirts, where large houses, once serving the monied classes, are living out their life as residential homes or nursery schools. Traffic zooms by. I let my thoughts linger over Tunnel Cottage and how much I'm drawn to the place. If I've got to stay in town for a few months, I might as well turn it into an adventure; that's my thinking, it's what I'll tell people. But the core of me is terrified I'll never make it back to White Platts again.

I pass by other relics of the town's Victorian heritage, cut sandstone in abundance, a pub on every corner. And an assortment of churches and chapels, many of which have changed their persona to match the needs of the tight-lipped industrial north. Though this is my home, I don't want to consider life without fellsides covered in bracken and the spine-tingling disorientation of peering into the depths of a freshwater lake.

The briskness of my pace, coupled with my high-tech jacket, has warmed me up considerably. I pull on the zip and allow some of the cool winter air to filter into the cocoon created by my sweater, then run a hand through my hair and prepare myself for Alex's office.

It lies along a small side street, away from the pedestrianised limestone-and-steel of the main thoroughfare. It is less an office and more a rejuvenated Victorian terraced house. The swish *Swarbrick and Murray* monochrome sign gives a hint that the place will live up to Alex's sense of style. And I'm not wrong.

I push open the shiny black front door and find myself in a small reception area, with a granite-topped counter, and a row of geometric-patterned easy chairs. A gleaming coffee machine gurgles in the far corner. Although there is a desk behind the counter, the office chair is quite empty.

But I can hear Alex's voice, coming from behind an open door.

'Al,' I call. 'Al. It's Evie.'

He appears, all open-neck shirt and snugly-fitting waistcoat, smiling out a welcome and casting an eye over my wind-mussed hair.

'Evie. Darling.' He walks around the side of the counter and holds out his arms. I lean in.

'You smell cold,' he says with a laugh. He smells of something florally expensive.

'I walked down,' I tell him. 'It's cool out there. But less bitter than yesterday. Are you okay?'

He steps away, catches me looking towards the immaculately tidy desk. 'We lost our front-of-house guy,' he starts to say. And then he's interrupted.

'Do not start speaking ill of Justin. I absolutely forbid it.'

Another man steps out from behind the door. This must be Paul Murray, Alex's partner. Small, slim, with a perfectly clipped dark beard. And the most welcoming smile I've seen in a long time.

Alex holds up his hands. 'As if. I said I'd never moan about *Justin-a-minute*, and I won't.'

Paul rolls his eyes. 'I guess you're Evie.' He holds out a hand. Looks me up and down. 'Al's description was *wild, fair hair and ruggedly pretty*. He lied. You're lovely.'

My face reddens. Compliment or not, the thought that I have been discussed causes a small bubble of anger in the back of my throat. My mouth tightens into a smile that I hope looks benign. Paul sees this.

'Sorry. What sort of dick are you, Paul Murray?' His hand beats lightly against his chest. 'Always trying to make people like you.'

I want to tell him not to be sucked into Alex's way of summing people up after one head-to-toe glance, but that's not what I do.

'Don't worry about it,' I say with a small shake of my head. 'I heard *rugged*. That's me, exactly.'

Alex is taking my hand and pulling me towards whatever lies beyond that door. 'Come through,' he says, 'and I'll get you a coffee. Then we can make a start.'

He leads me into another office, much less pristine, but still very modern-looking and stylish. A huge partners' desk dominates the space. Two computers sit back-to-back across the middle, and an array of papers and cardboard files spill into each other.

'Can you stay out front for a bit, love, so we're not disturbed?' he asks Paul.

'Sure can,' comes the response. 'Put the phones back through. And pass me out the Jackson file. May as well keep reading. Shall I have a scout around for a temp as well?'

Alex lifts a thick dun-coloured file from one side of the desk. It is tied with a piece of red ribbon. 'Good luck,' he mutters, passing it to Paul, then closing the door. He points to one of the black-and-chrome chairs. 'Sit. How do you have your coffee?'

'White, no sugar,' I tell him, then I roll out the chair and take a seat. 'Paul's lovely, by the way. How long have you been together?'

'Only living together for the past year. You must remember him; it's like I've known him forever.' He waves his hand in a way that makes me wonder if he's trying too hard to make that point.

'Good for you,' I say. 'Don't remember him, though.' He passes me a white porcelain mug and folds himself into the chair opposite. 'Alex and Paul: my mother's reaction was hilarious. If a little predictable.'

'We tend not to focus in on people's reactions.' He lets out a long sigh. 'So?' Steepled fingers, two pressed to his lips. 'Has your workplace been in touch again?'

I shake my head. 'Not since I sent the formal email. But I've found somewhere to live, like you said. I can move in anytime.'

'That's very canny of you, my darling.'

'Not canny. Just a way to preserve my sanity.'

Alex shifts in his seat and gives me the faintest of smiles. Then he's serious again, and I wonder what's coming next.

'By my reckoning,' he says, 'there won't be a criminal case brought against you. There would have been notification by now.'

'What do you mean?' I gasp. Criminal prosecution? I've never broken the law in my life. Never disregarded a speed limit or taken a sly puff of a cannabis cigarette.

Alex reaches across the desk and puts a hand on my arm. 'Woah,' he says. 'I just mean that if the Turnbull parents totally believed their son, they'd have gone through official channels – the CPS – to bring charges of grooming a minor.

They haven't. I would have heard by now. So, I'm expecting a formal declaration of their intent to pursue a civil case against you.' He clears his throat. 'In short, they want compensation.'

Anger is rising up from my stomach, breaking free from its acidic surface like bubbles of hot volcanic mud. I try to swallow it down but the taste and gas it's producing are threatening to choke me. I open my mouth, but all that comes out is a breathy exhale. Up to this point, I've let myself believe in the power of bottom-line world justice. I've done no wrong so wrong won't *do* me. Now Alex is using words like *criminal*.

'But don't worry,' he continues, shaking his head, 'they have absolutely no grounds. Which is why I need every detail from you, of your time at White Platts Camp.'

I can only nod in agreement. Alex has the legal understanding, the knowledge of how these things pan out. All I have is the complete indignity and utter bewilderment of a person who, until a few days ago, was minding their own business, and living their chosen life. Now, my choices are spooling away from me, on the word of a fifteen-year-old boy.

Paul steps through the door. His glasses are atop his head, and he is rolling his eyes heavenwards. 'Sorry, you two,' he says, 'but the pigging phone is ringing off the hook and I don't have the diary out there.' He riffles through a pile of papers on the desk. 'Here it is. We could do with two, couldn't we?' He waves a navy-blue diary in the air and fixes Alex with a hard stare.

Alex huffs and presses the heel of his hand to his forehead. 'We need to get another Justin. We really do.'

There is a beat of silence, then I find my voice again. 'I could come and help you out,' I offer. 'For a couple of months, at least.' I look at Alex. 'You won't let me pay for your services. This is one thing I could do for you. I did do some secretarial work, once. When I was first out of college.'

He says nothing.

'No problem, if not,' I stammer. 'I guess you need a properly qualified person.'

'You mean it?' His eyes stretch wide. 'Could you bear to be cooped up in a little office, after the glam of your White Platts job?'

'I would be happy to, if it helps you. I've been wondering how I was going to fill my days. There's only so much exercise a body can take.'

Paul throws his arms around my shoulders. 'When can you start?' he asks. 'Tommoz?'

'Let me get moved into the cottage, then I'll be here,' I reply. 'But I'll have to buy some bits and pieces to wear. Even back at my chalet, I don't have anything smart enough.'

'And that's something else we'll have to work out,' Alex cuts in. 'A trip back to your camp, to collect your things. When I fire off the first email later on, I'll give your old boss a date for visiting, one that suits you, not him. Then we'll go together.'

I'm not sure Malcom Fairley is my *old* boss, but I don't feel like pointing this out, not when Alex has been so helpful; I don't allow myself to feel *controlled*.

We spend the rest of the morning talking about my style of working with kids, my qualifications, my experience and every detail of the two weeks with Ian Turnbull. Including his intimidation of young Danni, and his fluid use of inappropriate language. Neither of which had been anything different from the character and reactions of most of the cocky teens that we encounter at White Platts. And therein lay the fun, the rewards, the sense of changing young lives.

At lunchtime, I say my farewells to Alex and Paul, with the promise of a catch-up as soon as I've got settled in Tunnel Cottage. Then I step back into the town centre, intent on tying things up with Rosina Kerr as soon as I can.

There is a smell of ordinariness about the townscape, overlaid with metallic fumes from delivery wagons and the odd motorcycle that is taking its chance on a short cut between the pedestrian bollards.

Kerr's estate agency is on the main thoroughfare and looks much more like a proper shop than Swarbrick and Murray's. Its frontage is all gloss-and-glass, and as I step inside, I notice that Rosina has many, many properties on her books. Every wall in the reception area is lined with beautifully presented brochures showing a wide range of houses for sale. And she has four members of staff, all smartly dressed, and all very busy.

I glance around, wondering what to do next. And there is Rosina, holding a telephone to her ear. She pats the air with her free hand, beckoning me forwards.

'*One minute,*' she mouths, then points towards a desk at the back of the shop. I nod and sit down. Admire her floral fifties frock and tiny cardigan.

'Evie.' She clicks off her call. 'It's brill to see you again. How did you find the cottage? Cute, isn't it?' This is Rosina. She doesn't need another person to hold a conversation. She just fills in the blanks.

I press my lips together and nod.

'There's not much furniture, I know,' she continues. 'But the mattresses are brand new. Still in the Ziploc bags, I think. Hope you've brought your chequebook.'

She sits neatly down opposite me. 'I've got all the paperwork together in a file. Rental details, the lot. There are just a few things to sign, then you'll have a six-month contractual agreement. How about that?'

She sifts through a brown paper file. Her nails are exactly the same shade of orange as the bigger flowers on her dress. Her lipstick ties in, too. I am suddenly conscious of my tatty jeans and nude face. As it's November, I'm not even wearing a tan.

'Great,' I say. 'Thanks so much for doing this. For giving

me priority, I mean.' I rummage around in my backpack. Then pull out my chequebook and fill in the details that will secure Tunnel Cottage. If only it was as easy to pin down the other details of my future. But I shake away that thought. Today isn't a day for feeling down. I can deal with whatever the next six months throw at me. I just have to be patient.

Chapter Seven

On the day I choose to move into Tunnel Cottage an icy slush is falling and brown clouds chase across the sky, helped by a fitful and angry wind. My mother shivers in the doorway of her bungalow as she waves me off. We have filled my car with boxes: food, crockery, cutlery, bedding, towels and electrical items; half her bungalow, it seems to me. This is her way of showing affection. My contribution is a pile of old clothes and shoes from my wardrobe, most of which I haven't worn since I left home.

The road to the cottage is quiet, empty of the usual dog-walkers and families. The ruin is deserted. I wonder whether it closes for the winter. The thought of those Tudor monks, living out their life of poverty in a place like this, makes me shudder. It would be beautiful in the summer months but mortally cold on days like today. I park at the end of the driveway, intending to carry down each box, rather than risk my car on the steep and uneven slope. But the weather worsens, and I change my mind; if the car is right next to the cottage, it'll probably be safer anyway. I'm not much of a driver: if I can walk somewhere, I will. I turn the key and stay in a low gear, but the adrenaline is flowing by the time I make it to the bottom.

I let myself into the cottage and, one by one, carry the boxes into the hallway, then close the front door and stop to catch my breath. I am wet and cold and feeling slightly off. Lonely. When I moved into my chalet at White Platts, lots of my new colleagues turned out to help with the lifting and carrying as much as with the inevitable feelings of disorientation that come with a change of circumstances. Now, I can't help thinking I've been abandoned. Perhaps I should have asked Alex and Paul to help. My mother, even. Though that would have to be balanced against her judgmental looks and comments.

There is an empty fireplace in the lounge. Rosina reminded me to buy some fire logs and a bag of seasoned kindling, but I haven't done that yet. I wish I had. There doesn't appear to be any other form of heating in the cottage.

Luckily, my mother has included an electric fan heater in the treasure trove of items she's given me. I search around for the box that contains her old kettle, and some bits and pieces to make myself a hot drink; true to form, she has tucked everything in with a clean tea towel, so that it looks like a picnic hamper.

I carry the box into the kitchen and put it down on the narrow countertop by the sink. There is a small electric cooker set into another counter on the opposite side of the room, and a tiny fridge sits on top of an old pine table. Red quarry tiles cover the floor, and there is a kind of scullery area just by the back door. The room is clean but simple.

I fill the kettle and plug it in. A red light flickers on, and I breathe a sigh of relief. Electricity. Something that Rosina promised, but I wondered about. It hadn't been turned off, she told me, though it should have been. There is no gas in the cottage. It's too far off the local grid. This is one of the things that has been putting off potential buyers, apparently. And tenants have struggled with its isolation.

I plug in the fridge and start to fill it with my supplies: milk, juice, bottled water, butter, cheese and a small loaf that was the last one on the shelf of the local Co-op. While the kettle boils, I take a trip upstairs to the main bedroom, carrying the pile of sheets and blankets my mother has donated.

This room gives a view onto the cottage's back garden, of ragged conifers and clumps of decaying bracken. The sky hangs heavy and low, and even though it is mid-afternoon, the light is ebbing. On each side of the wood-framed bed is a small table, both laid out with new electric lamps. I know this because the shades are still cellophane-wrapped, the bulbs in boxes. I unzip the mattress from its covering and make up the bed. With the curtains drawn the room feels homely enough, but cold. It also has an empty hearth with a small ornate surround, as do the other bedrooms. Unless I get some fires lit, the cottage isn't going to warm up.

Back in the kitchen, I switch on the cooker, for warmth more than anything, and make myself a hot drink. The window in this room looks towards the meadow. There isn't much to see, in the fade of the afternoon, but I can just make out small groups of the Herdwick sheep I'd seen before, huddling together in the icy rain.

A glance at my watch tells me there is still a couple of hours before the local Tesco closes for the evening. I can pop there in my car and buy some kindling for the fire, rather than rely on the electricity-guzzling fan heater. I could wait until tomorrow, but the move has left me a bit disorientated, and I want something to do.

After I have drunk my tea, I switch off the cooker, lift my parka from where I left it, then zip myself in. I slip my feet into my boots and pick up my handbag and the keys to the cottage.

Outside, the wind is still laced with slushy rain, and I pull up my hood and scoot towards the car. I click open the door and climb in, shaking myself dry and strapping on my seatbelt. I'm halfway up the drive when I see someone standing at the top.

Jay

Car headlights startle Jay back to reality. Less than an hour ago, the golden-brown woman had carried box after box into the cottage, and now she's leaving again. He slides into the tangled shadows at the top of the drive and flips up his hood. If she's seen him at all, she'll probably just think he's some local walker, having to put the miles in despite the weather.

Once the car splashes by, he stops walking and changes direction. It'll be risky, he knows, but he has to get inside the cottage and see what is in those boxes, see what she is planning. Now and again, people come and do small maintenance jobs, and he knows some mattresses have been delivered recently; he was in his den at the time. The delivery guys hadn't even tried to tackle the driveway. They'd parked where he's standing now and carried everything down.

It's almost dark and he is soaked to the skin, but he won't be able to settle unless he knows. Then he can plan. In the pocket of his coat is a torch, and the key to the French windows. He's had it for so many years, dreads the day when he can no longer let himself in, and remember.

The driveway is more slippery than usual; the rain has an edge of ice. He'll have to be quick. For all he knows, the woman could come back at any minute, though he'll hear her car and see the headlights before she gets anywhere near the front door.

Though his hands are wet, he slips the key easily into the

lock on the outside of the windows and pushes his way inside. They close softly behind him.

Nothing seems to be out of place in this room. An electric heater has been plugged in by the side of the fireplace, and a cardboard box sits on the sofa, but that's all. The last time he'd seen his mother she'd been in here, lying on a different type of sofa, with a knitted blanket across her legs and the curtains closed. He remembers her wan smile and his gnawing hunger, and not much else. Except that the television was always on.

In the kitchen he notices that the fridge has been plugged in. When he pulls open the door and sees someone else's items of food and drink, it gives him a tight feeling in his stomach and he's not sure if it is anger or something more complex. He can't imagine another life unfolding in this room, with meals at the table and boots in the scullery, can only picture his own mother at the sink, peeling potatoes for chips, while the afternoon sun slants in through the back door, lighting the terracotta floor tiles to a bright orange.

And now they are soaking wet from the rain on his boots. Chasing away intruders is one thing but leaving evidence behind – that's not his way. He needs to mop the floor and get out quickly. There is a tea towel on the kitchen counter. If he dries the floor behind him and takes the towel away, that'll be a good job done. There'll only be the smallest hint that something's a bit off, but no way of proving anything. Though he hates what he is doing, he has no choice. Tunnel Cottage is the only thing tying him to this world now, and he can't let anyone take it away from him.

Chapter Eight

The darkness has an impenetrable quality; I can't even see the cottage from the top of the driveway, but I'm going to leave my car here anyway. Better that, than risk losing traction and smashing straight into the outhouses in the backyard. There is a large bag of fire logs and kindling to carry down with me. I've done ice climbs with a full load on my back, so this is familiar territory. But my acute sense of isolation is not. Even the gentle buzz of the Tesco aisles has done nothing to lift my misery out of my boots. I'm not sure exactly what I'm feeling, but I guess it's something to do with not being at White Platts. And this creeping sense of the situation not being in my control.

Once I'm inside the cottage, I carry my logs into the lounge and switch on the electric lamps. It still feels bitterly cold, but the soft yellow light gives the room a homely glow and I flick on my mother's electric heater for good measure.

Setting fires is something I'm used to, though I wouldn't boast about being good at it. I have matches and some newspaper, and soon there is a mediocre kind of blaze flickering in the hearth. Closing the curtains might help to retain some of the heat, though there's nothing I can do to stop the French windows from holding onto the cold.

I lay my hand against the glass and peer out into the darkness, wondering if there had once been a patio or something just outside. Perhaps, when I get the chance, I'll have a go at clearing this side of the garden, see if I can't make the view from here less grim. I'd have to check the terms of my tenancy first, though. Don't want to get into any trouble.

As I walk away from the French windows, I notice that the soles of my socks have become wet. I lift each one and look at it, thinking it might just be the cold. Then I kneel to feel the carpet. In front of the windows, it is sopping wet. They must leak. It doesn't surprise me; I can feel cold air skulking through, too. There's another thing that will need fixing. For now, I'll have to roll up a towel or something and try to plug the gap.

While the fire logs catch, I go into the kitchen to make myself a hot drink and some toast. My stomach gurgles at the thought and I have to laugh: misery never stops me from eating. I can't remember a time when I was off my food. I wonder what my mother would think of toast for *supper*. She'll come and visit Tunnel Cottage eventually, I'm sure, and I can picture her face when she sees how *rudimentary* it is. She's never visited White Platts.

I look around for the tea towel she sent so I can wipe off a couple of plates I have found in one of the wall cupboards. When I can't find it, I rummage through some of the other boxes, thinking I'd stuffed it away whilst unpacking, but there's no sign. Odd, because I dried my hands on it just before I left for Tesco. A moment of unease slides itself across my shoulders and makes me shiver. Being on high alert is making me edgy and I need to snap out of it. The tea towel will turn up, I'm sure.

While I wait for the grill to heat up and the kettle to boil, I plan how I'm going to spend my first full day in Tunnel

Cottage. If the weather improves, I want to explore the paths and bridleways around here, maybe scramble my way to the top of the sandstone escarpment that faces the ruin itself. And what I won't be doing is letting myself get bogged down with court cases and wishful thinking.

By morning, I'm feeling much more like myself, and stretch out in the warmth of the bed, enjoying the way spangles of bright winter sunshine push between the mismatched curtains and fall across my sheets and blankets. Sleeping is something I'm good at and essential for the life I lead. Last night, I'd drifted off very quickly; there wasn't a sound from anywhere. Now, though, I can hear the click-clack call of a couple of magpies or other type of corvid: jays perhaps, or rooks. The trees around here are plentiful enough for whole flocks of birds to roost in. And with that thought, I pull back my bedclothes and swing myself into the sharp cold of the room.

Within an hour, I'm layered up with my warmest clothing, stomach full of porridge and coffee, and stepping out into the beauty of a late November morning. After days of rain and grim light, the air is crisp enough to drink, and I'm taking as many swigs as I can get. At the garden gate, I pause and let myself tune in to the landscape. From here, it is possible to look into the blankness of the railway tunnel, but also to take in the way the track stretches towards places yet to be discovered. And I'm certain of where I'm heading today.

Across the meadow, the grass hangs with glittering spiders' webs and brown thistle patches. Along the edge of the beck, pastureland has become a red-clay beach, under the hooves of Herdwick sheep. Now, they are munching enthusiastically from bales of summer hay laid out by the far gate. I smile to myself: there's a lot to be grateful for.

I call a hello to a lady with a small dog who is tramping along the footpath towards me, then let myself out of the meadow again, following a bridleway sign that is pointing upwards. This is exactly the way to lose yourself for a day, and that's my intention.

Jay

His aunt's house is becoming a dead weight. His shoulders ache with it; the place doesn't feel like his own. More than anything, he wants Tunnel Cottage, though he understands the impossibility of this. He's never had enough money to even rent the place, let alone pay out a huge lump sum for its purchase. Liz did so much for him, but she wasn't his mother. Rejection hurt; still hurts.

Jay closes the door of the house and steps into the brightness of the morning. It is early. For most of the night, he has been working on a commission from a company on the other side of the world, one that seems to adore his watercolours, which means he'll be able to eat, this month. He's tired though, so tired. Like everything he's ever felt, every jarring emotion, has pushed to the surface of his skin and is cracking him open. And it's all because someone is living in his cottage.

He's heading there now, wants to check on the golden-brown woman. Perhaps she has changed her mind; at this moment she might be packing her car up and fleeing. It's happened before. When a young couple stayed at the place a few years ago, it hadn't taken much to send them on their way.

There's been a new rental sign put up on the front, recently. From his forays inside he's seen that some tidying and maintenance has gone on. Then, there were the new mattresses. If he could bring himself to squat in the place, he would. But Jay has never been a law-breaker. His life has been spent trying not to alert people to his presence. Well, his life since Jamie, anyway.

He makes his way through a quiet housing estate and across the main route out of town. The cold is piercing this morning, and he feels it in the places where his coat is wearing through, and in his toes. Though his boots were expensive ones, they've long since worn thin with all the walking that he does. A bit like him. How his aunt had laughed when, at fourteen years old, he'd suddenly shot up past her shoulders then reached a height which made him duck to get through the doorways of her house. Only feeling settled in the outdoors has left him with a walking habit and a lean body that is bordering on skinny. And he hasn't been to a hairdresser for twenty years.

When the ruin looms up, he stops for a moment and lets his artist's eye take it in: the way the low gold of the sun washes clean the ancient sandstone, and sets fire to the shadowy places; the flash of a glossy black crow calling down its sarcasm. Painting this place makes him money. In that respect, he is lucky.

As he approaches Tunnel Cottage, he sees the golden-brown woman at the front gate. She is dressed warmly, muffled up in a thick coat and bobble hat, and striding away from him into the meadow. Tucking himself into the gloom at the mouth of the tunnel, he waits. And wonders where she could be going, this early.

Once she's out of sight, Jay stomps down the gravelly railway sidings, lets himself into the garden of the cottage and knocks on the front door. If anyone else is living here with her, he's got to know, though he thinks she's on her own. No answer comes, so he checks again, then slips in between the dark conifer hedge to the French windows. There's no smell of fire in the air, no sign that she'll be coming back soon, so he carefully slides his key into the lock and lets himself in.

Though the lounge isn't warm, he can smell coffee and

something sweetly floral, soap perhaps. And there is a woollen blanket folded onto the sofa, and a pair of flimsy slippers. It's like a punch to his stomach that someone is making themselves at home here, a punch he remembers from his other life. He's conscious of his wet boots; clean but creating soft outlines on the old carpet. They'll have to come off, he can't leave footprints: too obvious. He drops them just outside the French windows, then makes his way to the kitchen. This is where he'll do his work. The tea towel he'd taken last time is in his pocket. Freshly laundered. Folded. He lays it neatly on the countertop and lets his eyes flick round the room. His kitchen. Mam's.

In the sink is a bowl and a mug, and a small saucepan has been filled to soak on the draining board. This is what he'll do. The washing up.

With a sharp movement, he forces up the sleeves of his coat and sets to work. Looking out of this window, it is possible to see across the meadow to the beck. There are sheep today, wandering away from the place where they take their extra feeds, jaws moving frantically even as they walk. He likes sheep. And their sweet faces are perfect for the front of Christmas cards. Every year he creates a new set of pen-and-inks and every year they are snapped up by various local printers. Jay hasn't had a Christmas card sent to him for many years, not since he first left Kew.

He wonders about the golden-brown woman, what her story is, why she has appeared at the cottage. His father had taken the place because it was tied to his job: he'd kept the tunnel for British Rail, carried out the odd maintenance job on the track. Jay has no idea whether he's even still alive.

Then suddenly she's there again, at the edge of the meadow, striding through the morning, breath hanging in clouds and chasing the last Herdwick stragglers, so that they scatter in front of her.

He needs to get out, and quick.

Chapter Nine

I can't believe I've been stupid enough to leave my phone behind. First rule of setting off on an adventure: tell someone where you are going, and if you can't, take your phone.

Halfway up the side of a low fell, cheeks glowing, jacket unzipped, I'd patted down my pockets, out of habit, and realised I'd forgotten something. Not my regulation chocolate bar, though. That goes without saying.

It'll take five minutes to get back to the cottage, if I take a slow jog, so that's what I'm doing. And I'm surprised to find, when I'm almost there, that a man is pushing his way through a hole in the garden fence, just where a pair of Herdwicks are grazing.

'Nosy things, these Herdies,' he is calling to me. 'Sorry, but I've had to breach the fence to get them out of your garden.'

Something flickers across my thinking. *My* garden? How does he know? But he is speaking again, and I try to focus on what he is saying.

'If they get their fleece caught on the wood, they just yank and yank till they're free, without caring what damage they're doing. They're not very bright, sadly.' He lets out a small laugh, then comes to stand in front of me. 'Sorry. I noticed you setting off, this morning. Didn't mean to give you a shock.'

'No shock involved,' I tell him, 'but why were they in the garden?'

He swings an anorak-clad arm outwards and points at the fence. 'If there's a hole,' he says, 'a sheep-sized hole, they have to find out where it leads. Even if they already know. They can't help themselves.'

'What do you mean?' There is a joke going on here, and I'm not privy to it. Now that this guy is standing up again, I realise just how tall he is.

'This is the third time I've chased them out of the garden,' he says. 'And they've only been in the meadow for a week.'

'Are you a farmer then? Or their owner?'

He shakes his head, and snorts gently. 'No. I'm no farmer. I'm just… around here a lot. Walking and stuff.'

I take in the jeans and muddy boots, the looped scarf and long hair caught back in a braid.

'Oh. Well, I'll need to get that hole repaired then.'

Dark eyes snap to mine. 'You've bought the place?'

There is a second when I wonder why that information came out. I've no idea who this is. My brain works on a way to rein in what I've told him; my mouth decides not to follow suit.

'No,' I say. 'I'm just renting. But there's things that need doing, as you say. The fence, for instance. That just made it to the shortlist.'

The sheep have put themselves at a safe distance and I wonder, briefly, if I should do the same. But this man seems harmless enough.

'It'll be good to see the place with lights on and smoking chimneys,' he says, gazing upwards. 'But they'll need a sweeping first, I guess.'

'You know the cottage then?'

'A little.' He holds out his hand. 'I'm Jay Elliot, by the way. In case you're thinking some weirdo is hanging around Tunnel Cottage. I'm just an ordinary bloke.'

Our eyes meet. Only for a moment, but I'm almost knocked off my feet. There is an energy flowing from this man; it chases behind my eyes and down through my body, to Earth. I shake his hand lightly. 'Hello. Evie Cooper.'

We walk together towards the footpath that leads to the cottage gate.

'Beautiful morning,' he says, and I laugh.

'When in doubt, talk about the weather.'

'And are you?'

'What?'

'In doubt?'

I have to think about this for a moment. Is this guy, this Jay Elliot, flirting with me? After being found in my garden, looking ever so slightly embarrassed?

'I'm a decisive person, not a doubtful one,' is my reply. I can be flirty too. Though now I just sound like an idiot.

The energy fades.

'Good for you,' he says with a swagger, then shrugs his shoulders, and walks past my garden gate and back towards the railway track.

Jay

Damn, damn, damn.

Jay can't believe how foolish he's been. Letting himself get caught at the cottage, then making contact with the very person he's trying to get rid of. But there is something about the woman. Although she is probably around his age, there is a strength to her. Like she's used to being in charge.

And now he's tramping his way back to his aunt's house without any knowledge of what to do next. When this Evie Cooper gets back inside the cottage, she'll see that the washing up has been done and her tea towel is folded neatly on the kitchen counter. And her face might crumple in fear. Or it might not. Either way, there's not supposed to be any feeling about it on his part, only a calm and detached certainty that his actions are justified. Tunnel Cottage is his, after all. If not in name, then in every other way.

He can't forget the first time he'd seen the place: it had been high summer, with scribble larks singing in the meadow and a sprinkling of diamond on the surface of the beck. And his aunt had just been someone who came to tea. He'd been part of a family, then; he'd mattered. Now, it is just him and the depressing house he's been left with. Though his aunt had been a vibrant woman, her struggles had become his, as much as his became hers. They'd grappled with things neither of them understood. But she'd loved him, in her way. The last person who had.

When he gets to the front door, his legs feel shaky, and he is gasping for breath. Feeling weak is not something he usually allows; he's let himself lose control. Seeing the living room, with its cluttered surfaces and years of neglect, makes him lose it even more. He swipes his arms across his desk and his art materials smash to the floor. Then he does the same to his piles of books, and to the last of his aunt's ornaments. But nothing satisfies the deep uncertainty that has suddenly crystallised in his stomach and is clawing its way into his throat. He falls to his knees in the middle of the room and screams out for someone to help him.

Jay sits bolt upright, jolted out of his sleep. The pant of his breath is filling the shed with clouds of condensation and he's almost too cold to function. But he has to. Getting rid of this woman is top priority; he'll never settle until she's gone. His plan was to wait in his shed until she was locked safely in Tunnel Cottage for the evening, then make a few noises outside and watch for her response. But he'd fallen asleep, and now it looks to be the middle of the night. He doesn't own a watch, but one glance from the door of his shed and he can tell. There's not a single light on in the cottage and the moon is almost touching the ridge of the fell. So, way past midnight, then.

He slips through the shadows, making his way to the side of the cottage. There's no sound, except for the soft pad of boots on decayed leaves. He gently unlocks the French windows and creeps inside. There's a warmth in the lounge that he hasn't felt for a long time, and the smell of toasted bread. He slips off his boots and carries them with him as he makes his way into the hall. He stops at the bottom of the stairs. The woman will be asleep somewhere above him. That thought gives him a feeling he thinks may be anger, but could be envy. If he moves a few things around, she'll notice, and she'll start to worry. That's the plan, anyway.

Then there's a creak from the landing. A door opening. The door to Mam's room, he's sure. He moves back into the lounge. Makes himself secure by the French windows, just in case. Then he waits.

There's a slight sound on the stairs. Very faint, but he hears it. The woman is walking down them. She doesn't say anything, but he hears the banister move slightly; it's always been loose. All he can do is get out. Then his efforts will have been wasted. While she's still on the stairs, he touches the rocking chair and sets it in motion. Then lets himself out and turns the key in the lock, once again. From the shadows, he sees the woman switch on the light in the lounge. She is wearing pyjamas with a sweater over the top. Her feet are bare, and he enjoys the fear on her face as she sees the moving rocker.

Chapter Ten

'Evie, can you come through for a minute?'

Alex stands in the doorway of his office, shirtsleeves rolled, and his glasses pushed up to the top of his head. It's my first day of working for him, and I'm feeling pleased with myself, though my woollen slacks are itchy, and it seems odd to have a collar and cuffs. I've managed to answer most of the telephone queries that have come in, after only a short blast of training from Paul, and with the help of Alex's crib sheet and Post-it notes.

'Course,' I reply. 'Shall I put the phone through?'

He shakes his head as Paul pushes past. 'No, it's fine. We've got it covered.'

And that worries me. They have set up a situation where I can talk privately with Alex. Which means only one thing. They have heard from White Platts, or from the Turnbull family's solicitor. Almost a week has passed, and I've not been contacted, so it's about time there was some kind of communication. But now my stomach fizzes, like I'm standing at the edge of a cliff and imagining what it would be like to fall. And I know the strain of it all is starting to catch up with me: there have been small moments of forgetful panic when I'm at Tunnel Cottage on my own, losing things, setting off on a task that I'd already done, thinking someone's there, when they're clearly not. Little things, but they're starting to add up.

It is almost dark outside, and rain is pelting against the windows of the office in a way that makes me glad I'm inside. Alex and Paul's room is in the centre of the building; if there was any natural light, it wouldn't be finding its way in. Instead, two fluorescent panels have been installed in the ceiling, so the room is bright, but the effect is dazzling. I blink my way in and sit down in Paul's chair. It is holding onto a residual warmth.

'I guess you've heard from Malcom,' I say, but Alex shrugs his shoulders.

'Not directly, but I do have some news.'

His expression makes me lift my brows. 'Oh?'

I am surprised to see a wad of typescript in his hand. He flattens it down and brings his glasses back to the bridge of his nose, scans for a moment.

'Not an email, then?' Stupid question, but I can't help asking. A letter seems so *heavy-handed*, somehow.

'Nope. A full and formal set of findings and instructions from Odell's in Stratford-upon-Avon. The Turnbulls' solicitor. Shall I give you the main headings or do you want to read it all?'

'The headings,' I snap back. The fact that I am being directed by a solicitor is leaving a bitter taste on the sides of my tongue. Like I've bitten into hidden mould on the last piece of bread in the packet.

'Well,' he says. 'Firstly, I was right about no criminal prosecution forthcoming. Your boss had to inform the Local Authority Designated Officer about the accusation. I'm so glad I filed that detailed report early on. She found no case to answer because early witness statements provided no clear evidence for or against.'

I'm starting to have difficulty with the fact that I have become a *case*. I did nothing wrong, but I've found myself being reported to the LADO. That will be on my personnel records forever.

'I can go back to work then?'

'Sorry. No.' His mouth has a grim set to it, and I wonder what is coming next.

'As I told you before,' he says, 'the Turnbull parents don't want to drop the case. They believe their son, so they are saying anyway, and they want action taken against you.'

I inhale sharply. 'What sort of action?'

'They think you should be sacked.' A roll of his eyes. 'Impossible,' he says, 'but they have the right to bring a civil suit against you. The outcome of which would be a payout. And your removal from White Platts.'

'None of this makes sense.' I shake my head. 'One minute I'm an outdoor instructor, doing my job, and the next minute I'm this… this… criminal. And all on the word of a teenager.'

Alex lifts his glasses away from his face and rubs at his eyes. 'You're not a criminal,' he says. 'I'm not sure why the Turnbulls have still got a wasp up their arse, though, if you'll pardon the expression. Perhaps their solicitor has put them up to this. But I doubt it. A civil action will cost a fortune, whether they win or lose. We are not supposed to act in a way which will lead clients into recklessly spending their money.'

'But this solicitor has?'

'I don't know.' He frowns. 'But someone's encouraged them. They're seeking substantial damages, it seems.'

Damages? What is he talking about? I look at him, stunned.

'They want ten thousand pounds. Court costs, money for

Ian's counselling, and a sum of compensation. Sorry Evie, but there it is.'

'Fuck,' I say. Not my usual turn of phrase, but it slices through the weighted atmosphere and startles us both. 'Where does that money come from?' There is a small tremble in my bottom lip. I'm not sure if it's fear or anger or sheer bloody astonishment.

'Calm down. It's not something you would have to pay personally.' He rubs at his chin. 'Your employer would be liable for it, if the civil action ruled in the Turnbulls' favour. Or an out-of-court settlement could be agreed on. But you'll be going for neither of those, will you?'

'What do you mean?' I ask, feeling more out of my depth than when I had to jump out of a Wayfarer dinghy and into the middle of Windermere, to fish out an errant over-boarder.

'You'll want a *false* verdict, won't you? Even if it means appearing in court?'

I don't want any sort of verdict. I just want this whole fiasco to stop. As far as I'm concerned, there was never a case to answer, so how have I been dragged into this situation? 'Look, Alex,' I say with a sigh. 'Is there nothing I can do to make this whole thing go away? I just want to get back to my job and forget about Ian Turnbull.'

'You can make it go away,' he says. 'By facing them down in court. It will take time, but I think you knew that, didn't you? Or you wouldn't have settled yourself in Tunnel Cottage.' He stands up and drags open one of the drawers in a huge metal filing cabinet. 'I'll put this latest information with the other things in your file. Then we can draft a letter to Odell's.'

'I don't want to go to court,' I tell him. 'I haven't done anything.'

He huffs a little. 'Okay. Well, the alternative is that we write to Malcom Fairley and tell him that you want to settle with the Turnbulls. Then he'll have to fight it out with Odell's. But–'

The raised hands tell me that this isn't the course of action he would recommend.

'But what?'

'That gives Malcom too much power, in my opinion.' He hesitates. 'Can I ask you something quite personal?'

I shrug. 'You can ask.'

'Something about this boss of yours seems a little *off*. There was nothing going on between you, was there?'

'What sort of thing?'

'You tell me?'

I have to think about how I answer this. Alex hasn't sniffed something out for no reason.

'We were never romantically involved, if that's what you mean,' I finally say.

But I'm wondering what he's onto.

'I didn't necessarily mean that.' His eyes are narrowed on my face. 'I just get the feeling he's not on your side. When he should be.'

'Tell me what you know,' I hiss.

'I don't know anything. But there are a couple of things that have cropped up in my communications with the Turnbulls' solicitor, that makes me think that your Malcom Fairley would be happy if some blame was laid across your shoulders.' Alex presses his lips together. 'Perhaps I'm overthinking things?'

That's not something Alex ever does.

'You can't just leave me dangling, Al. Tell me.'

'For a start,' he says, 'there was no reason for sending you away from White Platts. That was Malcom Fairley's choice. He says it was to placate the Turnbulls. But he didn't have to do it. It implies that he didn't fully trust you.'

Incredulous, I stare at him. 'Go on,' I whisper.

'There's a sentence in his report to the LADO that jarred instantly with me. I'm not supposed to tell you anything about that report, so you mustn't ever repeat it to him or anyone else.'

'Like I would,' I mutter.

'He told the LADO that if he found there was any truth in Ian Turnbull's allegation, he would get rid of you straight away because he wasn't having any taint on White Platts. So supportive of him, wasn't it?'

Words fail me. In fact, they are trapped in the back of my throat, stopping my breath and making me gag. I put my hand over my mouth and shake my head.

'So, you see, Evie,' Alex is saying, as he slips my file away again, 'you have to face them all in court. Malcom included. Though he's supposed to be standing shoulder-to-shoulder with you.'

Later, when the office has closed for the day and I am driving back to the cottage, watching December flash by, a harlequin of coloured lights and strained faces, I allow myself to think again about what Alex has told me. Less than a month ago, I was a senior outdoor tutor, highly qualified and working in a place that I loved. Now, it seems, I have become a liability, and am being chased down and hounded into a court case that I neither want, nor deserve. But if I resist, I will never get back to being the person I was. And niggling away inside me is the feeling that Malcom Fairley can go to hell, that I never want to give my expertise to him again, anyway. Can I just hand in my notice, with the way things are? Would that allow me to get off this ridiculous rollercoaster that I've been forced to ride?

I chug along the main road with the crawl of traffic, tyres swishing and wipers frantic, leaving behind the rows of houses and shops that make up the town centre. The landscape darkens. I shiver despite the warmth of my parka and chunky scarf. The cottage will be chilly until I can get the fires lit. If I owned the place, the first thing I'd do would be to spend out on central heating. And a whole new set of windows.

The thick curtains are there for a reason, and it's nothing to do with 1980s décor. Unless they're properly closed, all manner of drafts and country smells creep in through the rattly windows, or under the badly fitting doors.

My chalet at White Platts was always warm, with its programmable heaters and silver-foam flooring. And I'm starting to miss Pip. She would always be there if I needed to chat. Perhaps I will give her a call when I get home. Find out what's being said about me. See if she has any insider information. *See if I can read between the lines.* The whole situation is starting to make me feel down. Nothing major, that's not me, just this tiny lump of darkness in the pit of my stomach, and nothing I'm doing seems to shift it.

As I turn into the top of the cottage's driveway, it crosses my mind that I should perhaps park here and walk down. I feel a flash of alarm as my car starts to slip forwards, losing any traction I might have had. But it's too late to stop. All I can do is crank into the lowest gear and hope I make it down.

I don't.

When I'm halfway, the car gets into a groove which I cannot steer out of, then slides off the tarmac and into a shallow ditch. It only comes to a standstill because of the ghostly white trunk of a silver birch, which groans slightly and then wedges me in.

I climb out and flip up the hood of my parka. Leaving the car here is probably the best option, unless I can find some kind of planking and slide it under the wheels. But my shoes are filling with water, and I can't think straight, or see well, with the rain teeming down.

I start to feel trapped. Which is ridiculous, considering I've been through a cave system at Ingleton and down Alum Pot, in

Yorkshire. But the thought of being stuck at the cottage with no means of escape is making my heart thud against my ribs.

As I glance up the drive towards the main road, someone is peering down at me. They wave. I'm pretty sure it is the same man that chased the sheep from my garden. Jay Elliot, I think his name was. Certainly, this person is wearing the same blue anorak, though the hood is up and zipped tightly.

'Having trouble?' The voice is the same. It strikes me as odd that he's here again, but I also feel an overwhelming sense of relief that I'm not on my own with the car problem.

'No, it's fine,' I call, but he's already walking down the drive towards me. Icy water drips from the peak of my hood, and I run a hand across my face, trying to get a better sight of him.

'It's dangerous.' He points at the tarmac. 'This driveway, I mean.' A moment's hesitation. 'And I only cross it up there. That's bad enough.'

I nod. He is wetter than I am, although I notice he's wearing waterproof trousers and what my mother calls duck boots. Strands of his hair have escaped from the hood of his coat and are plastered across his cheeks. He is standing next to me now. I have to look upwards to speak to him.

'I was thinking about looking for some bits of boarding.' I gesture towards the back garden. 'I'm sure there will be something. If not, I'm giving up.'

'Want some help?'

It is a simple enough question, but so loaded. I know nothing about this guy. I am on my own, far enough away from civilization that I should feel vulnerable. Though I don't.

'Sure,' I say, through the slicing rain. 'You have a rummage around in the garden for something that might prove useful. I'll start the car up and see what happens.'

He makes his way past me, towards the garden. I can always lock myself in my car, if he turns out to be an axe murderer. Then I let out a small snort of laughter and start again with turning the engine over, and revving. Jay soon returns with two pieces of half-rotted MDF. I open the window and pull on the handbrake once again.

'You try and reverse a little and I'll slide these under the front wheels,' he says, 'then get some kind of grip on them.' He blows the rain away from his face. 'Okay?'

I wait for him to kick the boards in front of the tyres then I try: more revving, a little wheel spin, then the car inches forward. But the back wheels are spinning on churned up mud and leaves.

'Let me find a couple more boards,' he calls to me through the rain, then disappears off into the garden. Once again, I wonder what I am doing. Relying on myself is something I'm used to. Letting a complete stranger help me is not. Yet, here I am, feeling elated when Jay comes back out from the darkness of the garden, carrying two more pieces of MDF under his arms. He forces them under the back wheels and slams his hand down on the roof, indicating that it is safe to try again.

Once more, I over-rev the engine and hold the car at the exact point where first gear engages. And it works. The car heaves itself out of the ditch and planes down to the bottom of the drive, where I skid to a splashy halt.

I hold onto the steering wheel for a moment as Jay jogs towards me, then I climb out of the car.

'Well,' he says with a laugh. 'That was a bit primitive. But it worked.' He tugs at the neck of his jacket. 'Wet now, though.'

'I'm so grateful. Thank you for that. Jay, wasn't it?' I'm not sure what else to say, but he is shaking himself off and walking away.

'No problem. I'll leave you to get out of the rain. Bye.'

'I'm Evie, in case you've forgotten. Let me at least make you a coffee or something,' I blurt out. 'It's one hell of a night.'

He stops walking and turns to me. 'A coffee would be welcome,' he says. Then sweeps his hands down his soaking wet jacket and trousers. 'But I'll stand outside, if that's okay. If I try to take my gear off, I'll just float away.'

We walk towards the front door of the cottage. 'I've just come back from work,' I tell him. 'Probably best if I get the bus on days like this, in future. Or walk.'

He smiles. 'Wait till proper winter kicks in. I'd leave the car at the top of the drive, in future. It'll be a pig of a walk back down to the cottage, but better than *Wacky Races* again.'

I laugh at that. 'Yeah. Just call me Penelope Pitstop.'

Jay stands in the porch while I unlock the door.

'I've got tea, if you'd prefer?'

He shakes his head. His long dark hair is loose and tucked into the back of his jacket. 'Coffee's great, thanks. Just milk. If you have any.'

I don't take off my parka. Instead, I head straight to the kitchen and flick the electric cooker on. Then the kettle. While I wait for it to boil, I stare out of the kitchen window and across the meadow. It is so quiet. I can't even see the surface of the beck, only fine sheets of rain and darkness. Where the sheep are, I can't even guess, though there are plenty of trees for shelter.

Who would be out walking on a night like this, I wonder. And why?

Jay is still in the porch when I carry through two mugs of hot coffee. He has unzipped his waterproof jacket and smoothed his wet hair back from his face.

'Thanks, I need this,' he says, as I pass him a mug. 'I've been out too long today. And I think my boots are leaking.' He takes a sip of his drink. 'That's good.' His eyes don't leave my face.

'Do you live nearby?' I have to ask.

'Not really, no. But I do walk here a lot.'

'I don't blame you,' I say. 'It is beautiful. Not the best weather for it, though.'

My eyes flicker over his hands, circling the mug. They are raw and paint-stained. And the cuffs of his jacket are none too clean.

'It's not. But I can't stand being cooped up. And walking goes with the job, as it happens.'

'Oh? What do you do?'

'I'm an artist. Well, kind of.' He shrugs.

'Woah. I'm impressed,' I tell him. 'What kind of art?' I realise I know nothing, wonder if that's a stupid question. And suddenly, I really don't want to appear stupid.

'Oh, I do all sorts.' Another sip of his coffee. 'Fine line drawing, oils, charcoal, even some sculpture. But I make most of my money from freelance illustration. For books and greetings cards and the like.'

I can't help myself. I'm fascinated. I've spent most of my life around people who grabbed the outdoors with both hands and explored its possibilities for excitement. Here is someone who responds to it in a totally different way.

'I'd love to see some of your work,' I say, then realise how *creepy* that sounds. 'Sorry. That's really pushy.'

He laughs. 'The coffee was great,' he says and hands me his mug. 'Well, I'd better get off.' He looks up at the black sky. 'The rain's not stopping, is it? But look—' He puffs out his cheeks and blows softly. 'The temperature has dropped even further.' A small cloud of frozen breath hangs for a second and then it's gone. He pulls up his hood. 'I'll probably see you again, now you're living here. I'm always in the woods, sketching or nosing at something. Bye now.'

Jay

Though he hates himself for it, a plan is forming in Jay's mind.

He pulls off his boots and hangs his wet jacket and trousers over the chairs in his aunt's kitchen. It's a room even more basic than the one in Tunnel Cottage, has never been more than a place to warm up cans of soup or boil water over the flames of an ancient gas cooker. And the cupboard where she kept her cider bottles is one that he can never bear to open. Remembering those evenings where she'd sent him over to what she called The Offy only adds another layer of misery to a time in his life he would rather forget. Along with so many others.

The woman, Evie Cooper, though: there is an aura of warmth and safety about her. Jay is good at picking up vibes from people. The talent comes, he thinks, from years spent leaning against playground walls, watching how other kids conducted themselves: even after he and Punchy-Boy parted company, Jay never felt included at school.

Punchy-Boy. A juvenile name invented at a time in his life when he only had the inside of his head for company. Taking a beating almost every day from a boy twice his size had at least given Jay some reason for his existence, when even teachers disliked him. Apart from the lady who ran the art department in his high school. She recognised the need in him to draw and sketch and paint and she'd protected him from the wrath of maths and PE.

There's something protective about Evie Cooper, too. And even though he knows it's a bad thing to do, he is going to woo her, an old-fashioned term that his mother used to describe what happened between her and Dad.

If Evie has worked out that he's been in Tunnel Cottage, she's given no indication, and she certainly doesn't seem to be a person who is easily scared; she invited him to share coffee, for goodness' sake, when she had no idea who he was.

He turns on the tap and fills a mug with cold water. Walking all day has given him a thirst, and his belly rumbles. There are some sandwiches in the fridge that he brought from the reduced section in the local Co-op earlier this week. They'll have to do for now.

If his plan works, he'll soon find himself welcomed into Tunnel Cottage, his cottage, in a way he never thought would happen again.

Chapter Eleven

I t's a raw night. One that transports me straight to evenings spent on winter fellsides, with air so sharp it would zing through your brain and clear away the shadowy parts of life in an instant. I would come back from those night walks with a sparkling outlook on life. And the effect would not only last for a long time, but would drive me to seek it out again and again. Breathing pure, cold air became my drug of choice.

I tug my scarf up over the bottom part of my face and jump off the bus. There is still about a mile to walk to Tunnel Cottage, down into the valley and across the railway line. When the splatter of headlights stops for a moment, and there is a gap in the traffic, I shuffle across the road, trying to hold onto my flat pumps by clawing my toes, which hurts. If I'm going to continue working for Alex and not driving my car into the town centre, I'm going to have to wear trainers with my work gear and keep these shiny slip-on contraptions at my desk.

More days have passed where I'm sitting on my hands to stop myself from phoning or emailing White Platts, to find out what the hell is going on. It's as if I was never there. Trying to get Pip to answer my messages has become impossible and when I mentioned this to Alex his shrug worried me.

'That's how things are,' he'd said. 'No talking, no communication of any kind until the whole thing is settled. I'd recommend you do the same. Keep schtum about your situation. This Pip character will have been told to keep you at arm's length, for now, and she won't have any choice but to obey. Don't take it to heart.'

But I have. These were my colleagues, and Pip was a friend. Or so I thought. That Malcom Fairley has told her not to speak to me makes me incredibly angry, though I can't deny I would probably have done the same, if asked. Malcom was one of those bosses – extremely supportive of his people, but if you didn't want the trappings of that particular clique, better look for a job elsewhere.

I have wondered why Ian Turnbull targeted me rather than Pip, or the other female instructors. One or two were much nearer his own age and did support me with the Apollonius group. But he'd only shown them scorn, much like he did with Danni. Poor kid, I wonder how she's doing now.

A few more drags of the night air get me downhill, moving towards the ruin. A layer of frost has already formed along the shadowed edges of the precinct wall, and it glimmers, white and soft. I run a finger along these mini-daggers, and they crumble under my touch. It's going to be cold in the cottage tonight.

I keep my eyes focussed on the one streetlamp at the bottom of the hill. Reaching it means I'm almost home. Tonight, there is someone standing at the railings, just in front of the lamp, staring into the darkness of the ancient abbey. As I approach, I recognise Jay Elliot. Again. And I am mistaken, he is not just staring. He has some kind of book in his hand. A sketchbook perhaps. He looks to be drawing, or maybe writing. A shuffle of my shoes, and he turns his face towards me.

'Evening.' A nod of his head.

I pull down my scarf.

'Hello,' I say. 'It's a chilly one.'

There is a smile. It fills me with light. 'Oh. Evie, isn't it. We keep meeting, don't we. Are you heading home?'

He remembers my name. That small fact sends a jolt of energy through my belly and down both legs.

'I am,' I tell him, then shuffle my feet awkwardly. 'But what are you up to? It looks interesting.'

'I've actually got a commission. The client wants an oil painting of the abbey at night.'

I crane towards the creamy page.

'Not easy,' he continues, 'when the only lighting comes from this,' he tilts his head towards the lamp, 'and the moon.'

'Can't you just paint it in daylight, then add an evening sky?'

'I could,' he tells me, 'but I really want to capture what you can see, right now. The sandstone has taken on a smoky sheen.' He points towards the enormous bell-tower. 'But only at the top, if you look. At the bottom, it's black.'

He's got it exactly right. I've scurried past the ruin every night this week, but I've never really looked.

'How do you remember everything?' I can see a very fine outline of the main buildings, but there is no colour. He flips over the page.

'That's where words come in handy.' He laughs, showing me hundreds of scribbly notes. I look at his hands. The knuckles are bone-white.

'You need to pick clients who want summery paintings,' I say. 'With buttercups in the meadow, and blue skies.'

'They pick me.' The sketchbook is snapped shut. 'I have to take work where I can.' He lifts his rucksack off his back. It is tatty, but a good make. He slides the sketchbook in, and pushes his pencil into one pocket. Then swings it back over his shoulder. 'I'd better get going. Nice to see you again.'

He begins to walk away. I don't want him to, want instead to spend some time talking to him. I think again of the cold cottage and the warmth I feel at the sight of Jay Elliot, and my rational brain opts out for a moment.

'Would you like to come for a coffee?' I ask. 'To the cottage, I mean?'

I don't get the chance to think any further.

'Sure.' He pushes his hands into his pockets. 'Could do with one.'

'Let's go then,' I say, and I'm suddenly conscious of a shift in my perspective. It's like my high-alert sense has kicked in.

Jay and I walk together, inhaling the atmosphere of the ruin, and batting between us comments about the weather. The path to the cottage is in darkness, the tunnel mouth a black hole in the hillside. Any moonlight is held back by the conifers in the garden, but when we swing open the railway gate and cross the track, it's like the place is welcoming me home. Jay follows me up to the front door and begins to unlace his boots. The toes are pretty scuffed, I notice. Here is a guy who likes to walk. My boots have similar damage.

'Come on in,' I say, as he kicks them off and tidies them onto the doorstep.

I flick on the hall light and unzip my parka, then hang it on one of the pegs behind the door. Jay steps inside and I get my first proper look at him, not veiled by icy rain or darkness, or hidden behind the backsides of a couple of Herdies and a broken fence.

'Take your coat off,' I say, 'if you like.' His long, dark hair is caught back tightly in an elastic band. His skin has the outdoorsy sheen I know so well. There are a few faint lines around his eyes, which are so dark as to be almost black, and they are smiling down at me.

'Thanks,' he is saying. 'You need a fire lighting?'

I hesitate. How does he know that I haven't got a gas or electric one that only requires the flick of a switch? Or did we have a conversation about fires and chimneys?

'That'd be great. If you don't mind.' I shrug one shoulder. 'Would you like coffee or tea?'

'Whatever you're having,' he says, stepping towards the lounge. 'No sugar, thanks. Is it in here?'

I nod, then watch his back as he ambles down the hallway. He is wearing a faded sweatshirt that is a little short in the length, and the oldest pair of Levi's I've ever seen. The hems are frayed and damp-dark.

In the kitchen, I fill the kettle and switch on the cooker, as is my habit. It will be eating electricity, but it helps to get the cottage warm quickly. I lay out a tray with two mugs and a plate of digestive biscuits, then wait for the water to boil. I can hear Jay banging about in the lounge, and now I finally ask myself what the hell I am doing. I've met the guy twice before and know nothing about him. Yet, here he is, in my house, shoeless and coatless and kneeling, no doubt, in front of my hearth. But that thought makes me smile. There is something very *warm* about Jay Elliot, and I'm sick of always playing by the rules. If I want to make new friends, I will.

'Got any matches, Evie?'

His call cuts across my self-talk, and I am glad of it. I pull open a drawer in the old kitchen dresser and flip a box of matches onto the tray, then carry everything through to the lounge.

'I have matches,' I tell him, 'and biscuits, too.' I put the tray down on the small coffee table in the centre of the room, then switch on the lamps and close the curtains.

He has built what I would class as an expert fire. It lights in an instant, and the kindling catches straight away.

'Wow. How did you do that?' I ask. 'I have to hold a

newspaper across the opening before I can get even the slightest flicker.'

He sits back on his heels. One of his socks has a hole in the sole.

'That's not what the newspaper is for.' He laughs, nodding towards the stack I have collected. 'I twist the sheets into a kind of stick, then pile them at the bottom first. Like this.' He peels off a sheet of the *Westmorland Gazette*, folds it neatly, then rolls it into what looks like a dog's toy bone. 'I'll make you a few,' he says.

I sit down on the sofa, fluffing up my cushions, the ones I chose to hide the slightly cracked leather, and make sitting less slippery. Jay positions himself on the slate hearthstone, his arms hugging his long legs. When I lift my mug from the tray, he does the same. Holds it up to me, in a gesture that says he needs it.

'Thanks for this.' That smile. 'It's been a long day.'

'How much time have you spent down here today?' I ask.

He takes a sip of his drink. 'Been here since eight this morning. But I haven't been working on my commission for the whole day. I like to walk around as well. See what's what.'

I let out a small laugh. 'For instance?'

'Sometimes I'll see something I like. A leaf skeleton. Or a tree shape I haven't noticed before. Then I stop to paint or sketch. It's how I work.' He shifts position, and then balances his mug on one of his knees. 'Been cold today, though.'

His comments have given my curiosity a tug. 'Could I have a look at your work?' It's a big ask, I know. These arty types are private people. Except for Rosina. A memory springs up in my mind. An exhibition, set up by her, and only about her and her work. I wonder how she became an estate agent, when all she'd ever talked about was letting her art loose on the world.

He doesn't say anything for a moment, and I cringe inwardly at the thought of overstepping some invisible mark, but then he puts his coffee down and stands up. 'Sure. I've got a few sketches and stuff. In my haversack. I'll just get it.'

He's soon back, sketchbooks in hand, and sitting beside me on the sofa, flipping through pages and bringing with him the smell of clean cotton and something chalky, paint perhaps, I'm not sure. But it takes me unawares, and his presence is more vivid because of it, more potent.

'These first ones are just general outlines of the ruin. In charcoal. Then I can smudge out the bits I don't like.' He waits as I peer closer, reach out my hand to the creamy paper.

'They look three-dimensional.' I stretch my eyes. 'The slabs of stone.' My index finger runs over a section of the bell-tower. 'How do you do that?'

'Just by looking, I guess,' he says. 'I spend my life just looking.'

He turns more pages. There is nothing artistic about his hands. They are large and raw-boned, the nails bitten down and split. But now he is showing me the most beautiful and intricate pencil drawing of a teasel. There is a slight tinge of brown to it, which I can see is watercolour paint, but it has no texture. It is glassy and smooth. Pencil lines create the fine spikes on the stems, and again, I have to touch.

'That's beautiful,' I whisper.

He turns his gaze on me.

'Have it, if you like.' The page comes away from its spiral binding, with a soft tearing sound. 'What I mean is, I'd like you to have it.'

The air between us crackles with a tension I can feel right through my body. Words of thanks don't seem enough, suddenly. It's like Jay has given me a piece of himself. And we hardly know each other.

'I'd really like to have it.' I pause. 'If you don't mind. There's something so evocative about your work. Like you've embedded yourself in it, somehow.'

He shrugs lightly and turns away.

'Ignore me. I'm rambling,' I tell him. 'I'm just so grateful, that's all.'

'No. You're exactly right,' he says. 'I do feel like I'm painting or drawing myself onto the page.' A shake of his head, then he takes the sketchbooks from my hand. 'But you haven't told me anything about you. Even though I've laid me out on the page.'

'Not much to tell.' I don't feel like talking about myself. 'I'm an outdoor instructor, between jobs at the moment, so I've moved in here for a while. Couldn't stand the thought of going to live back with my mother.'

I find that I don't want to give him any more detail than this. Because it's not his business, or because I don't want him to think badly of me – I'm not quite sure which of these reasons is the truth, but it doesn't really matter. He's off the subject and talking about the cottage.

'I could never understand why the place didn't sell,' he is saying. 'Do you know who actually owns it?'

'I'm not sure,' I tell him. 'A friend of mine has it on her books as a rental. She runs an estate agency.'

His eyes roam around the room, then he stands up and puts two more logs on the fire. 'Friends in high places, eh?'

'No.' My reaction surprises us both. 'I needed somewhere, and Tunnel Cottage was empty, that's all. Besides,' I say, peering up at him, 'I'm quite liking the place. It's got untold stories. Don't you think?'

A flicker of something crosses his face, though it's hard to determine exactly what it is. And then he's smiling again.

'I agree,' he says. 'Years of walking past, and I've never seen a curtain twitch or anything.' He darts his gaze away. 'It does make you wonder what's going on.'

'Where did you say you lived?' I'm not sure why, but we

need to stop talking about the cottage. It has become a spikey presence between us.

He nods vaguely in the direction of the ruin. 'Just up the hill. At the top of the estate.' He rubs his hands together and holds them in front of the fire. 'And I should be getting back there, before I get settled for the night.'

We both laugh at that, if a little awkwardly. I get up and lift our coffee mugs. He follows me out into the hallway.

'Thanks for the drink,' he says. 'And can I ask you something, Evie?'

'Course,' I answer, sliding my way into the kitchen. I put the mugs on the draining board and watch him from the doorway, as he slips his arms into his coat.

'Would you want to come for a walk with me tomorrow? Just across the local fells, or something?'

He lifts his eyes from his zip and looks at me. I get a small blast of that feeling again. Zingy and very unsettling. 'That'd be nice,' I murmur, trying to balance my voice. 'Morning or afternoon?'

'Both,' he says with a laugh. 'I'll call for you at nine.'

As I step towards him, he raises his hand and brushes mine. Gently, but there is a spark. Like the one that jumps from the metal carabiner to my fingertips when I've been climbing all day using nylon safety ropes. I wonder if he feels it too. We lock eyes, and I nod.

'Nine sounds fine. I'll see you then.'

He gives me one last sheepish grin, then opens the front door and is gone.

Jay

The feeling of being wanted takes Jay by surprise. He can't believe it was that easy. Though, if he's honest, it had felt less like a set-up, and more like something he actually chose. Meeting Evie, talking, sharing his work – he'd planned to do all those things. Now he wonders if he should back out and start again with her. But how can he? On the face of it, he'd simply asked a woman he likes out on a date. He laughs a little at this. Sneers, in fact. He's never had a date. Who'd look at him?

Sitting by the fire in Tunnel Cottage, with someone who wants him there, gives Jay a feeling he can't remember having before. It's like looking out on a field full of snow, and being safe inside. Usually, when he's in the cottage, it has a hollow feel, like an empty crisp packet. There is shape, but nothing firm for clinging to.

He's going to have to be careful about using his den, though. His shed. Evie's already talking about things that need doing around the cottage and in the garden. That she might discover the place he beds down, when his isolation overwhelms him, is a worry. What would she think? Knowing her even slightly, tells him she'd want to take away the tatty old sleeping bag she'd find and give the place a good clean. Then where would he go? He's only survived his worst nights by being able to let himself into the cottage and sit for a while, though he's never slept there through the night. To be discovered, and the trouble it would cause, isn't something he wants to think about. As long as he can be near to the place, he can survive.

For now, he'll go back to his aunt's house and try to hold his nerve for the morning.

Chapter Twelve

By the time nine o'clock the next morning arrives, I've worked myself into a strange mood.

For a start, I've never really cared about my appearance. My hair is long, and a soft brown, but I usually wear it in a loose knot at the back of my head, or tucked into a cap. I own a bag of make-up, but it's still at my chalet. A layer of Clinique is all that hides me from the world at the moment. And, as far as I'm concerned, clothing has to be facilitating. So, today I just look plain. Then there's the fact that I haven't thought about the Ian Turnbull situation once in the last sixteen hours, and that is some kind of record. Worse still, I am very aware that I don't do *relationships*, not serious ones, anyway.

There was Tim, during my sixth-form college years. Tim, who spent a lot of time posing in front of the mirror, checking out his latest mountaineering outfit. Tim, who, according to my friends – Rosina included – didn't have a neck, such was his musculature. But I'd fancied him at the time.

And there was the non-starter relationship with Rob, from White Platts. He tried, I didn't. I'd had a ton of intense friendships, Pip included, but not much sex.

The thought of something happening with Jay Elliot, it gets me. Right in the pit of my stomach. Making my thighs tremble with a fourteen-year-old's appetite. And here he is, right on time.

'Good morning.' He smiles from the open doorway. Same blue anorak, same tattered jeans and walking boots. But today, he is clean-shaven and his hair snakes down from underneath a knitted hat.

I lift my jacket from the coat pegs, and slip my phone into my pocket, then step outside to greet him.

It is a beauty of a morning. One that sends a sudden wave of bottled-up tears from my stomach to my throat. Bright blue and knife-cold used to mean only one thing on a Saturday morning: a flask of coffee and a trip across to Belle Isle in a Canadian canoe. It was one of the ways Pip and I used to avoid the drudgery of Clean Up. Especially when the camp was closed, and cleaning was simply for the sake of it.

'Is everything all right?' Jay is asking. Perhaps he has tuned in to my slight hesitation.

'Yep. Lovely today, isn't it?' I look upwards for a moment, then lock the front door and follow him down the path and out towards the meadow. He has a distinctive walking style, long strides, and a kind of lopsided sway. It's not a limp, but noticeable, nonetheless.

The meadow sparkles with early frost, and the rutted grass crunches softly beneath my boots. By the beck, a group of Herdies huddle together, thin streams of breath hanging above them.

'I thought we could walk up to the ridge,' Jay says, shielding his eyes. He is looking towards the highest slope. It's quite a climb, but I can't see a footpath. When I tell him this, there is a glitter in his expression.

'I know a way to get up there,' he says with a smile, 'and the view is worth the effort, believe me.'

We are marching towards a wooden stile. It will take us onto the main road, and I hope that we're not going to be tramping along tarmac. Jay climbs it easily then waits for me on the other side.

'Isn't it private land,' I ask, 'or farmland, perhaps?'

A shake of his head. 'There's a public right-of-way across those fields. But there isn't any access, so people don't know. But I do.'

'You're well embedded in this landscape,' I say, slightly puzzled. 'Were you born around here?'

The glitter fades. 'I just walk it a lot, that's all.' He turns away and looks along the length of the road. 'Better put your hood up for this bit, though,' he calls back to me. He tucks his hair into his and pulls it up over his head. I do the same, as he drags back an arc of naked blackthorn hedge. Some shrivelled fruit still hangs from the lichen-covered branches. He ducks, then pushes his way through the small gap he's created, almost crouching, before he springs into the field beyond. I do the same, though it's much easier for me. As I make it through, a twiggy piece of hedge catches on my jacket and stops me for a moment, making me pull away and causing a snag.

'Damn,' I mutter, looking at the tear. 'That'll let water in now.'

Jay reaches around my back and has a closer look. 'It's repairable,' he says. 'I've got a few like that on mine.' He lifts his arm, and I can see an assortment of patching and sewing. 'Make-do-and-mend. That's me.'

I lift my brows slightly.

'What?' he says.

'You're a talented guy, aren't you? Painting, drawing. Sewing.'

'Lighting fires,' he continues. 'And you haven't even asked if I can cook.'

'Can you?'

'No.' He hesitates. 'But I'm great at eating.'

We begin to climb the slope of the field. I match his stride, and he smiles down at me. For the next hour, we meander upwards and sideways, staying in the present moment and breathing in the freshness of the morning.

Jay is alert for anything of interest: he fills his pockets with spiral larch cones and feathers – one of which he tells me, is from a tawny owl – thistle heads and even a stray piece of what looks like seaweed. It's oakmoss lichen, apparently, a favourite of the crows that roost around here. They don't feed on it but treat it as a toy, which amazes me.

'I thought you were a creature of the outdoors,' he jokes, when I am astounded, yet again, by his knowledge.

'I am,' I say. 'But I want to conquer it, and that takes a lot of energy. Where do you get all your information from?'

I wait for him to tell me about some fantastical university course, or an immersive career in botany and zoology. But instead, he just shrugs and says, 'Reading.'

We are almost at the top of the fell now. What I thought was its ridge, is actually a grey limestone wall, with another stretch of wind-bleached moorland behind. There isn't a breath of wind. I squint against the vivid glare of the sun and wonder what's beyond this horizon.

Jay seems to read my thoughts. 'You want the view?' he asks. 'You're going to have to run for it. Race you.'

Then he is away, all arms and legs and hair streaming from the bottom of his hat. But this is something that I can do. Running. I am quick and fast. I soon catch him up and fly past, laughing and breathy, while he lumbers behind me. I stop when solid ground runs out. Or so it seems. As Jay catches up, I gulp down some deep breaths and try to make sense of what I'm looking at. Which amounts to five or six slices through the world. A layer of green falls away in front of us, and I can see a small chapel at the bottom, then rooftops, a haze of factories, and finally a strip of metallic-turquoise sea. I try to orientate myself. The roofs must be Dalton, a small market town on the road out of Barrow. And the water can only be the Duddon Estuary.

'Like a painting, isn't it?' Jay is standing right beside me. There is an emotional charge to the moment, and I can't help but lean into him. He slides his arm around my shoulder and hugs me lightly. Then steps away again. 'I've tried to relive it by looking at a map, but it's hard to pinpoint exactly where we are.'

I run my eyes from left to right, then up at his face. 'Amazing,' I agree. 'Have you ever tried to paint it?'

'Oh, I've tried, believe me.' A lift of his shoulders. 'I've sat up here for hours. Sketching and taking notes. I've tried to commit to paper, but it hasn't worked out right. Some things aren't meant to be captured, I guess.'

I'm still eyeing the landscape greedily. 'That must be Dalton Chapel,' I say, nodding towards the spire at the bottom of the hill. 'Shall we walk down and sit for a minute?'

Something happens in that moment. Like a cloud's crossed the sun. But there are no clouds. Only Jay's face. Shadowed suddenly, its shine gone.

'No,' he growls, then turns away.

Jay

He hadn't meant to bring her this far.

The chapel seems to have come from nowhere, looming darkly from the freshness of the landscape. That it's there, he knows very well, but the thought of going any nearer makes him feel sick to his stomach.

Only once has he been inside the place, more than thirty

years ago, though the memory of it hasn't ever faded: sitting next to his aunt, watching the darkly clad people who looked like a herd of sad animals sitting in a field, waiting for the weather. When his parents had come in, staggering behind a small blue coffin, he'd asked what it was. Finding out that his brother was trapped inside had made him vomit up his breakfast and he had to be taken out.

He'd lived with his aunt for a few weeks, after that. Mam didn't seem to want him back. His longing to be at the cottage had been as strong as his wish to be reunited with his parents, but only when the new school term had loomed, was he taken home. He's never forgotten the feeling of being dumped on the doorstep of Tunnel Cottage, not knowing who he belonged to. And his first night back was full of his mother crying, and his dad bellowing at him to get out, when he'd ventured into Jamie's bedroom and found it empty.

Evie has come to stand beside him and is looking at him quizzically. There's nothing he can tell her. The last thing he expected was to bond with this woman, but there's something about her. It makes him feel like everything that's wrong in his life matters not one bit. She has a vivid quality; it shines out from her face.

Chapter Thirteen

The tone of Jay's voice jars with the moment and sends a small trickle of fear across my shoulders.

'No worries,' I say, 'we'll just carry on walking, shall we.' I keep my voice light, as I'm without the slightest idea what I've said to make him uncomfortable. He is still staring out across the view, hands shoved in the pockets of his jeans. Sunlight bathes his face, but there is darkness, too. And suddenly we're making our way downhill, veering to the left to avoid the crumbling wall of the cemetery, where the chapel sits. He comes to settle at my side.

'Sorry,' he says, with a small shrug. 'I just don't like graveyards or churches, that's all. They give me a tight feeling, in my stomach.'

That makes me laugh. I can't help myself. 'In other words, you feel sad around graves. I've got news for you, Jay. So does everyone.' I slip my arm through the loop he has created, with his hands in his pockets, because it suddenly feels okay to do that.

'I'm daft, aren't I?' He smiles ruefully.

'I'll let you off,' I say.

It is lunchtime before we get back to Tunnel Cottage. Our walk has taken us downhill, over slopes of washed-out grass and limestone outcrops, along winding lanes edged with bare hawthorn, and to an area of beach known locally as Roanhead. As the ruin comes into view at last, relief washes over me. My thighs are beginning to burn, telling me that I'm at the limit of my fitness. I need a cup of tea, and something to eat.

I look at Jay. There is a pink tinge across his cheekbones, but no sign that he is feeling fatigued. The length of his stride suggests that he could carry on for another few miles at least.

'Want to come in and have some lunch?' I ask. 'Don't know about you, but I'm starving.'

We cross the road at a pace, and step towards the track leading to the railway line.

'I'd better get home,' he says, 'but thanks for the offer.'

His answer surprises me, considering how well we've been getting on; it's like he wants to get away from me. 'Oh. Okay then.' I frown my reply. 'No need to come all the way to the cottage. You get off.'

'I don't want to force myself on you, that's all.'

My heart flips over. Why would he think that? 'You wouldn't be,' I say. 'Let's not make a thing out of it. Come and have a bite to eat with me. I want you to.'

A smile spreads across his face. Wiping away that intensity and making him look a little less worried. It's only an offer of food, after all.

'I will, then.' He takes my hand, which flips me all over again.

On the doorstep, we toe off our boots, and I let us in to the hallway. After the brightness of the winter sun, we have to blink ourselves through the gloom and into the kitchen. I switch on the cooker and fill the kettle.

'Shall I go and set up a fire?' Jay asks. 'Although the lounge is probably the one room that will be warm at this time of day.'

I glance at him.

'That's where the sun is, I mean,' he adds, 'down that side of the cottage.'

'Go for it,' I say. 'Though that sun never gets to the French windows, does it?' I pause. 'What would you like to eat?'

There's an awkward moment. It stretches across the room and sends a shiver across my shoulders. Then Jay is speaking again. 'Anything. As long as you don't mind.'

I flick up my brows. 'Go and light that fire.'

He slides away, hunching down to clear the kitchen door. Same faded sweatshirt, hair loose down his back this time. He's a fit for Tunnel Cottage, that's for sure. And I cannot imagine Alex kneeling to light a fire and accepting food without checking out every ingredient. When we were kids, he'd had the best of everything. There was no other way to live, according to him. He's not much different now. Needle-sharp, but incredibly picky about simple details. Which is why he's had success within the law, I don't doubt.

I pull open the small fridge, which I have now stocked with the things I like, and wonder about feeding Jay. I pull out a tub of soup, bread, butter and cheese, and the milk for our tea. And some chocolate tiffin which I'd brought from Marks and Spencer because it was something I could shove in my pocket for energy, if I was out walking. Except today, I'd forgotten to take it with me. Bad form, when I was used to filling my pockets with sugary snacks if I was working. There was always a child or adult who needed a boost, out on the lake or halfway up a fell, not to mention Pip, who ran on an energy deficit most days.

By the time I have assembled our soup and sandwiches, and made a pot of tea, Jay has trained a fire up from the hearth and into the chimney. And now he is trying to dampen it down.

'You're good at that,' I say, as I lay the tray down on the small coffee table. 'Were you a boy scout, in a previous life?'

He is using an iron poker that I haven't really noticed before, to open a small hatch at the back of the chimney lining. His head is thrown back, cheeks glowing red.

'Not a boy scout.' He is interrupted by a spit of lighted ember that startles us both. With an expert hand, it is flipped back to where it belongs. 'But I have an open fire, at home. A temperamental one.'

He's given me a way in, so I take it. 'Do you live on your own?' I ask as I pass him a bowl. 'Help yourself to sandwiches, by the way.'

He sits on the hearth, back pressed against the red-brick surround, bowl resting on his knees.

'Yes. I'm on my own. The house was my aunt's, and she left it to me after she– when she–'

I wait, lift my spoon to my lips, but keep my eyes fixed on him.

'She died when I was in my twenties,' he continues. 'It wasn't pleasant.'

'Sorry,' I cut in. 'I didn't mean to be nosy. Change the subject, shall we?'

He lifts his chin slightly, and I take that as agreement. We eat in silence for a moment. Then he says, 'Tell me about your work, Evie. I blathered on about mine, the other day. What about yours?'

'It's more a way of life,' I say, 'than work. I climb and hike and sail and canoe and get paid for it. Good, eh?' If it's possible, I'd forgotten about the situation I'm in with regard to White Platts. And now, here it is again, and I don't want that thought to show itself in my expression. 'I'll be back at it soon, hopefully.'

Jay chews quietly, and it gives me the chance to think of something diverting to say, that will move us both into the future. I want to leave White Platts where it belongs – in a box marked pending, that I don't need to touch.

'What are you doing for the rest of the day?'

'Eating every crumb of this wonderful lunch,' he says with a smile, mopping up the last dregs of soup from the edge of his bowl. 'Why?'

I stand up and brush down my jeans. 'There's some clearing needs doing in the garden. The landlord doesn't bother, apparently. Whoever he is. And the woman who sorted out the rental for me said I could do anything that was needed.'

'Then I'm happy to help,' he says. 'I've always wanted to have a poke around in the garden.'

'Oh?'

'Legally, I mean. I've trespassed a few times to rescue sheep. As you know.' Jay starts to collect up our plates and bowls. 'Thanks for lunch, by the way.'

I shoot him a grin. Then watch as he balances the tray and shuffles out into the kitchen. He is all long bones and wide shoulders, but slim in a way that would cause my mother to say that he needed *feeding up.* This was something she'd threatened me with, many times over the years. She'd even tried to make it more practical, teaching me to cook substantial meals. But I never developed in the way she wanted, remained severely lacking in the curves she thought were needed to attract a man.

When I'd been old enough to vocalise my disgust at her attitude, I'd accompanied my anger with a spell of refusing every meal she cooked for me. Hunger had beaten me into submission, but my body remained lithe and athletic, built for running and scampering, and she had changed tack then. Overloading me with what she called women's magazines, trying to pique my interest with promises of swish clothing and even swisher hairstyles.

Her effort was largely wasted, but I'd taken what I thought was relevant: I'd had the best hair of my life, in those few years between the end of high school and the beginning of university. Running my hands through it now, I wonder how Jay sees me. Then I mentally slap myself down, and push past him, into the scullery.

I slip my feet into my wellies and open the kitchen door. Sunlight filters through the leylandii that have been left to dominate this part of the garden.

There is a patio on the other side of the gravel path. It is laid with concrete paving stones, blotched with green algae. Underneath the conifers are drifts of sticky brown bracken, choked over with ground ivy and bramble tendrils. With a couple of feet lopped off the thicket, and the rotting vegetation cleared, this could be a nice place to sit in the afternoons, especially when the sun is slightly higher. That's if I'm still here after my six-month contract is up. Though I fully intend not to be, it's hard to see beyond early summer, at the moment.

Every day that I'm not at White Platts stretches the disconnect I'm feeling. The lack of communication is less frustrating than I thought it would be, even if I'm pretty sure it has its origins in Malcom Fairley telling my colleagues it will be better for them if they keep me and my *situation* at a distance.

'I'll be out in a few minutes.' Jay is leaning back from the sink and calling to me through the open door. 'Just doing my chores.'

I smile. *Chores.* Such a past-era word. Clean Up was how we coined it, at White Platts. There it is again. That place. Embedded in my psyche like an earworm. There's a particular cure for one of those: fast-forward it to the end, let it run its natural course. I picture myself, driving along the pitted road that leads to the chalet park, unloading my car, then striding downhill, through the woods to the main camp. Where my colleagues will welcome me back and hand me a roster for up-and-coming sessions. But there are no colleagues, and it's not me.

'Have you got some tools?' Jay. 'Evie? Are they in the shed?'

His voice cuts into my negative thinking, and I welcome it. 'Haven't had a look in any of the sheds yet,' I tell him, 'except for the coal-hole.'

'That's an old-fashioned thing,' he says with a laugh. 'Coal-hole.'

I nod. 'But exactly the sort of thing that my mother would say. I'm sure she'd love to be back living in the 1950s. Though I doubt she can even remember them. She'd have only been a toddler.'

Jay steps away from me and into the greenish shade of a shabby-looking fir tree. He doesn't match my comment about *mothers*, doesn't even reply. He scratches at the ground with the toe of his boot, kicking at the brown thickness of fallen fir needles. Something makes me leave the scene. I am suddenly unwanted.

One of the outhouses is flat-roofed, with a Perspex window, smudged with age and cobwebs. It has an old-fashioned Yale lock that matches up with a key from the set given to me by Rosina. With one twist, it opens, the top half falling away from a rotting hinge. A metallic blast of air hits my nostrils and I sneeze. I can see an array of garden tools. Most are muddy or dusty, and all are covered in rust.

Jay crunches across the gravel behind me. 'What's in there?' His hand is on my shoulder, his face coming down next to my right ear.

'Tools, by the look of it,' I say. 'We need those long-handled scissory things.'

'Loppers, you mean.'

107

Whatever I mean, the proximity of him, the warm salt smell, sends a shiver across my shoulders. 'Yeah, loppers.' I don't want to move but tell myself that if we're on a quest for tools, it would look odd if I don't step forward into this shed. 'I'll go and see.'

Once inside, I realise that someone once had a pretty good set-up here. Though the tools are well used, they have been organised into tidy groups, and fastened into place with hooks or bungy elastic. There are shovels and forks, a pickaxe, an array of things that look like loppers, rusty-toothed saws, two wooden ladders, buckets galore and even an old pair of hard-toed men's wellington boots, with a strip of fluorescent paint around their rims. But everything is covered with stringy grey webs, clotted with dust and dried insect bodies.

'Come and have a look in here, Jay,' I call, from the furthest corner. 'Someone knew what they were doing.'

He ducks under the door-jamb and blinks at me. Then his eyes dart across the rows of tools and come to rest on the boots. He inhales sharply, and it startles us both.

'Are you okay?' I ask, looking into his face. His features have hardened, like he's zoned out for a moment. But now he's reaching for a pair of what look like bolt-cutters, with long handles and dirty-grey grips.

'Fine. Yes. These will be perfect. You take them, and I'll lift down the ladders.'

I'm glad to get out of the shed. The dust is catching at the back of my throat, and I'm suddenly the intruder. Which is ridiculous, considering I live here. I'm paying money for this outhouse, and the others. As Jay pushes the ladder through the open doorway, I take one end and guide it out. A swathe of sticky cobwebs come with it, some of which catch in his hair.

'We'll probably find electric shears in one of the others,' I say, nodding towards a shed at the end of the row. 'Should I look?'

'No,' he snaps, then, 'don't bother. It's padlocked anyway. We'll be better doing the leylandiis by hand.'

'Fair enough,' I say, though my interest is piqued now. There are so many locks and keys to Tunnel Cottage. One day, I will match up them all. But not today.

We stumble over to the hedge and drop everything.

'This is going to be a big job,' Jay says, looking skyward. 'I'll just have to do it branch-by-branch. Unless you want to?'

I jump in quickly. 'You're taller than me. I'll hold the ladder while you go up.'

'Here we go then.' He balances the loppers and leans his weight into the rungs, so that the hedge takes the strain. Within seconds the first branches, aromatic and dense, whizz by me and onto the ground. There are *oofs* and *grunts*, and more of them fall.

By the time we're on the fourth ladder-slide, half the hedge has been reduced. And the difference it makes to the garden light is startling. Where the sun had simply created a diffused green dankness, it now shines with silver intensity into every shadowy place on the patio.

'That's got rid of the last ten years.' Jay laughs down at me. 'These things are thirty years old. Probably.'

'I don't like them,' I say. 'They don't fit in with the other trees.'

'They don't.' He shakes his head as he steps carefully down. 'And there was really no need to plant a fast-growing hedge here, was there?'

I hadn't even wondered why the leylandiis are there. The garden is mature, and as the cottage is well over a hundred years old, I just presumed that its various residents had planted what they liked. But now I can see that behind these conifers is a wonderful view of the beck at its furthest point. Not something you would want to blot out with ugly trees.

'Perhaps I'll hire a man with a chainsaw and take them

right down,' I say. 'But let's have a rest, now. I'll go and make us a drink.'

We finish off the hedge in another hour, then spend the rest of the afternoon hacking back bracken and the vicious tendrils of blackberry bramble and wire-hard ground ivy.

When the winter light begins to fade and our breath turns to soft white powder, I turn to look at the results of our work. On the gravel to the side of the patio is a huge pile of shaggy conifer branches, spicing the air with their sharp smell, a mush of torn and decaying ground plants and then Jay's small heap of treasures. He has kept me entertained with his intense fascination for the minutiae of the natural world. And his wry observations about the human one. From him, I have learnt that the colour of a bird's egg depends on where it is laid, and I've also learnt about his lack of self-worth because he is an artist in a world full of techno-beings. He doesn't own a mobile telephone and he loves to read actual books. When I offer to cook us some supper, as the very least I can do after his afternoon of hard graft, he steeples his hands together across his chest and accepts with a gratitude I can't quite fathom.

'It'll only be mac and cheese,' I tell him. 'Not worthy of such high praise.'

The truth is, I don't want him to go. His company has completely obliterated my anxiety about White Platts. And there's a humility about him that's just a little bit enticing.

Inside the cottage, I close the lounge curtains and flick the switches on the electric lamps. Then wash my hands and scrub my nails over the kitchen sink. I have directed Jay to the bathroom upstairs. I can hear him moving about, making the water pipes gurgle and the ceilings creak.

When he comes down again, the water for the pasta is set to boil, and I am grating cheese for the sauce.

'I've nothing alcoholic to offer you,' I call to him as he passes the kitchen door. 'Is tea all right?'

'Tea would be lovely.' He swings his head back so that I can see him for a moment. 'I don't drink, anyway. Shall I stoke up the fire?' His cheeks are glowing from the cold afternoon, and he has knotted back his hair with a woven braid.

'Tea it is then,' I say, and he continues his journey towards my lounge. I wonder about that last comment. He doesn't drink. What does that mean, exactly? No alcohol at all, for religious or other reasons? Not much of a drinker, like me? Or something that he thought he ought to say? It makes me realise how little I know about him, despite our expansive conversations this afternoon. And how little he knows about me or my current situation.

Once I assemble the mac and cheese, I load up a tray with huge bowls of it, a pile of bread and butter and our mugs of tea. Something of a habit, but one that feels so natural that I smile, despite my small niggle of worries.

Jay is sitting with his back propped against the sofa and his long legs stretched out towards the fire. The lounge looks almost cosy now that its shabby edges have been muted by the low light. I lay the tray on the coffee table and sit down next to his shoulder.

'Poor but honest,' I say, as I pass him the pasta and a fork.

He nods his agreement at this.

'Looks great to me,' he says, and begins to eat. I do the same, and we're soon settled into an almost perfect silence, with only the scrape of forks and the spit of the fire hanging in the air.

When we've finished, Jay lets out a long sigh. 'I needed that,' he says. 'My shoulders are starting to ache a bit now.' His eyelids droop, and he rubs at them. 'A good day's walking and working though, Evie, eh?'

But I'm focussing on the long strand of sticky cobweb that is tangled in the hair at the crown of his head. From the tool shed, probably, but I haven't noticed it before because he towers above me. Without thinking too much about what I am doing, I loosen his hair braid and pull gently at the long, sticky strand.

'It's a piece of web,' I murmur as he leans back, 'with bits of moth trapped in it.' It comes away, and collapses into nothing more than a dirty grey clump. 'There you go.'

I hold it out to show him, but he turns his head, then cups the back of my hand with his. And plants a kiss on my palm.

'No one's touched my hair since I was a little boy,' he whispers. 'Not in a nice way, anyhow.' His eyes meet mine. I see darkness there. Which makes me slide my other hand around the side of his head and bring my lips down on his.

Jay

He never meant for this to happen. But Evie made it too easy. Lying beside her now, he can still sense the light in her; it has reached into him, somehow, and he's finding it exquisitely painful. There had been a moment of pure bliss last night, a reimagining of his life at Tunnel Cottage, and he'd wanted it, wanted it so much. When she'd kissed him, a pulse of pure energy had run from his lips to his feet, firing up everything in between. He'd been so hard that by the time she'd unzipped his jeans and touched him, he'd exploded into her hand. Connecting with himself like this is something he hasn't had in his life; it's terrifying.

He rolls back the bedcovers, taking care with his movements, and slips out of the bed, not his mother's bed, but the same room. The wardrobe was hers, and the dressing table, solid dark wood that had been part of the cottage when they'd first moved in. Dad never wanted him in this room, never stayed in it much himself, at the end.

They hadn't closed the curtains last night. Evie's body had become a shadowy form under his hands, like the objects he painted, only this one was warm and alive. The bond he'd felt had almost brought him to his knees. And when she'd giggled and said he should get out more, he'd wanted to tell her everything. But where would that leave him?

From the window, he gets a view across the garden woodland where he has spent so much of the past twenty years. It is close enough to the cottage that the tight knot in his stomach loosens when he's there.

Looking at Evie now, he knows the attraction is real; there is nothing *closed off* about what he feels for her. Which means he has a problem. He wants to punch himself for his stupidity. How did he think his ridiculous plan would end? That he can't find an answer makes him scared. Could he just pretend everything about their meeting and attraction is real, and let the relationship develop normally? He sighs. Normal; not him.

In his years at Kew, there had been a couple of women, co-workers who helped him feel less disorientated. But he could never commit, never give them what they really wanted, and they'd walked away. And when he'd had to come back, after Liz died, his life there came to an end. Where Kew had started as an escape from her demons as much as his, in the end it became a distant reinvention that rejected him as soundly as his own family had.

So this is what he's going to do: leave Evie in a politely formal way, imply that he'll be back, and let her decide the rest. Then he will go back to his old routines with the cottage, until she leaves. And she will. She's said as much. Phrases like *between jobs* haven't been wasted on him. This is a woman who will fly high; she won't want to be weighed down by him.

And now she is stirring, sliding her hand across the mattress in search of him. Two long strides across the room take him back into her bed and her warmth. She is soft and small and so strong. Her hands against his chest send desire knifing through his body and bring tears to his eyes.

Chapter Fourteen

It's early morning. I stand in the kitchen of Tunnel Cottage and look through the window at the meadow. The sun hasn't quite cleared the ridge of the fell, and the light still has that grainy turquoise quality, dregs from the night before.

The night before. What a night it had been. Just the thought of it makes my stomach flip over. My mother says I have a nose for adventure. But I've always gone with my instincts, and nothing about being with Jay feels wrong.

While I wait for the kettle to boil, I lift one of my bare feet and lay it on top of the other. With no fires lit, the cottage is freezing. I flick on the electric cooker. That should take the edge away, for now.

I pour the steaming water into the two mugs I've laid out and splash in a little milk. Then I carry the drinks upstairs and wonder, not for the first time, how I've ended up with a gorgeous man in my bed. And one that I hardly know.

The bedroom is still quite dark, though the curtains are open, and I can see the shadowy woods on the other side of the garden. This is the kind of view I will always want to wake up to. The floorboards creak slightly as I try to put down my drink.

Jay hears me and stirs.

'Coffee.' I gently shake his bare shoulder. His eyes snap open and dart around the room. Then come to rest on my face.

'Are you okay?' I try to pass him his mug. He slides up the pillows and runs a hand across his blurry face. There are a few strands of dark hair stuck to his lips.

'Oh, God,' he moans. 'You must think I'm a right... erm?' A shake of his head. 'I'm so sorry.'

I wasn't expecting an apology.

'For what?' I let my gaze wander across his wide, slim chest and downwards to where the matt of dark hair dips away underneath my sheets. 'I'm not sorry, that's for sure.'

But when I look at his face, there is a kind of embarrassment, and I realise something is off.

'I didn't mean that.' His thick brows lower. 'I don't want you to think I've taken advantage. Forced you into anything.' He looks away, across the bedroom towards the window. 'Yesterday was a good day though, wasn't it?'

I slip off my dressing gown and slink towards him, then lay myself along the side of his warmth. He gasps when my freezing feet touch his.

'It was,' I whisper. 'Let's have lots more days like it.' My hand slides across his flat stomach and he lifts his arm to let me in. But his body feels edgy, like he's wanting to be away. He lifts his coffee to his lips.

'That's good,' he says with a sigh. 'I still feel like an imposter though.'

'Well, you can impose anytime you like,' I tell him. Then I close my eyes for a moment and think about Jay's supposed imposition into my life. The truth is that I didn't know there was a space for him until he came along and fitted himself into it. On my own, I brood about things. With him, the present moment resonates. He makes me laugh. And he splits my heart open with his artist's eye and broken humility. I know hardly anything about him, but it doesn't worry me. There are things I've kept back from him, too. Not because I am hiding them, exactly, only that they might tarnish what's happening between us. Time enough to talk about White Platts, when the need arises. For now, I'm simply at the end of one job and waiting to start another. Jay will have things he is holding back, too. This isn't us being dishonest. It's more like we already have a connection, and the tendrils of our other lives will show themselves eventually, but they won't matter.

'I'd better drink this and get off,' he says suddenly. 'I must stink.'

I pretend a small sniff on his chest. 'Smell all right to me.' I laugh, then plant a kiss against his ribs. 'More than all right, actually. But you can have a shower here, if you like.' I pause. 'The bathroom's pretty cold though. Freezing, in fact.'

'I bet.' He takes another swig of coffee, then puts the mug down. 'Thanks for the offer, but I'd better go home. I've got some work to finish. And I need to post it off tomorrow.'

His words cut me a little, but I don't want him to think I'm clinging. That's not me. But something about this guy is causing a difference. I like it, and I don't.

'My mother's coming for lunch today, anyhow,' I say. 'Better not linger.' But I so want to linger.

He hugs me tightly, kisses my forehead, then swings his legs over the edge of the bed. 'Don't want to intrude,' he says.

I kneel behind him and slide my arms around his chest. 'Please come back later,' I whisper against his shoulder. 'I need your fire-lighting skills.'

He coughs lightly at that, and pulls away, searching the floor for his clothes. He is almost too tall for the room; it is suddenly filled with his elbows and knees and shoulders.

'It's going to be another beautiful day,' he says, glancing over his shoulder to the window. 'You can sit out on your patio. With your mother, I mean. Take a couple of kitchen chairs.'

'And a blanket,' I say with a laugh. 'Let me drive you home, at least.'

'No.'

My attention is immediately focussed on his snappy tone. I raise my brows.

'No. Thanks all the same, but I'll walk. It won't take me long. And, Evie.'

'Mmm?'

'Yesterday was amazing. Thank you.'

A kiss on my cheek and he is gone.

The bedroom seems down-at-heel now that I'm looking at it through someone else's eyes. The carpet is worn away, almost to its stringy weave, and the few bits of furniture probably came from another era entirely. But the sun has finally cleared the ridge and is sending rays of silvery light through the window, and that's worth more than any picture-perfect spread in a *Homes and Gardens* magazine. I wonder about Jay's home. And why he didn't want me to drop him there. But I don't wonder too hard, because a glance at my watch tells me that my mother will be here in an hour, demanding coffee and poking into every little part of Tunnel Cottage with her disapproving fingers and ideas of what's right.

After a lukewarm shower, where I wash away the traces of Jay that still cling, I rifle through the wardrobe, and select a thick sweater, jeans and some chunky socks that I used to wear for bivouacs, in my other life.

While I dress, I wonder about a trip to camp, to collect the rest of my clothes and my other belongings. They don't seem so important, now. Somehow, I am managing to survive in a way I hadn't thought possible on that drive back to Barrow a few weeks ago. I am still a person and I still count. And White Platts is existing without me.

By the time I'm fully clothed and breakfasted, my mother is knocking on the front door and getting her first glimpse of Tunnel Cottage.

'I've parked my car up by the bus stop,' she says as she gives me a hug that is more like a rigid chest-bump. 'I don't trust the roads around here. Where is your car?' She pushes a carrier bag of food into my hand. 'In case you're starving,' goes her reasoning. Like I've been cast away, on a desert island.

I lead her into the kitchen and jerk a thumb in the direction of the drive. 'Car's up the top there,' I tell her, 'it's far too steep to bring it down.'

'Well. That wouldn't suit me,' she says. 'I need access to my car, day and night.'

And so it begins.

She thinks the cottage is rustic, but at least it's clean. The noise from the rains would give her a permanent migraine. The place needs some heating. I haven't had the windows open, so it feels damp. There are still some dead flies trapped in the shadowy corners of the kitchen cupboards. The spindles on the staircase are wobbly – I need to get them fixed.

On and on she goes. I stop listening, and concentrate instead, on the blackbird who is hopping around just beyond the kitchen window, yellow beak scraping through the frost-hardened soil at the base of a dormant honeysuckle bush. I hope I'm still here when it comes into flower, standing at the sink, window open on the view. And Jay's in the picture, too, sitting at the table, scribbling away in his sketchbook.

'I still don't understand why you've put yourself all the way out here.' That voice. It cuts me. 'There's plenty of rentals in town that'd be much more convenient. Especially since Alex has been good enough to give you a job.'

I exhale sharply and rub at the fatigue in my eyes. 'He's told you,' I say. 'When did you see him?'

'I see him all the time,' she snaps. 'He's always over, visiting his mother.'

There isn't going to be a response to that one.

The kettle is bubbling and spitting, and I flick it off at the switch.

'Have you brought biscuits?' I ask, changing tack. 'Not coffee-time without shortbread, is it?'

She likes this comment. It sets her rummaging in the carrier bag I've dumped on the kitchen table.

'Ta-da.' In her hand is a small tartan box, which she rattles. 'You know me. Prepared for anything.'

And we both relax. This is how it is, between us. Brillo-pad abrasive, but the shine is always there, under the shit. I open the kitchen door and cold air pushes its way in. Perhaps Jay wasn't quite right about sitting on the patio, but when I step outside, I can see a square of sunlight to my left, just large enough to hold a couple of chairs.

'Shall we sit out here?' I call to my mother. 'We've tidied it up a bit. I think you'll approve.'

She steps outside, eyes firmly fixed on me. 'We? You said *we've* tidied up. Has Alex been helping you out? He never said. Why didn't he say?'

When she pauses for breath, I jump in and tell her Alex has never been to Tunnel Cottage. Which is why he didn't say. And then I explain about Jay. Enough to keep her listening, but not enough to earn myself another one of her reproachful mini-lectures. I get one, anyway.

'What do you know about this,' a pause, 'man.'

'I know that I like him. A lot.'

She frowns, then blows out a snort of air. 'Yet you won't give Alex a second look. I don't understand. I don't understand.' This last sentence is stretched to the point of no return. I walk back into the kitchen and lift one of the ladder-backed chairs that huddle around the table. It is heavier than it looks.

'Sit down and stop fussing,' I tell her when I've hauled it outside. 'I'll get another one. And our drinks.'

Her refusal to accept that Alex is anything but a heterosexual, single man, is quite frankly, ridiculous. She's seen him with Paul on numerous occasions, even invited them in for coffee and dinner.

'He'll move on from this *phase*, when he finds the right woman,' she's been known to say. She'd better not say it now.

We sit back in the sunshine and sip our coffee. The air is clean and brilliant, in that winter-morning way. From the cut stems of the leylandii comes a scent that makes me think of Christmas. And I am waiting for my mother to start on at me with her organisation of those particular routines.

Behind us, somewhere up in the nude white boughs of a birch tree, three crows call to each other. I turn to watch for a moment. Above them, a buzzard soars, chestnut-brown against the dazzle of blue sky. The boughs sway heavily, then the shiny black gathering gives a final caw, and scatters. There is something wild about this place, a sense of nature taking back its own. Jay has felt it, I'm sure. Why else would he be so drawn to tramping through these woods and fells, and the meadow, trying to capture it in his mind's eye and on his pages.

'When am I going to meet this guy then? Jay?' Her face is tilted towards the sun. A tanned face always looks healthy, as far as she's concerned.

'Any time you like,' is my answer. Evasive but agreeable.

'Bring him for tea, midweek then.'

'I'll see if he's free. And if I am,' I tell her. 'Then I'll let you know.'

She lifts her chin, just a little. 'It'll be a bit inconvenient,' she says, 'if you go back to White Platts. How will you see him then?'

The way she says *if,* sends a flash of irritation across my chest. I put my hand there, as though I can stop the word burrowing any further down.

'I'm sure we'll work something out,' I say. Then leave it. But she has a point. One which has been niggling at the edge of my consciousness for most of the last few days. In the graph of life, Jay's block is now ahead of White Platts' by quite a few points.

Later in the afternoon, when I have walked my mother back to her car and assured her that I will be in touch, I decide to have a wander onto the meadow, and look at the beck.

The light is fading, and my breath hangs in small clouds as I change gear to take in the uneven terrain. There are no sheep in the field today. Just a noisy song thrush mirroring its mate. Above me is a glassy blue expanse, harshly beautiful and dotted with a few early stars.

I hear the water before I see it. The banks are curved softly with grass and last year's river plants, and two ancient sycamores protrude at a dangerous angle, so that their branches drape the watery surface. Red clay is the local soil. It colours everything, even in the finely-drawn darkness. The sweet-water smell takes me straight to the shores of Windermere. There was nothing better than taking a walk down to the gravelly beach near my chalet, after a day of intense physical activity, and allowing any built-up human static to dissolve in the grainy darkness. Which is what I'm trying to do now. Watching my mother's continuous observations of my life simply floating away, out to sea.

Whenever I'm transported back to White Platts, the same thing niggles away at my thinking. Did I flirt with a fifteen-year-old boy in order to win him over, for the sake of an easy couple of weeks? Was that my teaching style with the other adolescents I encountered? That there could be any truth in what's being said about me, makes me feel sick to my stomach, and I can probe no further. Eventually though, I'm going to have to be honest with myself. But it's hard to approach self-talk when you've become an embarrassment. Perhaps I would be better off just walking away from my outdoor instructor career and looking for something more local. And if Jay's one of the reasons I'm feeling this, I can only shrug my shoulders and give myself a small, sniffy telling off. Then keep walking and become part of this watery landscape again.

Jay

The painting is unrolled and lies on his desk, mocking Jay with its beauty. That he created it is something he doesn't believe; there is never a personal connection with his art, though he always admires the results. It is one of the many he has worked, of Tunnel Cottage in high summer. When he paints the place, he is there, with the choke of cardboard dust in the back of his throat and Jamie sliding his feet into oversized wellies, begging to be taken across the meadow, to paddle in the beck. Those early days, when they'd first moved in, and Mam and Dad were happy, are the place where he lives. He can't walk past a hedge full of sultry August honeysuckle without tears forming in the back of his throat.

And he can't forget about Evie. She'd love the painting and he so wants her to see it. He can't understand how she's managed to slice through the thick murk of his life, but he knows one thing: he wants that feeling again.

That he becomes addicted to things easily, he knows only too well. From this room, he would be sent across the road to collect his aunt's ration of alcohol. And the shop next door, with the gaming machines, had drawn him in. It was more of a café really, and Liz had been friendly with the owner, so that her teenaged nephew was allowed to spend some of his pocket money playing the machines. Just so long as he took her cider back home first.

No one at Tunnel Cottage had been checking up on him by then, and within a year he was pushing every coin he was given, earned or otherwise, into the slots of the one-arm bandits. They never gave anything back.

In his mind, he was always just about to win, just about to be able to buy his way back into his mother's heart and his father's high regard. But it never happened.

Going to work at Kew Gardens had been an escape, and it had torn him in two. Waving to Liz on the platform, as the London train pulled away, had broken him. By the time he arrived in the capital, he'd decided to leave the tragic John Pickthall behind, and begin again as Jay Elliot: his aunt always called him Jay-Jay, and he took her surname as a match. An escape from his past had worked, to an extent, though it had lingered, waiting for him in the quiet of evenings spent alone. He saw his aunt one more time after that, wearing her saggy floral dress and even more saggy skin. But her death had been a shock, one that made the last frayed shreds of his connection with the world snap.

And now the previously numb Jay Elliot has been slit open and peeled back, and he doesn't know whether he will survive.

There can be no normal relationship with Evie. His darkness won't allow it. And she'd find out about him, eventually. But he wants her, he wants her, he wants her.

Chapter Fifteen

When I get back to the cottage, I find Jay waiting for me at the gate. He is wearing a different coat, dark and woollen, with his hair tucked into the collar.

'Hello.' A scintillating smile. 'I got us these.' He lifts a white carrier bag, and I am treated to a waft of warm vinegar. 'There's a fish-and-chip shop across the road from my house. They start serving at five on a Sunday evening.'

'Pure genius,' I say, taking him by the arm. 'You're welcome anytime.'

Once we're inside the cottage, Jay stokes up the fire while I slam through cupboards to find the biggest plates. Then I set the kettle to boil and butter some slices of white bread. The food comes inside apricot-coloured polystyrene, terrible for the planet but great for retaining heat.

'I preferred it when they came wrapped in newspaper,' Jay says as he comes into the kitchen, with a duck of his head under the door lintel.

'You remember that?' I ask. 'When did it become frowned upon, I wonder. We didn't have chippie teas when I was a kid. My mother didn't approve.'

He shakes his head. 'Not sure.'

'How long have you lived opposite a fish-and-chip shop?' The question means nothing, but his expression has darkened.

He lifts one shoulder, then lets it drop again. 'Forever.'

'Lucky you.' I laugh, as I tip the golden battered portions on to our plates. A few of the chips slide off, so I stuff those into my mouth. 'I'm starving.'

'I can see that. Have you got salt and pepper?'

I nod towards one of the kitchen cupboards. 'Just in their packets, I'm afraid. This place doesn't run to those little shakers with holes in the top. I do wonder who's behind setting it up as *furnished*. There's too much of some things – garden tools, for instance – yet some of the basics are missing.'

Jay is quiet for a moment. He lifts out the salt and pepper packets, and gazes at them. I wonder what he is thinking. There is a tautness to his jaw, a grimness to his expression. Then it lifts. And he smiles.

'Sorry. What were you saying?' He blinks. 'I missed that?'

'Don't worry about it.' A tilt of my head towards the door. 'Let's go and get started.'

In the lounge, the fire spits and crackles. We sit, plates on our knees, and eat. There's a tension between us, suddenly, and I'm not sure why. Jay is hungry: he eats his food with fierce concentration; it's soon gone.

'Want half my fish?' I ask, cutting across the long body of batter. 'It's huge.'

'No. It's fine,' he says. 'Unless you're leaving it? My aunt used to say I had hollow legs.'

I slide the bisected fish body from my plate to his. It drags with it a trail of oily gold. 'Did your aunt bring you up? You've mentioned her before, but not your parents.'

Jay finishes his mouthful. The muscles of his jaw and throat working together. Then he shakes his head. 'I don't have any parents,' are his words, but the tone implies *leave it.*

The other half of my fish disappears pretty quickly, then he says, 'Oh, I forgot. I have something else for you.'

'As though the supper wasn't enough.' I am intrigued. He wipes his hands on his jeans and walks towards the door of the lounge, then picks up his coat from the banister and brings it into the room. He fumbles with a long roll of paper, in what I realise is a pocket in the tatty lining. He pulls the roll out. There is a string bow, and the paper is crumpled on its edges.

'Have a look,' he says with a secretive kind of smile, then hands it to me.

I lay my plate down on the coffee table and clean my hands on the wad of kitchen paper I brought in with me. One look at his face tells me this is important. He is watching me with an intensity that would be uncomfortable, if it wasn't for the incredibly unsophisticated joy in his eyes.

I pull at the tail of the bow, and it slips away. The paper comes to life, springing itself out of a roll and into both my hands. On it is a painting of Tunnel Cottage. Muted and soft, with the garden in high summer. The house blends beautifully with its surroundings, and there is not a flaw in sight. From the green-gold birch trees to the pale-orange roses twined within a hedge of velvet-yellow honeysuckle, to the play of intense light and cool shadow, this is the cottage through the eye of a perfectionist. Or someone who loves it immensely.

Finding words is difficult, but Jay is waiting, watching my reaction. In the end I shake my head and whisper '*Unbelievable.*'

He sits down beside me and gazes at his work. 'You like it then? I thought I'd sign it, too. In case I ever become famous.' A small laugh. 'I did it a couple of years ago, but only put my name on it yesterday. When I realised it might mean something to you.'

'And it does,' I say. 'It really does.' I roll the paper up again and lay it on the sofa. 'Thank you.' I swing around onto my knees and slide my arms around him. Then my hand is in his hair and on his cheek and we are kissing again.

I pull closed the front door and lock it. Jay is already outside, the collar of his long coat turned up, and a pale fatigue spreading across his face. Last night was the second he had spent with me, in Tunnel Cottage and in my bed. And now we are heading into town, me to my work and him… I'm not sure what he's going to do, apart from walking with me.

Once more, I have offered to drop him off at his house, and once more, my car remains unused, at the top of the drive.

It is eight o'clock in the morning, and painfully cold. A sharp silence spreads outside the cottage. We crunch along the track, over frosted ruts of mud, and cross over the railway line. Jay shoots a glance towards the tunnel, and I wonder if he's worried about us being ambushed by a train. Though there is always a rumble underfoot and the twin-horned alarm to give fair warning.

The ruin itself is bathed in a pale-orange light, making it appear as a sepia image from another time entirely. This is how I feel, too. That I am living another life, without having made an active choice to be there. But it is a creepingly beautiful life, nonetheless. When Jay is lying with me, his vulnerability unprotected and wanting, I can't help but respond. There is something in him that calls out to me. If I consider us being apart now, it feels wrong. Which has come as a bit of a shock, when I thought I was trying to claw my way back to White Platts.

'Beautiful morning,' he is saying, 'but I could do with wearing about three more layers. This coat isn't the warmest.'

'Go straight home,' I say, slipping my hand through the

crook of his elbow, 'and I'll jump on the bus. You must have things to do.'

His face loosens. 'I will if you want me to, but I'd much prefer to walk with you.'

I sneak a look at him.

'If you want me to,' he says.

'You look tired,' I tell him, but he just laughs softly, and says that it is entirely my fault.

'I can't comment on that. We're both shattered.'

When we reach the main road, it is like stepping into another world. Traffic trundles past, a mix of buses, delivery lorries and cars full of people wearing lanyards and collared shirts. Jay clings tightly to my hand as we weave our way across, and step along the narrow pavement that trips into the town proper. An orange sun hangs low in the sky and the air is beautifully bitter.

Victorian gentrification created the outskirts here, and we pass sandstone and limestone houses that have no right to be part of a working-class town. They are acceptable only in their rebranding as public and private service buildings: a nursery, a care home, a bed-and-breakfast hotel.

At the end of the first block is a church in the New England style – a sore thumb against the other buildings – with a small school attached to it. Not one that I attended, but it had a reputation for prayers and parades. I remember thinking how silly the kids looked, in maroon uniforms and grey caps.

And now Jay is dragging me past.

'Are you okay?' I ask, peering at his taut jaw and downcast eyes.

A mumble. I ask again.

'I'm fine,' he says, 'just don't want you to be late.'

'It's not that kind of job,' I tell him.

'You have a forgiving boss?'

'I don't have a boss at all, as a matter of fact.' I explain to him about working for Alex as a favour, though I veil what the favour is with a story using the phrase *friend of a-friend*.

'Like your estate agent,' he points out. 'I've said it before; friends in high places.'

'I just know some people, that's all,' I mutter, then, as we are about to pass a petrol station and its advert for free mince pies with every turkey bap, 'soon be Christmas.'

He snorts lightly. 'Yeah.' Then sets his mouth in a grim line. I say nothing else about it.

By the time we get to the town centre, it is full to bursting with delivery wagons, the coffee-carrying workforce and even some early-morning shoppers. The pavements are silvery, the faces raw. Jay still looks uncomfortable, casting his eyes about and hunching down so that his collar covers half of his face.

'I'm not used to this,' he mutters. 'Shopping. I rarely come down here.'

I slip my arm through his again and lean my head against him.

He smiles down at me. 'Sorry. I'm grumpy this morning, aren't I.'

'Yep,' I laugh, 'but I'll let you off. Shall we go and get a coffee from Greggs?'

We are heading towards Swarbrick and Murray's, but I'm sure Alex won't mind if we take a slight detour.

'Coffee sounds good,' Jay says. 'I'm starving. Again.'

But as we approach the office, I catch sight of Alex and Paul, striding towards us, all dazzling white collars and matching navy Puffa jackets. A wave of my hand and Jay is casting his eyes after my stare.

'Here's the guys I work for. Right on cue,' I say, as the pair of them saunter towards us. 'Alex. Hi.'

'Evie. Darling,' he drawls, his eyes flicking sideways. I'm about to answer with some introductions, when Jay lets go of my arm, spins around and charges away in the direction we have come from. I think I hear a very quiet *bye*, but I can't be sure.

Jay

He has to lean against the side of a building to steady himself. Coming into town was probably not the best idea. He'd passed by the school, and that was bad enough, though he thought that perhaps a solution to some of his fears lay on the far side of it; solace might be found there too.

Then he'd seen Punchy-Boy again.

In his mind's eye, Jay can see him as he was, tall and blond and Persil-white. Picking on the new boy with such hatred in his eyes. There had been name-calling at first, the state of John Pickthall's clothing, his hair, the skinny knees that knocked together during football matches. Mam had still been in Jay's life at that point, but she never seemed well enough to talk to about the perfect giant who was making his life a misery.

Punchy-Boy hadn't stopped at name-calling. To further impress his friends, he'd taken to kicking John to the ground, then punching him on the muscles at the top of his legs and arms. Never his face. And never in the sight of grown-ups. In the end, John stopped going to school. His time would be spent in the woods around the cottage, immersing himself in nature and wishing he had a brother to be there at his side, to provide some solidarity, although Jamie had been a few years younger than him.

Inhaling deeply through his nose, Jay tries to steady his raging thoughts. In Evie's face, as he'd stormed away, there had been confusion, and something he thought might be anger. And he didn't blame her for those emotions. He was a grown man and he'd turned on his heel and fled like the small boy he really was. But seeing this bully again, this Alex, has opened up the last of Jay's hidden places. That this man works with Evie can mean only one thing. The end of their relationship, before it's even really started.

God, he's been such a fool. Letting his newly discovered desires mean anything; thinking he deserved to feel good.

Trying not to attract too much attention, he breaks into a slow jog. Though his breath is coming out in loud gasps, he manages to keep going. Past the shops and houses of the town centre, along the wide pavements that finally narrow and fall away. And down towards the ruin, and Tunnel Cottage. It is here that he comes to find any relief from himself, and today, he wants only to cross the meadow and sit by the beck.

Glitter on the surface of the water makes Jay want to dip his hand and scoop. He kneels and reaches out. This is what Jamie was doing, on that last day. When John should have been watching.

Chapter Sixteen

'Oh. Was it something I said?' Alex's hand is flat against his chest, and Paul is peering along the street.

'I'm not sure what that was,' I say with a frown. 'Sorry.' I think about going after Jay, but he is almost turning the corner now, and I should offer further information to my colleagues. 'He did have some jobs to do.' I accompany those words with a shrug, but Alex narrows his eyes.

'Your face is burning,' he says to me. 'Who was that bloke?'

'I was about to tell you. I've met someone. That was him.' I tilt my head in the direction of the main road. 'Jay Elliot.'

'Not quite ready to be introduced, I guess.' Paul is reaching towards the office door and unlocking it. 'Let's get inside. It's bloody freezing standing here.'

I don't know what else I can say, or why I feel there should be any explaining to do. That Jay simply ducked away does worry me a little. But he'll have his reasons. I've already worked out that he's not the most sociable people. Something I quite like. We're similar in that respect. I can play-act a gregarious nature while I'm working, but at day's end, I'm happiest walking by myself in the landscape.

I follow Paul and Alex inside and hang up my coat while they deactivate the alarm and activate the coffee machine.

'So, this is a boyfriend then, Miss Evie Cooper?' Alex is asking. 'You've kept that quiet.'

Have I? Friday was the last time I'd seen Alex, at the end of the working week. Jay had been on my radar by then, but why would I have mentioned it?

Paul is switching on the office computers and running his hands over two old-fashioned radiators that are the sole heat source for both rooms.

'Stop being so damned nosy, Alex Swarbrick,' he snarls, though his lips are telling me he's not really annoyed.

Alex holds up his hands. 'Okay. Okay.' A stretch of his brows. 'I won't mention it again. But I do need to talk to you, Evie. There's been a couple of emails over the weekend that you need to know about.' He shivers a little in his shirtsleeves. 'Bring some drinks through, my darling man,' a twinkle at Paul, 'and we'll crack on. I've to be at family court for eleven.'

In Alex's office, I drag Paul's rotating chair so that it aligns itself with the corner of the partner desk. Then I sit down and wait, enjoying the early morning aromas of expensive aftershave and Pennington's Colombia Suarez.

Alex comes to settle beside me and begins tapping away on his keyboard. 'I've had an email from Malcom Fairley. It came in on Friday night. And another from Jackie Odell, the Turnbulls' solicitor.' He makes one final heavy click, then swings his monitor around so that I can see it. 'Neither contains anything good, I'm afraid.'

He explains about a date being set for the civil court in Stratford-upon-Avon. When he says June the fourteenth, I think I've misheard.

'Next summer,' he tells me, 'which is sooner than I expected.'

While I'm trying to take this in, he also lets me know that Malcom Fairley would like me to collect my belongings from White Platts on the Sunday before Christmas, when the place will be quiet. I'm to speak to nobody about the *situation*, apart from a named representative from the camp.

'A Philippa Joy,' he says. 'I'm guessing you know her?'

'Pip Joy?' I snort. 'Of course I know her. She's my friend.'

Alex looks puzzled. 'I'm surprised he's chosen her, then. It could put your friendship at risk, do you not think?'

I shake my head. 'I don't know what to think, if I'm honest. I've hardly heard from Pip since I left. I get that once you're on the outside, insiders find it hard to deal with you. It's the same in any workplace, isn't it? And you did say there had probably been a gagging order placed on the staff. But I thought Pip would be on my side, rather than supporting the management.'

'Well.' Alex leans back in his chair as Paul brings us cups of coffee and a stack of sealed envelopes and dun-coloured flyers. 'I'm guessing this Pip Joy will be a ferocious advocate, then. And as she'll probably be the rep at your hearing, it's not a bad thing. It does mean she'll be kept informed of everything that's going on. It could work in your favour.'

'You think?' I groan.

'I do.' He peers at me. 'Look, Evie. Whatever the rights and wrongs of this situation, I want to win it for you. Which means you need to trust me.'

'Oh, Alex.' I tut. 'That goes without saying.'

He falls silent, and I wonder why. Then realise he must have so much more to do than over-prepare for my small case.

'I'd better get on,' I say. 'And you need to do the same.' But he isn't listening, so I make my way back to the reception area and sit down at the computer. That's the thing about Alex. One side of him is helpful and attentive and so, so sharp. Then there's this other guy; the one who used to stop me throwing loose change into the polystyrene cups put out by rough sleepers in the town centre *because they'd only spend the money on booze.*

Through his teen years, I'd watched him struggle with his sexuality; he wanted an attractive woman on his arm like the rest of us wanted flashy handbags. But his obsessions were always men, and in the end, after years of emotional fights with himself and a lot of angst for his mother, he'd come out as gay and those close to him felt relieved. The change in him was marked.

While I was a diligent and quiet student, his mother was constantly being called into school because of one tearful outburst or another. Alex was always a head taller and much more developed than his peers, and throwing his weight around became something of a habit. But when we played together, usually out of school, he was great fun. I laughed at his brand of humour, and he liked to join in with my physical pranks: cycling for miles, climbing anything that looked dangerous or just rambling through the countryside. Those truly were the days. There's an edge to the guy, though, so I'm going to make sure I retain some control.

As I start typing my way through a list of standard email replies, I can't help thinking about Jay, running my mind over those last few moments before he literally just stormed away. And the only explanation I can find, the only scenario that fits, is one where he's this insanely jealous guy and I regret ever having got involved with him.

But am I involved? I certainly fancy him like crazy; he's attractive and dryly funny and hugely gifted. And the sex is red-hot. He's vulnerable and passionate and so needy.

Some things strike me as odd, though. How at home he is in Tunnel Cottage, for instance. Like he's lived there before. Which is ridiculous, because he would have told me. Then there's the weirdness of him turning up in the garden and then on the driveway, at moments that were perfect for meeting up with me. Jay's no stalker, though. I know that about him. They're people with mental-health problems, and Jay seems so stable. Introverted, yes, but stable. Though I can guarantee my mother won't like him. Which seals the deal for me.

Chapter Seventeen

A few days later, when I'm sitting at my desk in the reception area of Swarbrick and Murray, trying to undo a mess I've made by sending an email to the wrong client, I suddenly sense Alex's presence, his breath on my neck. It sends a weird little flutter across my shoulders, and I spin around to check it's him.

'If you're going to stay, Evie,' he says, 'I want to pay you.' He peers over the rim of his trendy black specs. Then nods at the computer screen. 'And that one's fine.'

The email is for Rosina Kerr, letting her know the legal position in reference to one of her clients. It's a small town we live in. And it'll be a smaller one for me if all I'm ever to do is work in this office, with this guy.

'You're already doing that. By saving me hundreds of pounds on legal fees. I'd have had to rely on White Platts and their blunderings if it wasn't for you.'

'Talking of which,' Alex says. 'Do you want me to go with you on Sunday? To retrieve your belongings. I could hire a van.'

He walks towards his office door. He is wearing an

immaculately pressed lilac shirt and navy slacks and I struggle to imagine him driving a transit van. 'What do you think, Paul? Fancy a trip to The Lakes on Sunday?' He has a foot in both rooms. Blue suede shoes, too. I can't hear Paul's response, but Alex informs me that he will telephone a couple of rental companies and see what he can get. So, that's settled then, and I haven't even agreed.

'By the way,' he is saying, as I press send on the email, 'what did happen with that guy of yours? Have you asked him why he scuttled off?'

The truth is that I haven't seen Jay since that morning. And now it's Friday. But this is none of Alex's business.

'Don't say *scuttled*.' I shoot him a frown. 'It's a horrible word.'

He folds his arms and leans against the door-frame. His body fills the space. He's a big guy, is Alex. Shoulder muscles of that quality can't be hidden under a shirt. I can see them flexing now, quite clearly.

'When he made a *sharp exit*, then?' A flick of his head. 'Whatever you want to call it.'

'Alex Swarbrick. Get back in here.' Paul's voice, much larger than his size, and deliberately loud.

'God.' Alex tilts his hip, then turns. 'I can't do anything, can I?'

'If by *anything*, you mean bully Evie, then no you can't.' Paul appears in the doorway. Also in shirtsleeves, and with a pen tucked behind his ear.

'There was no bullying involved,' Alex snarls, but his lips are turned upwards. 'Was there?' He looks at me.

I say nothing, just hold up my hands, with a shrug. Then the telephone rings, and as it's my job to answer it, that's what I do. Both men retreat to the back office and leave me to it.

The calls that come in are usually low-level – a wish to know the progress of a property purchase or the date of an appointment – they're nothing I can't deal with, because Alex and Paul keep a detailed diary and are methodical with their recording and tallying of events. What they are not good at is the physical aspects of typing, copy-editing and small talk with waiting clients. And that's where I come in. The job's nothing like I'm used to, but I kind of like it. There's a gentleness, a sense of quietly being useful. There was nothing quiet about throwing groups of kids into the outdoor environment, then jumping in there with them.

From my desk, I can look out into the high street. It's three o'clock in the afternoon, but it could be much later. A claggy mist has descended, and without a breath of wind, it sits along the street, coating everything in a layer of tiny, jewelled droplets. I think about Jay, and wonder if he's on one of his walks. There is a strangeness in not being able to contact him, a disorientation of senses. He will have his reasons for ducking out of an introduction to Alex and Paul, I'm sure. But the *not knowing* is tapping away at me, like a tenacious teacher picking at the empty brain of a switched-off child. The answer is just not there.

The afternoon stretches. People are heading home, dark coats covered in fine spray, hair in watery diamonds. Next week, Christmas will be almost over, and I'll have spent some of it trying not to kill my mother. But at least she's extended the invite to my *new boyfriend*. If he ever turns up again.

Then Alex puts his head around the office door. 'You get off, Evie, if you like,' he says. 'And sorry about before. I've booked a van for Sunday at nine. If that's not being too controlling.' This last word is much louder, and with a look back at Paul.

'Don't be daft,' I say. 'I'm the one who asked you to. Was it very expensive?'

He shakes his head. 'Paul Murray spends more on his skin-care products, so I've heard.'

'Cheeky.' A call from the depths of the office. 'We can't all have perfect complexions.'

Alex dimples his cheeks. 'He loves me really.'

'You are very loveable,' I say, 'in an overgrown-puppy kind of way.'

'That's not an appropriate thing to say to your boss.' He lifts my coat down from the line of stainless-steel pegs next to the coffee machine. 'And I am going to start paying you a small wage. It's only right. Don't bother arguing.'

I take the coat from him. It's my parka, and I'm glad I wore it. A glance outside shows me that the fine mist-droplets have joined forces with each other, and now strongly resemble rain.

'Let's just get Sunday over with,' I say with a sigh. 'I might get there and be asked to stay. You never know.'

'You could be that unlucky,' he says, through gritted teeth.

Out on the street, I inhale the stony dank air and pull the zip of my parka up under my chin. The strap of my handbag goes over my head, then I break into a slow jog towards the bus stop. There's a pleasing kind of anonymity in waiting for a bus. No one demanding anything of you and nothing to focus on except that moment when someone you don't know will drive you home.

That word. *Home.* Tunnel Cottage has become this for me. What White Platts and my chalet will feel like when I get there on Sunday is anybody's guess. Though I have to stop thinking of it as *my* chalet. Someone else will have taken residence by now, I am sure.

When the bus arrives, quite a few people have taken up their places behind me in the queue, and we file on, smelling of wet coats and hunger, and rubbing small viewing circles in the streaming windows as we take our seats.

The bus trundles out of the town centre and past the residential areas. I peer into the gloom and try to second-guess what type of house Jay might live in. Would it be one of the tall red-brick terraces that stand together facing the town's Victorian park? Or a smaller, more homely place on the grid-line streets running away from it? Then there are housing estates like the one where my mother lives. Full of 1970s semis and bungalows. I can't imagine him anywhere, and that is starting to bother me. He's been very vague about where he lives. Perhaps he simply doesn't want me to know. And that thought sends a shiver across my shoulders that's nothing to do with the weather.

When the bus pulls up at my stop, I step carefully through other people's wet footprints and into what is now a hazy darkness. Cars swish along the main road, sending up arcs of spray, giving the mist a shiny yellow glow. There is a short run down the hill to the railway track, then a quick shimmy to the cottage. I tug up my hood and make a run for it.

I see Jay before he sees me. A jolt of emotion tells me how much I've missed him. He is standing at the gate of the crossing, peering in the direction of Tunnel Cottage. He turns as I step onto the track. His hair is covered with a fine layer of mist, and he is smiling.

'Evie.'

'Hello,' I say. 'Stranger.'

I catch the worried expression that crosses his face.

'I'm only messing,' I add, then push my arm through his. 'Let's get inside. It's a pig of a night.'

His shoulders relax. We cross the track and make our way up the garden path. Twiggy fingers of honeysuckle and forsythia, dripping and earthy, brush against my coat. The darkness feels solid, and I have a sudden sense of how isolated this place is.

'Could do with one of those lights. On a sensor,' I say. 'It's pretty basic here, isn't it?'

Jay has stepped onto the porch. He's ducking down to

avoid a rusting bracket that might once have supported a hanging basket.

'I always kept a torch–' His head turns away sharply.

I fiddle with the key until it catches in the lock. 'Where?' I ask. 'You always kept a torch, where?'

'Just in my pocket. When I was a kid.' He stumbles over his words. A distraction comes when the door won't open straight away, and I have to lean in my shoulder, and push hard.

'It's the weather,' he mutters. 'The door. Doors swell up in damp weather, don't they? Solid wood doors. I have one. It does the same thing.'

'Are you okay?' I have to ask. He is unzipping his waterproof coat. The blue one, with the paint stains and strip of grime around the cuffs. 'You seem a bit–'

He interrupts. 'I'm sorry about the other day. That's all.' The coat slips from his shoulders. 'When you tried to introduce me to your – friends.'

I step towards him and take his hands in mine. They are ice cold. 'Don't worry about it,' I say. 'You'll have had your reasons. And they were work colleagues as much as friends.'

My hands are lifted to his lips. Soft, but just as cold.

'I thought you wouldn't want to see me again.' There is a tremble in his voice. 'I'm just not very good with new people. That's all. Then these two guys appeared, all smart and part of the world. It's a thing I find hard to handle.'

Something in me crumbles. There is no other way to describe the feelings I have for this man. It's like every layer of toughened emotion and fibrous mistrust that have built up through my life, have been peeled away. Leaving me raw, and beautifully unstable. I reach out to move some strands of wet hair that are sticking to his cheek.

'I'll always want to see you,' I whisper. He kisses me then. With his eyes wide open and locked on mine. It takes away my breath. And when he pulls at my hand and leads me upstairs, there is nothing but that in my head.

Jay

He's come back.

In the end, there wasn't a choice. For days, he's been wandering about the fields and fells around the cottage, hiding in the tunnel, and watching Evie as she leaves in the morning, and lets herself in at night. Mostly, it's been cold and wet and miserable, and for that he is grateful. Better to be as downcast as the weather than to walk in bright and beautiful December days with an empty heart.

Something has shifted in his life: not a change of mood, exactly, more like a subtle warming of snow by the sun. No one sees it melt. One moment it's there, cold and blindingly harsh, and the next it's mush. That's how he feels now. Like all his insides have turned so soft, he's having trouble holding onto them. It's frightening, but he longs for the change.

What he's struggling to get used to is that every time he turns up feeling like the most pathetic man on the planet, she welcomes him into her arms and makes him feel like he'll never want to be anywhere else again.

Chapter Eighteen

J ay has lit a fire.

We huddle on the sofa, under my one blanket, and my sanity is restored enough to remember that on Sunday I am travelling to White Platts with Alex and Paul. I should ask Jay to come with us, though I've a feeling that these hire vans only have three seats upfront. But I don't want to send him on his way again, come that morning. And I'm pretty sure he wouldn't want to be sent anyway.

'I've got to take a trip to my old workplace this weekend,' I tell him. 'You're welcome to come. Alex, my boss, that is, he's going to take a van, but I could drive. If you trust my driving.' I am thinking about that night. The one of frozen rain and slippage. And Jay with his soaking wet hair and dazzle of a smile.

'Do you need me to?'

I peel myself away from his side and sit up a little. 'No,' I say. 'It's only to collect the rest of my clothes and belongings. I just thought you might like a run up to The Lakes, that's all.'

The muscles in his jaw flex, just a little, but there is a

change in his expression. 'I won't, if you don't mind. I can't take up your whole weekend.'

'I don't mind.' I hesitate. 'And I want you to take up my whole weekend, actually. Spending time with you is a choice. You're not forcing me.'

He doesn't even look at me. I swing myself away from his side and kneel up on the sofa. 'Jay?'

He gives me a crooked smile. 'I'm struggling with this, Evie.' He lifts my hand. 'Why would you want to be with me?'

I open my mouth to begin a huge list of reasons, but he cuts across them. 'No. I'm not fishing. But you're so... together... with friends. Workmates. A mother. I'm just...' A pause. 'Nobody, really.' He flicks his head, like he's shaking away a fly or something. 'God, I sound like such an idiot.'

'Right,' I order. 'Stop this. Now.' There's a hard edge in my voice, like I'm standing up in a metal canoe, waving a paddle at kids. Then he's smiling and that surprises me. 'I want to be with you. You're exactly my kind of guy.'

'You mean it, don't you?' A pink blush across his cheeks.

'Either that,' I tell him, 'or I'm a bugger for jumping into bed with men I've only known for a few weeks.'

I drop my head onto his shoulder. He sighs lightly and leans into me.

'The truth is,' he says, 'I'm not good at judging people. Or situations.' There's a shift in his shoulders. 'Things haven't always been... easy for me, that's all.'

'In what way?'

There is a stretch of silence. A moment when I want to take back my asking. Here is a man who is very protective of the facts behind his life. I already know this. Yet I am pressing him for what now feels like *gossip*. Before I can apologise and do something to change the mood, he begins to speak again.

'I told you that my aunt left me the house I live in.'

I nod.

'Well, she brought me up. Or at least guided me through the growing-up years. And I didn't make things easy, that's for sure.'

'Who hasn't gone off the rails at some point in their teens,' I interrupt, then wish I hadn't.

'I tore up the rails and sold them for scrap metal,' he snaps, 'if we're using that metaphor.'

'What did your parents think?'

'That was one of the problems.' A spit of words that shocks me.

'Oh,' I whisper.

'They didn't want anything to do with me, Evie. Not even my own mother.' He sits forwards, head sinking. I run my hand across the hunch of his shoulders.

'They're both gone now, anyway,' he says, the energy draining from his voice.

'Gone where?'

'Dead, I mean.'

'I'm so sorry,' I say and slip down in front of him. 'Let's talk about something else. The past isn't somewhere to store our feelings, is it?'

He lets me into his embrace. I lay my head against the itchy wool of his sweater and breathe in his warm sandalwood smell. It reminds me of the spicy hand-cream my mother keeps on the windowsill of her kitchen, next to the sink.

'No, it isn't,' he murmurs. 'Let's just focus on you and me, shall we?'

'Let's.' I slide a hand into his hair and kiss him.

———

A rainy Sunday morning and we're standing in the kitchen of Tunnel Cottage and waiting for the kettle to boil. Jay looms above me, all woolly hair and a fine layer of stubble. We'd spent the previous day talking and cooking and sloshing through water-clogged woodland and meadow. And now he is going home, and I am heading to a place that feels anything but.

He slides his arms around me and kisses the top of my head. 'Shall I pop back later? To help you unpack?'

'Can do,' I say. What I really want is for him to come with me to White Platts. To be a reminder that there exists, for me, a life away from the place. And I want him to be comfortable around Alex and Paul. I so want that.

'I have some bits and pieces to do anyway,' comes the reply. The one I expected. Although he has agreed to accompany me on my Christmas lunch date with my mother. So that's progress.

'Let me drop you off at home, at least,' I continue. 'It's horribly claggy out there. And I've got time. The guys aren't coming until after nine.'

He puts his hands on my shoulders and moves me away from him slightly. 'Evie. I'm fine to walk, honestly. And, who knows.' A shrug. 'I might just find that small slice of something interesting.'

I smile. 'I know. The one you're always on the lookout for. Your house must be full of—'

'What?'

'I was going to say *crap*, but I don't want to offend.'

He laughs at that. 'No offence taken. And you're exactly right. My house is a storage facility for art materials and so many rejects of nature.' He holds up his hands. 'Including me.'

That comment gives me a tight feeling in my throat. Here is somebody with a wonderful talent, and a gentleness. Yet he calls himself a reject. I wonder, momentarily, what that makes me.

'Well, everyone else's loss is my gain,' I murmur up at him

and his eyes tear up, just slightly. 'Now, make that tea, would you?'

At the front door, Jay flips up the hood of his waterproof, kisses me once on the cheek with the promise of coming back at six o'clock to help me unpack. Then I am left to wait, in the edgy silence of the cottage, for the arrival of Alex and Paul and the van.

I hear it before I see it. At just after nine, I decide to stand on the doorstep and work on some of the deep-breathing exercises that I usually reserve for panicking climbers or nervous potholers.

Across the garden, the light is grainy, the birdsong muted. A match for my mood. Jay had tuned into it, had asked me why this trip was weighing so heavily, and I struggle with what to tell him, finally saying that it was the end of an era. Which is exactly what it feels like. Perhaps I need to cut ties with White Platts forever, call a halt to any court cases and pay-outs. A couple of months ago, I'd never have allowed myself to think about any such thing.

But now? Working back there would mean a swift end to my relationship with Jay. However much I'd like to think we could continue to see each other, life in a place like White Platts becomes all-consuming. You jump into the merry-go-round world of outdoor adventure with a heap of other people, and they become your family and your life. No one else gets a look-in. There are in-jokes, heart-to-hearts in the darkest hours of the night, and also there's the bottomless well of support through every kind of danger. If you're not part of it, you don't exist. I couldn't drag Jay into that.

Three toots of a vehicle horn cut across the maudlin of my

thoughts. Then Alex appears at the top of the drive, and the greyness of the morning lifts a little.

'Evie, darling,' he calls. 'Ready when you are.'

I push my hands into the pockets of my parka, then take a slow jog towards him. In a couple of hours, three at the most, we'll be back at the cottage, and I might just have a little more clarity about my feelings. But I doubt it.

Paul slides himself into the middle seat, and I scramble in beside him. Mixed in with the rotten-apple smell of van-insides generally, is the more upmarket aroma of a citrus-based aftershave, and Listerine. Alex isn't one for seedy Sunday clothing. Paul has followed his lead. They are a match of grey wool sweaters and artfully scruffy jeans, held together with a leather biker jacket on the one hand and a belted combat number on the other. I run a hand through my loose hair and hope I don't look too sleep-deprived.

'No sign of your fella, then?' Alex starts up the van and buckles himself in. 'Jay, wasn't it?'

I catch a small sigh from Paul.

'What do you mean by *no sign?*' I hiss. 'Don't start this again, Al. Please don't.'

'I thought he might have come to help, that's all. Or haven't you seen him?'

'He's just left. Not that it's any of your business.'

The van judders against the gradient and he over-revs, just a little. 'Staying over, eh? He's becoming a *thing* then, is he?'

Paul clears his throat, then mutters Alex's name.

'What?' he groans. 'I'm curious, that's all.' A flick of the indicator and we're pulling out onto the main road. The traffic is sparse, and he relaxes back into his seat. 'Look, Evie. I'm only after protecting your interests. Can't blame me for that.'

There is enough adrenaline fizzing around my body, without the extra blast that arguing with Alex would cause. So, I choose not to be offended. 'Well, there's really no need,' I say gently. 'Jay's a lovely guy and we're getting on well. He's good company. When you finally get to meet him, you'll like him. I guarantee it.'

A lift of his chin tells me I've made the right call. After a moment, he asks another question. 'Did you say his second name was Elliot? I couldn't remember.'

A growl from Paul, low and full of exasperation.

'Yes,' I tell him, 'Jay Elliot. Local, and honest and incredibly artistic. Look him up if you like, Al. You know you want to. I'm sure his work will be in the digital world somewhere.'

And that seems to satisfy him. We settle ourselves into the journey, watching the landscape change from winter-blanched pasture and craggy red outcrops, through small hamlets and villages that straddle the road, to the first clean and sharp margins of the Lake District proper.

When Windermere itself comes into view, my stomach flips. It is a strip of lead, shiny and fluid, and supporting the pale-grey sky. But the van soon takes us out of its eyeline again, and we begin to wind along the tarmac route that parallels the water. There are no kerbs. Trees and spiky shrubs, and the skeletons of cow-parsley and hogweed, bleed straight onto the road. Slate-built cottages are set back slightly, their gardens built to incorporate the craggy limestone escarpments poking out from every fellside. Then a more open area, where a hotel sits alongside a cluster of private and very expensive-looking houses with names like *Heron's Reach* and *The Landing*.

I tune out Alex and Paul's conversation, which has turned to holidays and property prices, and whispers about something I can't quite hear, though the word *love* is in there somewhere. Ian Turnbull has reared up in my thoughts and I can't seem to flick him away. The nearer we get to the camp, the more tenacious he becomes, grabbing at me, and leering out his misplaced teenage lust. What I find baffling is that he wasn't simply put in his place, by his parents or my colleagues, or even his peers. Perhaps I will have the chance to talk to Pip while I'm at White Platts. It's been made clear to me that I can't talk to anyone else. Except Malcom, of course. He'll be there to meet me and do the handover, so I'm told.

'Are you feeling okay?' A hand on my knee. Paul. 'We're almost there, aren't we?'

I snap my eyes towards him, and he smiles compassion at me.

'I just want to get it over with,' is all I can find to say. Adrenaline has numbed my face and blunted my ability to play join-the-dots with conversation. The huge camp sign will flash itself at us within seconds, and I'm counting every one.

'This the place?' Alex slows the van with a tap of his foot and checks his mirrors.

'Sure is,' I say as the wide gateway appears, with its welcome lettering and gaudily painted fir trees, which should have been plane trees, in my humble opinion. A group of them, with their creamy trunks and lofty foliage, stand in the meadow to the left of the gates. I remember pointing this out to Malcom when he showed us the graphics for this latest sign. There had been no response.

We pull onto the drive and Alex stops.

'How do you want to play this?' he asks.

Do I want to play it? I'm not sure. Games will be the last thing on Malcom's mind.

'Get in, get my stuff then get the hell out,' I snap, before I can stop myself. The words are fuelled by a mix of anger and something much more subtle, like I'm sitting on a high horse and can't get off: they hang in the air for a moment before Alex coughs, then says 'Right,' in a long and stretched way.

I turn my gaze away from him and across the rough grassland that flanks the driveway here. It is used for archery and wide games, though there's no evidence of this at the moment. It just looks muddy and a bit down-at-heel.

'Can I take the van right down to the camp?' he continues, 'or shall we just wait here for you?'

'There's probably quite a few boxes,' I tell him. 'So, it'd be good if you came down with me. If you don't mind.'

He reaches across in front of Paul and takes my hand. 'You're the priority, my love,' he says. 'They've treated you very unfairly, in my opinion.' He leans back. 'Oh, in the eyes of the law, they've been bob-on. But this guy. Malcom Fairly. He could have shown a modicum of compassion, and it wouldn't have detracted from his *safe* position.'

Paul has been listening, but suddenly chips in. 'Have you thought about leaving this place? Finding work elsewhere? You're more than qualified.'

Alex interrupts before I can say anything. 'Not until this case is over. I have a feeling your boss would love that to happen. His tone has been very much along the lines of you being a rogue instructor and his camp not having any taint attached to it. Am I right, Evie?'

'It seems you are,' I say with a sigh. Had Malcom been a friend and supporter, I doubt there would have been a case to answer. To me, the Turnbull parents have sown a few seeds and found unexpectedly fertile ground. In short, I've been scapegoated.

'If you want my honest opinion,' Alex says, 'I think the whole thing could be settled long before the court case, with a small amount of compensation for the Turnbulls, perhaps. Greedy, I know. But that would also mean a minor disciplinary meeting before you could get back to work. No one wants a full court case, civil or otherwise, unless it's absolutely necessary. I'm starting to think that might be best.'

'Why should I have to face a disciplinary meeting, when I did nothing to merit it?'

'Woah. Don't shoot the messenger,' he barks. 'I know you deserve better, but in these cases, as time passes, people tend to get fed up and just want things to be resolved. That's all I'm saying.'

A shake of my head. 'Not me.'

'I don't agree with the principal.' Paul's words float in between us. 'But Al has a point. It really depends on what you want, Evie. Back to work and quickly, or total absolution?'

'You need to ask? That was your original suggestion, if you remember.' I turn myself away from them both. 'Can we go now?'

Down in the main body of the camp, everywhere is quiet. Sunday mornings were often like this, low season, but I know there will be someone manning the office, especially as I'm expected. Alex parks the van in front of the refectory and waits. From here, we can see a very small section of the lake itself, deep grey nestled between the faded greens of winter. Someone in a bright orange camp jacket is on the beach, moving equipment about, but I can't tell who it is.

'I'll go through to the office,' I say. 'Is it all right if you wait here for a minute?'

'Course,' replies Paul. Alex nods lightly.

My pulse hammers at the base of my throat. A deep breath helps me to slip out of the van and into the cold grey morning. I straighten my coat and turn my face towards the slatted wooden building that contains Malcom's office. The glass doors are not locked. One is offset from the other, and the lights are on in the reception area. I push against them, and that familiar smell filters out: burnt coffee and vanilla, overlaid with dubbin. Inside, it is warm and tidy. Though I have a memory of waterproof jackets strewn across the horseshoe of low armchairs, and a mix of mud and crumbs on the carpet, a place like White Platts has to be well maintained. Someone has hoovered recently. There are stripes.

Stacked to the side of the door are five white plastic boxes. With handles. Each has a piece of masking tape with the word *Evie* scribbled in black felt pen. Before I can take in anything else, the door of Malcom's office opens and out comes Pip. She looks sickeningly healthy, as always.

'Evie,' she says. 'How are you?'

We don't hug. It's as though we're meeting for the first time. She seems so *cold*.

'I'm okay, thanks,' I lie. 'You?'

'Good, thanks.' She runs her eyes over the stack of boxes. 'I've been put in charge of making everything right for you. Starting here.'

I smile in a way that doesn't really convey anything.

'I hope this is all of your gear. I was very careful.'

There was nothing in my chalet that was fragile, as I recall. But I did have a radio and a very small television. Perhaps that's what she means.

'That's good of you.' And here is my old life, care of five tatty boxes.

'Have you got time for a chat?' she asks, all blonde eyelashes and pale gaze focussed on me.

'Sure,' I say, 'but can I just ask my *friends* to get the boxes loaded?'

She nods, then walks towards the office again. 'I'll just be in here. When you're ready.'

Alex and Paul are out of the van and sitting on the low wall where camp inmates and staff tended to congregate whilst waiting to be fed. I doubt these two would have approved of the food: the emphasis was on filling the stomach rather than teasing the palate.

'Hi guys,' I call. 'Not what you're used to, is it?'

'We were just enjoying the peace. And the birdsong.' Alex stretches his arms wide. 'Where is everybody?'

'It's December, Al. Hibernation time.' In truth, outdoor

pursuits sessions go on right through the winter, but on a lesser scale, with no weekend sleepovers or bivouacs.

'Oh, right,' he says. 'What's happening with your stuff? Where is it?'

'Boxed up and waiting,' I tell him, then nod towards the main building. 'I've just got to have a quick word with Pip, if that's okay. Could you put the boxes in the van?'

They follow me back inside and I leave them to it, while I knock for Pip, then let myself into the office. She is sitting at Malcom's desk, mug in hand and spinning small half-circles with his chair.

'All right?' she asks as I close the door behind me.

'Not really.' I look around for somewhere to sit. There is one armchair, way across the room. 'I'm wondering why Malcom isn't here... and why you're sitting in his chair.'

'Well.' A light cough. 'For one, he's had a pig of a week, with this and that. Then there's his paranoia over the whole Ian Turnbull incident. He's terrified of taking the wrong course of action.'

Malcom Fairley? Terrified? That doesn't sit well with me. Not at all.

'Who is he getting his information from?' I ask.

Pip leans back in her seat. Malcom's seat, actually.

'He's been in touch with his union's HR department from the start. They suggested he put you on extended leave until the whole situation was resolved.' She hesitates. 'I don't think that was very fair. I told him how upset you were about it, but he insisted on following their guidance rather than getting emotional about things.'

'Oh?' I tilt my head. She meets my gaze. 'I think I had every right to expect an emotional response, Pip. He's my boss, and you're my friend. Don't you feel anything for how I might have been struggling with the situation?'

She thinks about this for a moment. 'What I mean is, he

didn't have to send you off-site. It wasn't a legal requirement. He was just trying to clean up after you. Too quickly, in my opinion.'

'Does he know your opinion?' Something is telling me Pip is now firmly in Malcom's pocket, tucked away and there when he needs to blow his nose.

'We have had words about it, yes,' she says. 'And I told him he needed to be supportive. He'd rather have things dealt with by somebody else. Someone who might be better able to cope with your reactions. Hence–' she throws out her hands '–me.'

Everything has now been served with a gigantic question mark. Can I trust Pip? Is Malcom distancing himself from me for a different reason to the one I'd assumed? Have I actually been treated unlawfully? It suddenly dawns on me that I couldn't possibly come back here to work. Not when the person I'd thought of as a best friend seems to be anything but. And certainly not when someone who should have sent the Turnbulls packing, decided to find another use for their complaint. Malcom's distance has served its purpose; he'll never have to face me again. Clever, that. I have one last question, and it will illuminate everything, as long as Pip doesn't overthink before she answers.

'How's Malcom covering the role of course convenor?'

'That'll be me, again,' she says, with an edge of sarcasm. And that's when I realise she's into this *getting rid of Evie* as much as he is. Pretending to be Malcom's antagonist is all part of the façade. Clearly, she suits the position of senior henchwoman much more than I did. It makes me want to plant my feet in the field outside and refuse to move.

'Oh dear.' I force out a laugh. 'Never mind. I'll be back before you know it.' I watch her reaction. 'My solicitor is top-dollar. He's been so good.'

A slight flicker of something crosses her face. Flaring

nostrils and one blink of those pale eyelashes. 'Lucky you.' Words with a slice. 'Now. Was there anything else?'

I shake my head and step away from the desk. 'Don't think so. You'll be in touch before June, I guess?'

'I will.' She pushes herself up out of the seat, but I don't wait for her, don't look back as the front doors open and close behind me. With absolute certainty, I know I won't be coming back again. Not to work, anyway.

'Just drive,' I say to Alex as I climb up into the van. 'Get me away from here.'

Jay

There is a beauty to the morning, though the air is grey and damp. That anyone could want him, makes Jay's heart sing. He is a small boy again, taking in the sights and smells of nature for no other reason than he wants to. Here is a day to rival those he had before Jamie died; even crossing the railway line doesn't weigh him down. A memory comes, then: standing on the railway track and waiting for a train, thinking of how, if it hit him, it would break so many of his bones that he'd never have to go to *Big School* again. And the best part of this daydream was always that Mam and Dad would nurse him back to health; they'd touch him, cuddle him, bring him drinks and comics in hospital or on the sofa, and they'd be glad of him. But it never happened, in the end; he was always too careful, choosing instead to dart across the line in his flappy shoes, that crying feeling twisting sideways in his throat. He was not wanted at school, and not wanted at home.

Back at his house, he unloads his pockets and lays his latest finds out on the table he uses for a desk. Seeing the space where the painting of Tunnel Cottage had been, makes him smile again. Evie's face when he'd given it as a gift is something he'll not forget. Evie: so full of warmth and light and intelligence. This has been his problem; never having the kindness of human contact, never wanting it, nor trusting it.

He flicks through his pile of sketchbooks for his favourite: the one full of Jamie. He's only ever had photographs and his imagination to work with, though his brother is well and truly alive on the pages. But when his dad had seen his work, he'd flung the book back at him and called him the sorts of names that come from the school playground.

Capturing Evie on the page is going to be Jay's next job. So that when it's all over, he'll be able to look back and remember her. That thought makes him sick to his stomach, so he won't dwell on it. Better to pretend that he's in the first flush of a normal relationship and things can only get better.

He spends the rest of the day sitting by the window of his back room, making drawings and allowing the light to change them slightly as it moves position. When it eventually fades, he takes himself off for a bath and a change of clothing, then slips himself into his waterproof jacket and heads outside.

The evening air is still and smoky. Though it's only six o'clock, the day feels ended and Jay just wants to be inside the cottage with Evie and her softness. Hope is something new, like the first day of spring, with air so clean, and greens so radiant. And he's holding just a tiny bit of it in his heart.

A white van is parked at the top of the driveway when he gets there, so he stands in the shadows and waits. It's not long before two men come out through the front door; the same two he's seen before. Evie's work colleagues. And one he remembers as Punchy-Boy. It's an infantile name, he knows. Zan was what the teacher called him, and from Evie he's heard *Alex*. Whatever the name, the deeds were the same. But he won't think about that. Though he's a match in size and stature for this guy now, he can never meet up with him. John Pickthall would be brought back to life, and that can't happen. So he will wait.

Once the van pulls away, Jay takes himself up to the door of Tunnel Cottage and knocks loudly. When Evie opens it, she bursts into tears and falls into his arms. All he can do is soothe her and listen. There had been a friend at her old workplace who'd let her down in a cruel way. She's not sure if she's angry or sad, or both. But she doesn't want to see her again. And while he can understand only too well how her betrayal must feel, he's glad Evie's broken with this person: he doesn't want to share her.

While she talks and dabs at her eyes and fusses in the kitchen, Jay can't stop looking at her, thinks he'll never stop looking at her. And when he helps her carry her newly-claimed belongings up to the bedroom, the thought of sleeping with her again, her warmth against his back, makes his knees feel shaky, so that he has to sit down. She creeps onto the bed behind him, and her arms slide around his shoulders, making him shiver with desire. When she bunches up his hair and presses her lips to his cheek, he can't hold back any longer. He reaches up and pulls her onto his lap, sliding a hand under her sweater to connect himself to her skin. Then she's kissing him back so hard that he can do nothing but match her intensity.

And afterwards, when they've pulled the bedcovers around them and he's lying with his head between her breasts while she twists her hand through his hair, they talk about how he's going to spend Christmas with her in Tunnel Cottage and how she's not going to take no for an answer, and he thinks he might die from the tenderness of it all.

Chapter Nineteen

'This is it.'

We are standing outside my mother's bungalow. The day is cold and drab. Nothing like the imagined Christmas Days from childhood. They were snowy and twinkly, and fake. At least this one is authentically northern, from its knife-sharp wind to its strings of fairy lights twined around garden holly bushes or pinched between the twiggy fingers of last year's clematis.

'What's *Blengdale*?' Jay is huddled up in the dark woollen coat I have seen once before, and he's brushed his hair into a tight ponytail. With his shoulders rounded and his hands deep in his pockets, he could have escaped from the pages of a Dickensian novel. And I know my mother will think it's her place to comment on that.

'It's an area of forest, in The Lakes,' I tell him. 'She likes to visit and walk there.'

'We'll have that in common, then,' he replies, and I can't bring myself to tell him that my mother doesn't do *common*. She likes to take any common ground, and trample all over it.

'You will,' I say, instead.

He opens the gate, and I follow him up the path, swinging my rucksack off my back. A clink of glass. The bottles of sparkling wine that are my contribution to this meal. And I've tucked a box of after-dinner mints in there too. Expensive ones, a gift from Jay, though I told him there was no need.

Since I'd returned from White Platts with the rest of my belongings, he's been staying with me at the cottage, helping with the garden and being the perfect house guest. But I still can't bring myself to tell him the real reason I'm not at the camp anymore, and he hasn't pushed to find out, because that's what he's like. Accepting, supportive and very private himself. Which means I must swear my mother to secrecy; that will be as inflammatory as if I'd asked her to tell him everything. And she's at the door to meet us. In full Christmas finery: soft plum-coloured sweater, and a string of milky pearls.

'Evie. Merry Christmas.' My arms are held by my sides as she kisses my cheek, then looks over my shoulder. 'And you must be Jay. Merry Christmas to you, too. I'm Fiona. Fi.' No kiss. We step into the warm fug of cooking meat and heated goose fat.

'The weather's not very Christmassy, is it,' I say, 'but your tree looks nice.' I can see it, all tartan ribbons and a twinkle of white lights, in its usual place, in front of the lounge window.

'Let me take your coats,' she purrs, 'and you can just relax, while I cook.' We find ourselves propelled forwards, and through the lounge door. Jay is unbuttoning his coat, and I notice a flush across his cheeks, where he is usually quite pale.

'Are you okay?' I whisper.

A weak nod.

'Thanks,' he says as he hands my mother the coat. 'Thanks for inviting me.'

'That's okay, dear.' Her nostrils twitch, just slightly. Calling Jay *dear* is a dead giveaway. That's a word she uses for keeping someone firmly in their place. And she doesn't approve of the coat, I can tell.

As she walks away, I settle Jay on the sofa. His arms and legs suddenly seem too big for this tiny bungalow. He looks awkward and gangly, all frayed cuffs and wrist-bones.

'I'll get us something to drink,' I tell him. 'Non-alcoholic for you?'

'Please.'

'Won't be a minute,' I whisper, 'and just ignore my mother's posturing. She can't stop being a parent when she's around me. Even though I'm nearly forty.'

'She's not posturing.' His eyes meet mine. 'Is she?'

'That's her default position.' I laugh, then head towards the kitchen to find her, retrieving my rucksack en route.

The table has been set for three, and she has put her cooking pinny back on and is stirring a saucepan full of gravy.

'I've bought the Asti,' I say, pulling out two dark-green bottles, 'and these are Jay's contribution.' I lay the box of mints in the middle of the table. 'And on that subject, I haven't told him about what happened at White Platts.'

'Oh? Is there a reason why not?' She puts down her wooden spoon and turns to look at me properly.

And as I don't know what the reason is, I can't answer. I want to tell her that I'm embarrassed. That it's nobody's business but mine, but I know she won't accept either of those reasons. Because she'll know they're not true.

'Confidentiality.' I give her that, instead. 'Alex advised me to say nothing to anyone, in case there were *connections*. There won't be, but I get where he's coming from, so I'd appreciate it if White Platts is kept out of the conversation.'

She pulls a pretend zip across her lips and shrugs. The gesture makes me sigh.

'It's not a game, Mother, it's my life,' I snap, but she turns her back on me.

Her best crystal-cut glasses have been arranged on a tray on one of the countertops. 'Shall I open this?' I lean around in front of her and hold up one of my bottles.

'Oh, yes,' she says, 'but do it outside, will you. It makes the floor so sticky when it sprays.'

While she decants the gravy, I pop the wine and pour two glasses, then stick an empty one under the cold tap.

'Are you driving?' she asks. 'I didn't hear the car?'

'No, the water's for Jay. He doesn't drink.'

I wait. For the tutting, or the comment. None come. Instead, she gives me a silent smile.

After some loud clattering of saucepans and a final peer into the oven, she announces that she's ready to serve up the dinner, so I leave the glasses on the table and go back to the lounge to fetch Jay. He must have been listening, because he's already on his feet and waiting.

'Don't worry,' I say, because of the grim expression on his face. 'Just compliment the meal and leave the small talk to me.'

'I can do that.'

I lead him into the kitchen, get him tucked into his place at the gold-and-red-themed table. A sequined runner is draped across a layer of paper cloth, and gaudily traditional crackers are lined up alongside my mother's best cutlery. She flaps away my offer to help with the serving up, so I sit opposite Jay and give him a wink. He gulps down his nerves and tries to return the gesture.

'Turkey or ham?' my mother asks, her favourite Christmas one-liner. And woe betide the vegetarian or slimmer.

'Both,' chirps Jay. 'Thanks.'

'Just turkey for me, Mum. Though you know that already.'

She is soon handing us round white plates, piled with meat. Then loading the table with dishes of potatoes and vegetables, sauces and gravy. Finally, she brings herself.

I lift my glass. 'Merry Christmas,' I croon, then wait for Jay to catch on and lift his. My mother clinks glasses with us.

'Tuck in,' she says. 'I can't abide people who are fussy about their food.' Her eyes dart across to Jay. 'And you look like you could do with a good meal, if you don't mind me saying so.'

'Mother.'

But Jay beats me to it. 'Every time I'm offered a good meal,' he says, 'I take it.' A pause while he swallows a mouthful of turkey. 'I can't help my skinny genes.'

'Are your parents tall and thin, then?' She takes a glug of her Asti. 'Sometimes it skips a generation, doesn't it?'

Part of me wants to drag Jay out of here, away from her inevitable probing into his life, but on the surface, she's just asked a pretty ordinary question. And besides, I'm curious, too. Beyond knowing that his parents are dead, as is his guardian aunt, there are many gaps in my knowledge. Especially since the guy is practically living with me.

'My mum was tall and slim, so I guess I've turned out like her.' It is hard to tell if the mumbling is because he is eating, but I'm as interested as my mother.

'She's dead now though,' he adds. 'So's Dad.'

From underneath my lashes, I pretend to be scraping round for some mashed potato and gravy. Her hand is spread out across her chest, one finger touching her pearls.

'I'm so sorry,' she says. 'Evie never told me that.'

'Mother,' I whisper, but Jay stops me with a twist of a smile.

'It's okay. I was brought up by my aunt, in actual fact.' No interruptions come, so he continues. 'Elizabeth Elliot was her name. I live in her house.'

I want him to continue, to give me some further insights into his life before me, but I know how much it will have cost him to say even this, so I search my mind for something to divert the conversation. 'Jay's an artist, aren't you?' Patronising, but it does the job.

'Oh,' says my mother, patting her mouth with a tartan serviette. 'What do you paint?'

'The natural world, mainly,' he tells her. 'But not only in paint. I draw and sculpt as well.'

'Goodness me, you are a busy bee. How do you fit it all in around work?'

Why she can't think beyond her own understanding of the world, has always been a source of embarrassment and annoyance to me. And I can see Jay's colour rising. I want to jump to his defence, but from my many years of experience at handling my mother, I know this will make her consider what she's saying even less.

'Art is my work and my life,' he replies simply, and I want to punch the air.

'And does it pay the bills?' she asks, quite brittle now. But Jay has his answer ready.

'I live a simple life, so I don't have many bills.' I have never heard him talk in such a piercing way. But she needs to understand.

'Jay's artwork is beautiful,' I tell her. 'He's shown me a few of his pieces. And I've got one on the cottage wall.'

She snorts. 'The cottage. You make it sound like a sweet, thatched kind of place.' Her attention flicks to Jay again. 'What do you think of Tunnel Cottage? It's rather *crude*, isn't it?'

He tidies his knife and fork to the middle of his empty plate, then finishes his last mouthful. 'I really like the place, actually.' A soft smile. 'And the setting is perfect if you're a naturalist, like me. Thanks for the lovely meal, by the way.'

'You're welcome,' she says, with a purse of her lips. 'I hope you like Christmas pudding.'

Jay has finished his food much more quickly than either me or my mother, and the gap stretches awkwardly between us.

Eventually he excuses himself with a request to use the bathroom, more from embarrassment than need, I guess.

'Have you gone back to your *hippy* roots?' my mother hisses when we hear the door close behind him. 'A long-haired artist with no job?' She shakes her head. 'Honestly, Evie, is this what you've given up your camp job for?'

I slam down my cutlery. 'You never wanted me to work at White Platts in the first place. So what are you saying that for?' I inhale deeply, then pick up my plate and move towards the sink with it. 'Can't you be a bit nicer? Just this once?'

'I thought I was being,' comes the reply. 'Inviting you both for Christmas lunch, when I hardly know this man.'

'Don't call him a man. Like he's some random stranger,' I snap. 'His name's Jay. And he happens to mean quite a lot to me.'

Then he reappears at the door. Sheepish and rubbing his hands together. 'Did someone mention Christmas pudding?'

Jay

He's struggling with Evie's mother, but not for the reasons she'd probably think. This woman has her health, her strength. Her daughter still alive. How can she not appreciate that, love that?

Jay's own mother had none of those things. Not in the end, anyway. Her life had been about lying with her feet flat against the arm of the sofa, a cushion under her head; drawn curtains. And she'd lived off tablets, white ones from a brown tube with a snapping lid, that made her sleep as deep as he'd ever seen.

When he came home from school, with its odour of disinfectant and chalk, he'd notice the cottage smelt stale, of old fish and even older cigarettes. There were no longer any of the house-proud cleaning days or shopping days, or any other kind of days. His aunt might drop over some things that stopped the family from stepping into starvation or filth. Or she might not.

And when the offer came to live with her on a more permanent basis, Jay couldn't see that there was a choice. Not if he was to survive.

That first Christmas with Liz had been full of warmth and food, clean sheets and her solid presence. As a boy, he'd needed those things so much. He still does. Within two years, his aunt had become as insubstantial as his mother, and he'd started to look around for something else to lift him up. He'd found his own way through, in the end, but the struggle left him numb. Like he was living one step removed from everyone else, crouching in a place of safety, while his other self got on with the humdrum of existence. Only when he was connected to nature did the tendrils of human sentiment cause him to react. Not strongly, but there was something.

On the day Jay found out that his aunt had died, he'd been about to fell one of his favourite trees: an ancient ash that hung over the west wall of Kew's riverside walk and was shedding larger and larger boughs. He'd been a team leader by then; people looked to him for advice and support, and he'd started to believe that he could finally leave John Pickthall behind.

Then everything changed.

Liz had no other relatives and no one to sort out her estate. Not that there was much: a run-down house and a small sum of money in savings bonds. But it was all his, and he couldn't deal with it. Not without her, and now she was gone.

It had been his intention to sell the place, cash up and ship himself back to Kew as soon as he could.

Once the funeral was over, he'd decided to visit Tunnel Cottage one last time, to try and speak to his father. That had been a disaster. The place was closed up, the furniture gone.

When he'd peered through the letterbox and called into the gloom of the hallway, he could hear only the echo of his own voice. And there was no one to ask about it; his father had become a stranger.

Jay had stayed on the doorstep for the whole of the day and most of the night. His father didn't return. He was gone: the last connection Jay had with family. At two o'clock in the morning, he'd tried to drag himself away from the cottage and return to his aunt's house. As soon as he'd hit the railway track and felt the thick darkness coming from the tunnel itself, something shifted in his mood; he started to panic. Blaming the pound of his heart and the gasp of his breath on the more recent stresses in his life, he'd tried to carry on walking. It was impossible. Tunnel Cottage was calling him back, pulling at the bond he had with the place, demanding he return. And when he did, the panic had subsided. It took two further attempts before he'd managed to get away, but all the time he was fighting the urge to get back there and feel safe again.

He never returned to Kew. Instead, he spent his days as near to the cottage as he could get. There was no way inside, but if he could just rest his hands on the sandstone walls or stand at the gate and look at the beck, he felt soothed, felt his mother's presence, and Jamie's. That she never recovered herself, after his death, is something Jay still struggles with. And blames his father for.

Now, though, there's Evie. She's helping him to scramble down from the safe place where he's been hiding, without even knowing it. But it's making him feel like a liar, a cheat and a fraud.

Chapter Twenty

It's a Christmas tradition to visit The Bay View. Which is why Jay, my mother and I are stepping briskly through the smoggy night air, under a starless sky, and talking about pubs.

The day hasn't been easy. My mother has called a temporary truce with her disapproval, and Jay has been quietly charming.

'I didn't think pubs opened on Christmas night,' he is saying, 'but what do I know?' His shoulder lifts against my arm. 'Haven't been in one for many years.'

'Well, don't expect much,' I tell him. 'It's open, but full of sad hopefuls trying to extend the buzz of Christmas. With alcohol.'

But my mother's not having that. 'You're such a cynic,' she huffs. 'How did I get a daughter who is so cynical? You don't get it from me, that's for sure.'

And once again, her comments make me want to scream. I wonder what her definition of cynicism is. She certainly questions the validity of everything she doesn't deem worthy. Am I the same? I don't have time to think about this any further because she's changing the subject.

'I wonder if Sheila will be in.' She glances at her watch. 'Remember how we all used to meet up here, didn't we? You and Alex would try to outdo each other with your Christmas gifts.'

We've reached the car park of Bay View. It hasn't even occurred to me that Alex might be here with his mother. There is an image in my mind, of him and Paul, cuddled up in front of *Scrooge and Marley*, sipping Baileys and basking in the glow of their perfectly co-ordinated and pine-scented tree. Not trudging to his mother's bungalow, then treating her to a pint of Wainwright in a pub with fake ceiling beams and an anaglypta border.

We push our way through the swing doors, and into the black-and-scarlet glow. Most of the tables are empty. A youngish man is standing at the electronic gaming machine, drink in one hand and smashing the *play* button. Jay is hunched in his coat and walks behind us towards the bar. There is that awkward moment when each of us is wondering who is going to take the lead. I don't wonder for too long.

'What are we having?' I ask. 'Mum? Brandy?'

'Oh, go on then.' A dimple of her cheeks. 'Just one. A small one.' She uses her thumb and forefinger to show me just how small, in case I haven't quite understood.

'Jay?'

When I look into his face, I can see something isn't right. Understandable, after a day in my mother's company, but I have tried to mitigate where I could.

'Just a soft drink, thanks.'

The music from the games machine pierces the air as I turn towards the bar.

'We'll go and sit down,' my mother says, behind me, and then she mutters something about there being plenty of tables to choose from.

'Merry Christmas,' I say to the landlady when she appears. 'Skeleton staff tonight, eh?'

This is Belle, from the dynamic duo that are Belle and Brian. They took over the pub somewhere back in my university days, and have been here ever since, have brought up their children here, and are now on the verge of letting them run things themselves. Belle is a whippet of a woman, white-haired, with the stature of an eleven-year-old boy, and language to match.

'He's in the back, watching the bloody telly.' She laughs, and thumbs over her shoulder. 'The other two are out supping somewhere else, would you believe.'

'Traitors.' I join in with her banter, but in my peripheral vision I can see Jay and my mother pulling out chairs from a nearby table, then lifting off their coats and draping them. He's had one hell of a day, but he's managed it. His life is a solitary one, that hasn't been a secret, but there is a fine line between enjoying solitude and privacy, and being a recluse. Where he falls on that continuum, I'm still not sure. And it's not for me to judge.

I order our drinks and carry them over to the table. The set of Jay's shoulders tells me he's struggling with this whole scene. And I would be, too. Someone else's mother, and judgemental to a fault. I want to tell him that he's made me proud today. But that's not the way we talk to each other. Instead, I sit down next to him and take his hand in mine. It is ice cold.

'All right?' I ask.

He nods and lifts his drink to his lips. 'Tired though,' he whispers. 'I was never very good at socialising.' A dart of his eyes. 'Pubs are just not me.'

'Nor me,' I say, quiet enough that my mother won't hear without deliberately trying to. But when I look across at her, she is craning towards the door.

With a whoosh of cold air, in walks Sheila Swarbrick.

Closely followed by Alex and Paul, all pea-coats and Nordic-patterned scarves.

'Sheila. *Woo-hoo.*' My mother is beside herself, waving her hand and knocking the table as she stands up. My lemonade slops everywhere.

Alex heads to the bar, while Paul clinks change in his pocket then begins to feed coins into the gaming machine. Sheila comes to our table and takes my mother into her lilac embrace.

'Fi,' she sings. 'Merry Christmas to you. And Evie. I haven't seen you for such a long time.' Her eyes flick across to Jay. 'Hello.'

Alex calls to her.

'What are you having, Ma? Anyone else?'

There is already a fizzing in my stomach. I don't want to add to it. As I'm about to refuse, Jay stands up. No one is aware of this, particularly. But I am. The colour has drained from his face, and he mumbles something about needing fresh air. Then he crashes away from the table and out through the swing doors.

I catch up with him.

A metal handrail follows a line of concrete steps out of the pub, and Jay is holding onto it, knuckles livid, and gulping down the muzzy night air. I reach up and run my hand across his shoulders. They are granite hard and don't respond.

'What's going on?' I ask.

Nothing.

'Jay. Do you want to go home?'

He shudders, telling me all I need to know.

'Stay there and I'll get our coats and make our excuses. Won't be a moment.'

When I step back inside, all eyes are on me.

'Was it something I said?' My mother, sympathetic as ever.

173

'It's nothing,' I snap. 'Jay's not feeling himself, that's all. So, we're going to get off.'

She harumphs slightly.

'Thanks for everything today. It's been lovely.' I reach for our coats.

'Can I do anything?' Sheila is a retired counsellor. Well-meaning, knowledgeable, but not what's needed.

'It'll be fine,' I say, searching for my calm voice. The one I once used for panicking kids stuck up rock faces. 'Too much food and drink, I suspect.'

'Everything all right, darling?' Alex has joined the throng of concern. He is clutching three chunky glasses of amber liquid. Whisky, I guess. One is full to the brim with ice.

'I'm having to love you and leave you, I'm afraid,' I start to say, but he jumps in straight away.

'What is it with that guy? Whenever he sees me, he runs a mile.'

A prickle of interest starts up in the middle of my mother's face. Then it spreads to her eyes, and finally her mouth. 'What do you mean, Al?' she asks.

I lock my eyes with his, try to make him feel what I'm feeling. But his words are already escaping, drawn out by the gravitational pull of my mother and Sheila's gaping stares.

'Last time I bumped into Evie and her– Jay, he stormed away, too. Outside the office, wasn't it?' He is looking over his shoulder at Paul now.

'Alex Swarbrick, you are an old gossip,' Paul says, with just the smallest tinge of outrage. 'There was no storming being done. Either time. You've just got an oversensitive nose for a bit of drama.'

He smiles at me. 'Ignore him, Evie. He's unbearable on bank holidays.'

Jay

That woman. Evie's mother. Jay is struggling to believe how nasty some of her comments have been. He has been dealing with this reaction from some people for most of his life. Even before Punchy-Boy and his cruelty.

And then there was the pub. Jay hadn't been in one of those places since he'd been a team leader at Kew. There had been the time when he'd felt the need to take his colleagues for a drink, then embarrassed himself by having a panic attack. All he could think of to save the situation was to put fifty pounds behind the bar then flee with the excuse of some family emergency. Ridiculous really, when they all knew he had none.

He can't be anywhere near those machines. They swallowed up so much more than his money. Having to admit to his aunt that he had a gambling habit hurt almost as much as Jamie dying.

It had started with the simplest of things: keeping the change from his daily errand of collecting his aunt's cider; the guy in the shop letting him play the bandits, just for fun.

Then there were the television programmes she watched. *Dallas* and *Dynasty*, he remembers. American. Full of lovely-looking people, with beautiful houses and marriage and happy endings. When he'd caught glimpses of the opening scenes, someone was usually kissing or driving away in an open-topped car. There was never rain, or rooms piled high with magazines, or shoes with the toes kicked out.

Money made a difference, was what he thought back then; the more you have, the glossier your life. If he could just get a lot of money, and give it to his parents, theirs might be better. They might have even wanted him back.

Living with Liz was as good as he was going to get, but she wasn't a parent, and there was always a difficulty when he tried to explain this to his school. There were sideways looks and straight mouths, and whispers of the word *guardian*, like it was something filthy. Worse than sex. Not that he knew much about it, back then. None of the boys in his form at school would let him in on their private little worlds, and the girls avoided him completely.

Jay's attention had been immediately captured by the two machines, robot-square and silver, standing in the corner of the shop, with their coloured numbers, and Blaze Seven painted along their fake-wood sides. One-armed bandits, his aunt called them. Watching grown men grabbing at the arm, and the jangling spew of coins, sent a thrill through Jay he'd never experienced before. And he'd imagined his mother's face if he could knock on the door of Tunnel Cottage with an armful of flowers and a box of chocolates. Proper ones. He'd seen them once, in the window of a shop in town. Smooth globes, brown as soaked conkers, each with a diamond of violet jelly crowning the top. And all sitting in a gold box with a ribbon on the lid. They would make her smile like she used to. Before.

But every one of his spins on those machines had been followed by a silence.

Jay wants to cry. The watery heat of tears is building up at the back of his eyes, and he tries blinking to relieve it. But the pressure is too much, and the tears push their way out. He rubs them away with his index fingers, but not before Evie sees. And he's surprised when she simply slips her arm through his and leads him away. What must she think of him?

He's going to have to tell her something.

Facing up to his reaction at seeing Punchy-Boy again isn't something he wants to do. So, it's time to tell her about another part of his life.

Chapter Twenty-One

Once we've cleared the housing estate, arms linked, and marching like soldiers, Jay unfurls himself enough for me to start up a conversation.

'Do you want to go to your house?' I ask. 'I'll walk there with you, if you like?'

'No.' There is an energy in his voice that surprises me, considering how unwell he looked only five minutes ago. 'Unless you want rid of me? I'll make my own way, if you do.'

Up until this point, we haven't had any sort of disagreement. There has been no vying for position or realigning of personal space or any of the other things I've felt in relationships before. So, I don't know quite where to go with this sudden petulance. Unless I've got it completely wrong. When Jay speaks again, I realise I have.

'That sounded pathetic, didn't it? I'm sorry, Evie.' He clears his throat. 'I have to tell you something. About me. It's not fair that you're being put into embarrassing situations by only knowing half a story.'

I have to stop him there. 'Don't worry about embarrassing situations. I'm a master of those.' I stop walking and stand in front of him. 'But if you need help with something, please let me be the one to give it. I want to. I'm starting to care very deeply about you, Jay.' His eyes fill up again. 'Weird. But true.'

'It's not weird.' He takes my face in his hands. 'I care about you, too. A lot. And I don't want to mess it up. So, I must tell you why I struggled in the pub, earlier.'

'Okay,' I say. Then turn my head to kiss one of his palms. 'Let's walk back to the cottage, and you can tell me all about this *thing*.'

I can see Jay through the kitchen window. After the revelation of his teenage gambling addiction, we have become closer. I believe him when he says he's had the problem under control for more than twenty years now. That it was the manifestation of a mental health issue is something he's still struggling to accept.

Back then, he told me, problems like his were taken at face value and dealt with as such. When I asked if there was help from his parents or aunt, he'd shrugged off that question with one of his own. One that made me realise just how much he'd been on his own with his demons.

'Why would they care?'

His spit of words warned me against any further interrogation about his parents. And though I wondered if he'd any siblings, they were never mentioned, so I presumed not. He was well and truly alone in the world. He'd left the area aged eighteen, he told me, to take up a post at Kew Gardens, as a labourer. My guilty conscience prevented me from asking questions that would join up the dots.

I've been evasive about the situation at White Platts, after all. That veil will cause problems in the end, I'm sure, so now I'm wrestling with how to explain fully. Perhaps I'll wait until

I'm back at work in a couple of days, when I've had the chance to catch up with Alex again and find out how the land lies. For now, I intend to enjoy the last days of the Christmas and New Year break, without analysing things too much.

Jay straightens his back, looks at me through the window, and waves a handful of dry brushwood at me. Then performs an elaborate drinking mime. His hair is loose across his shoulders and there is a pop of pink in each of his cheeks. And suddenly I realise. This is what I want. A life with him. That simple.

I lift the kettle and wave it back. How will he react when he finds out he's in a relationship with someone who is being looked at for inappropriate conduct? There I go, analysing again. The only solution is to be in the present moment and enjoy it. So, I step out through the kitchen door without waiting for the kettle to boil, and throw myself into the *now*.

––––––––

Jay

When Evie's mother turns up unannounced, on the day after Boxing Day, Jay wants to try again with her. Any relationship with the daughter must involve at least a truce with the mother, or so he thinks. Not that he's an expert on parents and their children. There'd been no *truce* with his own father, just the naivety of a ten-year-old boy, trying to understand what he'd done.

It crosses his mind that Fiona Cooper has planned this visit deliberately, having had a telephone conversation with Evie earlier about which shops might be open for stocking up on milk and bread, and sending her off to Tesco.

Christmas Day lunch had been a trial, and Jay had sensed Fiona's dislike from the moment they'd met, but perhaps things could be mended. He offers her coffee and asks her into the cottage, but she refuses, preferring to stand on the doorstep with her coat buttoned around her, gloved hand emphasising her words as they stab at his conscience as surely as if she'd been holding a long-handled knife.

'I think you're a freeloader,' she says, with a spit in her voice. 'Taking advantage of Evie's good nature, living in her cottage, eating all her food yet contributing nothing. You don't even work. *Art.*' She snorts. 'That's ridiculous.'

And though his face burns with anger, he tries to explain what his contribution actually is, but she doesn't let him finish.

'And you look so… tatty,' she continues. 'How can Evie be seen out with you. Her people are *professionals.*'

He's not sure what she's implying: he's already been out and about with Evie and there didn't seem to have been a problem about his clothing. The situation needs calming, but he's not sure how to do it without his anger shooting out and smothering her in an almost tangible way. He pictures her slumping against the porch, gasping, clutching at her throat, while he turns his back and slams the door.

When she does pause for breath, he tells her quietly that he will let Evie know she's called, and thanks her for her input. Then he closes the door and collapses behind it, wondering again if he should just get the hell out.

He doesn't tell Evie about her visit.

Chapter Twenty-Two

On the day before I'm due back at work, Jay arrives early from spending the night at his own house. Which I haven't been invited to. Yet.

'Here I am.' He smiles me a hello when I open the front door.

'You need your own key,' I say with a laugh. 'Or you could just keep some of your stuff here.' I step back and let him into the cottage. He is clean-shaven and wearing fresh clothes; a black roll-neck sweater and a pair of jeans that are faded to almost transparent at the knees. But it's the smell of him I can't resist. Warm and earthy, plain soap and line-dried cotton. I slide my arms around his waist, inside his jacket.

'You missed me then?' he asks. 'I thought you might be glad to see the back of me.' His chin on the top of my head. 'I can be a bit clingy, you know.'

'Cling all you like,' I tell him. 'As long as you shout me breakfast in town this morning. There's a few things I need to buy. Not that you know much about shopping.'

'What does that mean? *Shout you breakfast?*'

When I let go of him and frown out my confusion, he

continues. 'I've led a sheltered life, as you know.' A wry smile crosses his lips. 'In some respects, anyway.'

'Buy me breakfast. That's all it means. There's a little café tucked away down one of the side streets in town. I saw it when I was wandering about, one lunchtime.'

'Get your coat on then, and we'll walk down,' he says. 'It's a beautiful morning. You can steer me through café regulations when we get there.'

The air outside is sharp, and icily refreshing, the sky a picture-postcard blue. We decide to take the back route into the town centre, which means crossing the meadow. Jay slides an arm around my shoulder as we tramp across the frost-crisp grass, and make our way to the narrow footpath alongside the beck. The water level is high, almost overflowing, and a few stray sunbeams that have cleared the trees, cast patches of brightness across its surface. We don't say much: Jay seems lost in his own thoughts, giving me time to enjoy the serenity of the place.

A road, little more than a country lane really, takes us past a looming fell that is scarred with quarry damage. Gorse has grown within the fault lines, stark green shadows against the red stone bloom, and a few Herdwicks dip for their breakfast. Jay stops for a moment, scanning the highest ridge.

'No matter the damage, nature always returns,' he says.

'Wow. That's profound, for this time of the morning.' More flippant than I meant, so I follow it up with, 'Tell me about your time at Kew. I had no idea you were actually a trained plantsman.'

He lifts one shoulder, then starts walking again. 'Not a plantsman, as such, but I did learn a lot during my time there.' He hesitates. 'It was only a few years, though. Then I came back.'

By the time he's finished telling me about his London experience, our journey has taken us away from this hard-edged rural landscape. A sprawl of faded dockland industry leads us into the centre of town, which isn't as busy as it would be, had it not been the day after New Year's Day. Most of the local white-collar workers have given themselves an extra day's holiday to take them up to the weekend.

The inside of the café is warm with the fragrance of coffee and toast. Jay starts to rummage in his pocket, then pulls out an old-fashioned wallet, leather by the looks of it, and sewn around the edges with a thick black twine.

'You go to the counter,' he says, pushing two ten-pound notes into my hand, 'I'm not very good in these situations.' His eyes flick across to an empty table. 'I'll get us a seat.'

'We haven't looked at the menu yet.' I shake my head and frown.

'There's a menu? I am out of touch, aren't I?'

I unzip my jacket and hang it over the back of one of the chairs. Jay edges himself in, folding his knees under the table. An elderly lady is sitting nearby and smiles a hello at us. He beams and she blushes. I push the propped paper leaflet towards him.

'Choose something,' I tell him, 'then I can get in the queue.'

'I'll have anything.' His words are almost a whisper. Like he doesn't want to draw any attention to himself. 'As long as it's with coffee.'

While I wait to be served, I watch him, although he is facing away from me. His shoulders are set square and both elbows are resting on the table while he chews at his nails. Then he runs one hand around the back of his neck to smooth down his ponytail. I wonder if I've done the right thing, bringing him into another unpredictable place. But there are no gambling machines here, just the gentle hum of coffee and ice-cream makers, and the local radio station thumping out nondescript eighties music.

I order us bacon rolls and large cappuccinos with a slice of the local bakery's caramel shortcake on the side. After paying, I carry our drinks back to the table, smiling again at the elderly lady, who is now sliding her shoulders into a turquoise raincoat.

'He's a good-looking chap, isn't he,' she says, nodding towards Jay, then twitching her eye into a covert wink.

'Don't tell him that.' I join her banter. 'He's vain enough as it is.'

'I heard that.' A glance over his shoulder. 'Vanity is the quicksand of reason, so they say.'

We all laugh then, though I have no idea what he is talking about.

'What does that mean?' I hiss, as the lady heads for the door.

'I'm not sure,' comes the reply. 'My aunt had it cross-stitched into cloth and framed, on the wall of her living room.'

'So, is it still there?'

He shakes his head. 'I can't remember what happened to it. Only that I used to puzzle over what it meant, when I was very small.'

I slide his coffee towards him. 'Did you go to live with her when you were quite young?' I ask.

He plays with packets of sugar from a glass container in the middle of the table. Have I crossed a line again, I wonder? The subject of his house and his aunt have come up from time to time, but the facts I get are scant, and spoken with reluctance. Something I understand, given how much of my life he still knows nothing about.

The conversation is halted by the arrival of our food, delivered by the café's round-faced proprietor, along with another slice of northern banter. Jay follows my lead, and we engage in a round of wordplay before the guy leaves us alone to enjoy our breakfast.

'This is tasty,' Jay says, after a few mouthfuls, and when I nod enthusiastically, he continues. 'Can you tell I don't get out much?'

'It's not a crime to lead a quiet life,' I tell him, crumbling some of the shortbread to eat with my bacon. 'Too much drama can be disorientating. Sometimes, in my old job, I forgot I was an actual person because of the constant demands on my time. The worst shifts were twenty-four hours on, for a block of three days. Sometimes I didn't even get to clean my teeth.'

His eyes are on my face as he swallows his last bit of roll. 'Is that another reason why you left?' he asks. When I don't answer straight away, he adds, 'Sorry. I wasn't being nosy. You don't have to tell me.'

In the moment that I decide I am going to tell Jay about the whole Ian Turnbull incident, the door of the café bursts open and in strolls Paul Murray, crash helmet under his arm, closely followed by Alex and a blast of chilly air.

He spots us immediately. 'Evie,' he calls, 'small world. Happy New Year.'

The atmosphere shifts. I smile back a greeting, but my instincts tell me that his focus is going to be on Jay. And I don't want that.

Paul's eyes dart between us all. He taps Alex's leather-clad forearm.

'Cappuccino or latte?' he asks, rather loudly. 'Al?'

But Alex doesn't answer. Instead, he says, 'Happy New Year. Jay, isn't it?' A hand, extended across the table, while I can do nothing but watch the situation unfold and hope it turns into something quite ordinary. That doesn't happen.

Without looking up, Jay shoves his chair back, picks up his coat and bolts for the door. I can only shake my head at Alex, and follow, mouthing an apology as I go.

Outside, Jay is pulling on his coat. I step forward and stand in front of him. His mouth is set in a hard line.

'What's going on?' I murmur, taking his hand. 'Tell me.'

He shakes his head. There are words on his lips, I can almost see them. But he is struggling to speak, though I'm finding it hard to guess which kind of emotion is blocking him. Anger? Fear? Hatred? None of those match up with what I know of Jay. He's been nothing but gentle.

This can't be a simple case of what we used to call, at White Platts, *settling of pecking order.* No matter what the disparity and diversity of our groups of young men, the first day or two of their training or outdoor education visit would be bogged down by some imagined competition. Once ranking was established, and feathers were smoothed, it was over. Groups of young women rarely had that dynamic. Their actions were the polar opposite: at the start of the visit, they would be all about love and fairness and equality, but by the end, the leaders amongst them had an edge of strength so phenomenal they were trusted by all to run the show.

No, this isn't a simple case of pecking order.

'Let's go back to the cottage. I can get my shopping another time.'

'I'll be fine,' he says suddenly. 'Your friend doesn't like me, that's all. And I can tell.'

'He's my boss as well as my friend,' I snap, 'and I've yet to meet someone he doesn't like. You could have at least tried to face him off.'

Jay pulls away from me. 'You go back inside,' he mutters. 'I'll be around later.' And the look he gives me before walking away crashes my heart.

Jay

Jay runs. Though his world is tilting away, he slams one foot down and then another. How did he ever think there was a place for him in this jagged world, this brittle landscape full of shiny judgement and false hope? He can't have Evie. To think he could makes him want to scream out loud. But all he can do is run. Past a townscape that is laughing at his stupidity; under the skeletal canopy of winter trees; down into the valley that has trapped him as surely as his actions. Not even Tunnel Cottage could provide solace today; that scares him more than anything.

On the other side of the ruin is a series of steps, cut into the woodland floor and leading steeply upwards. Jay follows the steps as far as they go, then stomps his way across the tangles of dead bramble and ground ivy to an area that is clear and flat. From here, it is possible to see trains as they emerge from the tunnel. Watching them gives him a sense of release, of escape. He remembers the time when a train had carried him away from his life, once before. And though it had been profoundly sad, there was a feeling of freedom, too. It would be so easy to do this again; he wants to do it again.

Chapter Twenty-Three

The low thrum of an engine wakes me from my fretful doze. I sit up and blink into the fading light. The lounge is freezing. When I'd arrived back from the town centre, weighed down with shopping bags, I'd expected to find Jay, waiting on the doorstep or gazing at the ruin. There was no sign of him, so I'd sat on the sofa and stewed about the situation until my brain shut down under the pressure. And now someone is hammering on the front door and calling my name. I slide my feet back into my slippers and shuffle out into the hall. Alex is there, leather-clad, crash-helmet in hand, as I pull open the door.

'Hi,' he says. 'I thought I'd come and check that you were okay.' He peers over my shoulder, just for a moment.

'Jay's not here,' I say, 'and I'm fine, thank you very much.'

Alex drops his brows. 'No need to be like that. You looked really uncomfortable when–' A pause. The silence does its work.

'When Jay stormed off. Might as well say it.' I step aside. 'Come in. You haven't seen the cottage properly yet, have you?'

That's the thing about Alex. His confidence never deserts

him; there's never a time when his humility holds him back. A great skill, if you work in law, I guess. He strides into the hallway like he owns the place, laying down his helmet and unzipping his jacket before I've even had the chance to close the door behind him. A trail of cold smoky air comes in with him.

'Get the kettle on,' he shivers, 'I've just driven over from the island. A blast, I know, but a bitterly cold one.'

'Paul at home?' I ask as we make our way into the kitchen.

'He is. There are a few emails to answer before we're back to it tomorrow.' He casts around. 'This is quite basic, isn't it?'

'I like it.'

'Oh, I didn't mean to sound patronising. It's a fabulous setting. But the cottage doesn't look like it's had any work done recently. And that driveway.' He shakes his head in disgust. 'Dodgy or what?'

'Let's stop talking around the reason you're here,' I say. 'Honestly, I have no idea why Jay can't cope with being anywhere near you.' I hold up my hands. 'Sorry, Al. But there it is.'

My own reaction surprises me. There is a choke at the back of my throat, and tears on the rims of my eyes. Because I so want to know what is going on. And I so want to know where Jay is now, and if he's okay.

Alex puts his arms around me. 'Darling girl,' he murmurs. 'I'm not taking it personally, I assure you. It's only that you've had so much to cope with, lately. I do wonder if this guy is just adding to your woes.'

I snap myself out of his embrace. 'That's the last thing he's doing. And I'm coping just fine.' I turn away and lift the kettle to fill our mugs. 'Jay means a lot to me, actually. Enough to make me wonder if I want to go back to White Platts, whatever the outcome of the court case.'

I hadn't meant to give Alex that piece of information.

Saying it aloud sends a strange jolt through my body. Am I really that attached to Jay? But if I'm not, what have I been doing? Using him for companionship? That's just not me. And now, I'm wondering if I understand myself at all.

'But what do you know about this guy, Evie? Tell me honestly, because I can find no trace of him, wherever I look.'

'Where have you been looking?' I can feel myself getting agitated. 'And why, more's the point.'

Alex takes a sip of his coffee. 'He's got no digital presence, as far as I can see. You told me he was an artist.' He tightens his lips and shakes his head. 'Nope.'

'Well, that's strange,' I hiss, 'because I've seen his art.'

'I'm only saying that he's not selling online. As far as I can see, anyway. And he's got no social media presence whatsoever. Whereabouts does he live? What schools did he go to?'

'Schools? For goodness' sake, it sounds like you're asking if he went to Eton or Harrow. He went to one of the local comps, I guess.'

'You guess? Don't you know?'

What I can't understand is why Alex is so worried about any of this. Jay is, by my reckoning, round about forty years of age. Which makes him part of a more discerning generation, where a life could be lived without electronically displaying it.

'He's a quiet guy,' I say. 'He doesn't want to talk about himself. It's one of the things I love about him, actually.' That word. Love. Have I really said it?

As I walk into the lounge, Alex lets out a huge sigh. Then he follows me. No point in me expecting him to light the fire, though. I put down my mug on the hearth and start to scrunch up balls of newspaper, which I push into the empty grate, then overlay with fire logs and coal.

'Don't fall out with me,' Alex says suddenly.

'I won't.' A small yellow flame starts to lick at the logs. I blow it gently.

'Put yourself first. That's all I'm asking.'

'Yes, Mum,' I say with a laugh as he sits down on the sofa. But his words have got me thinking. I've been sleeping with a guy I hardly know. However strong my feelings for him are, I have to wonder if I'm being duped in some way. What the reason would be, I can hardly fathom. I don't have money or looks or a fabulous lifestyle. If Jay has hooked up with me for any of those, he must have realised by now that there's been a mistake made. I'd like to think he was interested in me for other reasons. We do get along well, so perhaps he enjoys my company. And the truth is, I haven't been any more honest with him than he's been with me. Not so much dishonest. More like opacity for self-preservation, something that I only ever intended to be temporary. So, I have to give him the same chances that I'm giving myself.

A low rumble comes from the side of the house. It builds to a loud metallic clattering. Then the two-horned note and ear-splitting shriek that never fails to impress.

'Jeez. What the hell's that?' Alex's expression makes me laugh. It's like he's just taken the first dive on a rollercoaster ride.

'Every half hour. On the dot,' I say loudly. 'Train from Barrow to Lancaster, and back.'

He sticks his tongue in his cheek. 'You don't half pick 'em,' is all he says.

We wait until the roaring has faded, then resume our conversation.

'I meant to tell you.' He sips his coffee and looks at me over the rim of the mug. 'I had an email in from the Turnbulls' solicitor.'

'Oh? Unexpected?'

'Yep. They've requested a mediation meeting. Which is unusual.'

I lean back on my heels, then turn to sit on the hearth and look at him. 'Why?'

He shrugs. 'Those meetings can represent a desire to find some middle ground. Before things get too formal. Like a *thawing out*, if you will.'

'But the Turnbulls are dead set on bringing me down, aren't they? Or at least getting some money out of White Platts?'

'This is why I'm saying it's unusual. I don't believe for one moment that they are backing down.'

'Ian Turnbull can hardly back down, can he? All he'd be then is a liar.' I spit out that word and Alex raises his eyebrows.

'We already know he's one of those, Evie. What I'm wondering is whether they want a meeting to imply that a completely private payment would solve the situation.'

'An out-of-court settlement, then?'

'Not even that.' Alex shakes his head. 'A back-hander, if you will. Not strictly legal, but a way of ending a bad situation for everyone.'

'You're not suggesting we agree to it, are you?' I don't want to be part of any unsavoury pay-offs to make the situation go away. 'Alex?'

'Not at all. In fact, I'd say that their request is even more of a reason to go ahead with the civil court case.'

'I don't understand?'

'Well.' He scowls and I wait. 'Well, it makes me think some new evidence has come to light. But I can't imagine, for the life of me, what it would be. Can you?'

'What sort of thing?' I ask.

'Do you know, Evie, I have not an inkling. My hope was that you did.'

'I don't.' My words are loaded with anger. 'And I'm not sure I'm even bothered anymore.'

The fire crackles. It is starting to bring some warmth into

the room. I get up from the hearth and move to close the curtains. Outside, the garden is enveloped in thick darkness. Not for the first time, I realise just how isolated the cottage is. Perhaps Alex is right. I should look for somewhere a little more modern, and nearer town. No limit has been placed on the time I'm going to be working for him. When I started, the presumption had been a few months of office chores while I waited for my reinstatement to White Platts. Now, the future seems as elusive as the glittery surface of the beck; what the hand tries to grasp, flits away, cold and artless.

We sit in silence for a moment, watching the flames. Then Alex decides he'd better be getting home. When I stand at the front door and watch him go, an immense wave of something like sadness washes over me, and I wonder, not for the first time, what the hell I am doing.

The following morning, huddled up in two sweaters and my parka with my work clothes underneath, I wait for the bus at the stop near the main road. The air is raw, and an orange sun hangs low, tinging the clouds of my breath with a smattering of apricot. There's still no sign of Jay. And, as Alex pointed out as he was leaving last night, I have no way of contacting him. Despite my layers of clothing, I shiver, and stamp my feet lightly to try and hold back the creep of numbness in my toes, and in my heart.

When the bus arrives, I jump on and pass my fare over to the driver. He chats cheerfully about the chilly air and about another Christmas being well and truly over. I smile my agreement then find a seat at the back, where I can watch the landscape and townscape blend and get some headspace before the start of another day with Alex and Paul. Not that I don't appreciate the job they've given me. It has meant my savings, such as they are, remain almost as solid as the day I left White Platts. Though my wages from the camp have continued to make their way into my bank account, suddenly having to pay rent and bills, and to feed myself, is costing far more than I ever imagined in those halcyon days of living *all-found*.

I get off the bus right next to the Victorian monstrosity that serves the town as a registry office. The windows in its red-brick and terracotta façade reflect back broken bits of sunlight. Huge oak entrance doors at the top of its portico are open to the morning. And at the top of them, peering at his phone, stands Alex.

'Hello,' I call as I step away from the bus stop. Shock flashes across his face.

'Evie.' He is clean-shaven and muffled up in a thick overcoat. 'I was. Erm. I was just–'

'Not getting married, are you?' I nod at the sign declaring this building's express purpose. Then realise that I've said the one thing that is unlikely to be a joke. His face takes on a hot pink tinge.

'Rumbled.' A nervous laugh that answers the question for me.

I step towards him and sling my arms around his shoulders. 'You can always make me smile,' I say. 'But where's Paul? Shouldn't he be here?'

He gives me a squeeze, then moves his face back to look at me. 'Paul told me to surprise him, so that's what I'm doing. We've discussed marriage. So many times.' He stretches that sentence. 'I thought I'd just fix up a wedding then spring it on him. If you can even do that.'

'Can you?'

'That's what I'm here to find out. I can get access to all his documents, but I want to be sure of the final legalities.'

I'm surprised by this. Alex is pin sharp where the law is concerned. His obsession has spanned the decades that we've known each other. Even when we were children, he had an elevated sense of what was right. I particularly remember his sense of outrage if I ever suggested teen boundaries were there to be pushed at, or that areas of the town considered *no-go* might be quite fun. He even complained that I was letting the side down by wearing socks with holes in at one of his pyjama parties.

'What? You don't know?' I grimace. 'How can that be?'

He slaps my arm. 'Cheeky. Do you want to come in with me?'

'Won't Paul wonder where we've got to? It's gone nine?'

'I'm not daft,' he says, with a tap of his nose. 'He's out with clients all morning. I said I'd open up on my own today, and we knew you'd be in, anyway.'

I slide my arm through his. 'Come on, then. Let's go and get your marriage licence.'

Inside the building it is warm with the smell of lemon furniture polish and dusty radiators. The reception area is dominated by a beautifully crafted oak countertop with etched glass panelling. I stare upwards at the cathedral-like cream walls, bordered with green crackle-glaze tiles. The effect is stunning.

'No wonder people want to get married here. It's beautiful,' I whisper to Alex. He is busy patting down his coat, pulling out folded poly-pockets with papers stuffed inside.

A clatter of heels, then a young woman appears, smart in navy blue with a lacy blouse. She smiles a hello. 'Can I help?' she asks.

Alex mutters something about booking a wedding and she cuts him off mid-sentence. 'I'll take you and your fiancée through to the office,' she tells him, then beams a shiny red smile at me.

'It's not me. I mean, I'm not anyone's fiancée.' I hold up

my hands and shake them a little, but she doesn't look convinced.

'She's just a friend,' Alex says, with a flick of his thumb. 'I'm wanting to surprise my... boyfriend with the wedding date. If you get what I'm saying?'

'It's a confidential service.' The young woman isn't happy. 'Your friend will have to wait here.'

'No worries,' I reply. Then to Alex, 'I'll go to your office. If you trust me to open up?'

He rummages around on the countertop for a pen and writes the alarm codes on a till receipt he finds in his pocket. Then pushes a bunch of keys into my hand.

'It's the one with the red sticky dot on,' he tells me. 'Just text if you get into a tizz with anything.'

A tilt of my head and I step away. 'Good luck.' I wink and then walk out of the front door again.

'Thanks, darling,' he calls after me.

As I make my way back across the main road and through the town centre, I think about my place in the pattern of things. While I quite like the feel of mixing in with the bustle of office workers and retailers, with their coffee cups and text-neck, could I see myself becoming part of that set in a more permanent way? I'm not sure. But can I see myself as I was, manipulating the physical environment, day after day, so that others might enjoy it as much as I do? Would I still want to be doing that for the next twenty years? I shrug to myself.

Then there's Jay. The mornings we'd walked together into the thick of it, then I'd gone home to the cottage and to him, they felt like the best of times. Does any of the other stuff even matter? It doesn't, now I'm thinking about it. Only he does. So, I'm going to tell him the full story about White Platts, when I see him next. And I'm going to make sure I do everything to clear my name.

Three school-aged boys, all black skinny-trousers and

shoulders tensed against the chill of the morning, step around me as I approach the office. They guffaw and nudge each other, while their hands remain stuck in their pockets.

'No school today?' I ask, before I can stop myself, 'only, it's gone half past nine.'

To my complete surprise, one of them replies. And quite politely. 'Soz, miss,' he stammers, 'we've got a free period. We're on our way now, though.'

'Get on, then,' I tell him, laughing to myself. But then, as I put the key in the lock of the Swarbrick and Murray office, an idea starts to crystalize in my mind.

'Evie.'

Someone has come to stand behind me. I smell who it is before I even turn around. Chanel. Overdone and sickly sweet.

'Hello, Rosina,' I say. 'Haven't seen you for a while.' I push at the door. 'Let me just deactivate the alarm,' I tell her as I dive inside. She waits at the open entrance.

Once I've punched in the code, the high-pitched wailing stops and we're left in a kind of awkward silence, where I'm not sure what she wants, and she's looking very confused about something.

'You okay?' I ask, trying not to feel drab next to her peacock-blue velvet coat and Egyptian eye make-up.

'I am.' She smiles. 'You're looking quite the *efficient secretary.* You're a fast learner. I've always said it.'

I'm not quite sure what she's implying, and the telephone is ringing so I don't have time to think too much.

'Excuse me a mo,' I mouth, then am conscious of her stepping into the office and closing the door behind us both.

Once I've explained what I can to the person on the end of the phone, I start to undo my coat and turn back to Rosina again.

'Sorry about that,' I say. 'Were you just passing? Have you

got time for a coffee? I've been meaning to come and see you, but–'

Her snappy tone cuts me off. 'I came to see Alex Swarbrick, actually. I'd love a coffee, though. If you don't mind.'

I notice she is carrying a leather portfolio, which she lays on my desk. Her fingernails are exactly the same shade of blue as her coat, incredibly smooth and shiny. She pops open the case and slides out a large brown envelope, sealed and tied.

'I have to tell you this, Evie. Someone has made an offer for Tunnel Cottage. I want Swarbrick and Murray to handle the legalities, if they can. It's all a bit murky.'

While I swallow down the sudden lump that has appeared in my throat, I switch on my computer and fill up the coffee machine. Rosina is wittering on about death while intestate and lack of heirs. She drapes her coat over one of the armchairs, then wafts the envelope at me. Its smell fills the reception area, and suddenly I can taste dust and cigars. When she asks to leave it for Alex, I take it from her hands and push my way through into the back office. Without the radiator on, the room is damply cold, and I shiver. Perhaps I should just dump the envelope in the bin and pretend I've never seen it. Leaving Tunnel Cottage isn't something I want to contemplate.

'Is there a loo?' Rosina is calling. I direct her to the door at the bottom of the stairs and tell her to be careful, as the rooms above are nowhere near as swish as those down here. She laughs faintly at this and makes a comment about her own premises and the rateable value of properties in general. But I'm finding it hard to communicate, because in my mind is a picture of me packing up my belongings and driving away from the cottage. And from Jay.

I know Rosina has found the *ladies*, by the gurgle of water in the antiquated pipe system. Then she comes down the stairs in a flurry of floral dress and net petticoats. How she keeps up her appearance, I'll never understand. The office is warming up a little now, and the coffee machine is sending out small puffs of fragrant steam.

'You're a dark horse,' she says suddenly, making me stop what I am doing and look up in surprise. Not having a clue what she's talking about, I can only smile, though the force of pressing my teeth together is quite painful.

'I've seen you with a guy,' she adds, with a wink.

A flush of heat starts at the base of my neck and travels across my face. She must be able to see it, because she giggles as she sits down. 'Don't deny it.'

'I won't,' I tell her. Small town, less space to hide.

'And he was bloody good-looking.'

I give her a shrug, then busy myself with the coffee.

'Do you take milk?' I ask, keeping my expression neutral.

'I do. But don't you change the subject, Miss Evie Cooper. And I've seen the guy before somewhere. Who is he?'

What is she talking about? That someone else knows Jay hasn't even occurred to me. From what he's told me, his life has been lived inside a tiny bubble for the last twenty years. And some of that not even in the town.

'Well, he's an artist, if that's any help. Maybe you know him in that context?' Though I doubt it.

I pass her a cup of coffee and she takes an exaggerated sip.

'I needed that,' she says with a sigh. 'And I didn't say I *know* your guy. But I've seen him, might have even talked to him. Now. Let me think.'

The way she draws out those words; it reminds me of my mother. She stretches her legs out and makes a drama out of the moment. I don't remember her being this *disruptive*. Or perhaps I have changed. Then the telephone starts ringing and there is the opportunity to excuse myself.

'I'll have to get this,' I say, and she gives me a silent

thumbs-up. I add that it might be confidential, and she finally gets the message.

While I'm being polite to the person on the other end of the phone, she swigs down her coffee and slides on the vivid coat, then makes a pantomime out of buttoning it. I wave my hand and use my eyebrows to say goodbye, but then she picks up a pen from my desk-tidy and scrawls on my memo pad.

I swing away from her, but she taps my shoulder and points to the pad.

'Toodle-oo,' she croons in what I gather must be her quiet voice.

I glance at her note. Then I read it again, properly.

I know where I've seen your guy, now. He was in the garden of Tunnel Cottage when I first prepared the brochure. He was really helpful x

Chapter Twenty-Four

'Cheers.'

Alex lifts his glass, and the rest of us join him.

'To the happy couple,' says his mother; the polar opposite of mine. Sheila Swarbrick is wearing fashionably large spectacles, and her smile is genuine, unlike my mother's. She has never been known for her warmth. Now, her glass is raised in a congratulatory way, but her lips are tight. I can tell she's blow-dried her hair to within an inch of its life.

'Shame your new *boyfriend* couldn't be here,' she mutters at me. 'Taken the hint and left, has he?'

'What hint are you talking about, Mother? Jay's not a boy anyway,' I say, 'and we're not joined at the hip.'

But Paul is interrupting. 'Unlike Al and I,' he says with a laugh, then takes a gulp of his champagne. 'He's even started following me into the loo.'

'Too much information.' A grimace from Alex. 'Why don't we get a bottle? It's a long time since I've had a fizz-hangover.'

'Go for it,' his mother says. 'Let me pay, though.'

They slide out of the small booth where we are all huddled. A town-centre bar on a Friday night was always going to be chock-full. This one has an industrial vibe, with slabs of bubbly glass and large globes of light hanging from bare wires. Young adults, aglow with enthusiasm, stand shoulder-to-shoulder with office workers and glammed-up people making a night of it.

I wonder what Jay would think of the place. Or if he'd even have stayed long enough to form an opinion. Not that I've seen him. A week has passed and there has been no contact. I'm starting to wonder if that's the end of things between us. Which makes no sense, and it's gnawing away at me that something is wrong. The more I think about him, the less I understand. But I'm missing him like crazy.

'Where will you be having this wedding?' my mother is saying to Paul. 'Not in a church, surely?'

I want to slap her, but Paul doesn't seem to mind. He has been so full of this wedding since Alex sprung the date on him, I doubt he's got room for bigoted opinions.

'I want the registry office,' he tells her. 'Then a walk through the town centre to The Duke. That's where I first met Al.'

Her look is blistering, but it's not enough to stop him.

'Early April.' He fans out his hands. 'All the daffodils will be out. Sparkling spring sunshine. It'll be glorious. We've thought about asking everyone to wear yellow.'

I can't help but laugh at my mother's expression, in fact I can almost hear the cogs of her brain scanning through the outfits that hang in her wardrobe.

'Yellow?' A twist of her lips. 'That'll be nice.'

By the time Alex and Sheila come back, I have listened, once again, to the way the wedding day will pan out. Made even more enjoyable by my mother's feigned interest. It must be killing her. She would dearly love to see me married, preferably to Alex, but I guess any guy would do. Not Jay, though. Her dislike of him has been clear from the start.

'The girl behind the bar hadn't ever seen a fifty-pound

note,' says Alex, laughing. 'That's Barrow for you.' He slides in beside Paul and gives him a light kiss, lips and everything. My mother looks away.

By nine o'clock, even though I've hardly drunk any of the champagne, I'm ready for going back to Tunnel Cottage and climbing into bed. It's been a busy week as far as my office job goes. A backlog of clients and enquiries, on hold because of the Christmas break, have been dealt with. As has my own case. I've decided to meet with the Turnbulls for what they're calling mediation. Alex is going to accompany me, and as the meeting is in less than a month's time, we've got our script to sort out... or that's what Alex calls his narration through the whole process. I've only to say what he tells me to say. And that's fine by me, because I'm determined to clear my name completely, and leave that family looking foolish and grasping. Then, I've decided I'm going to tell Malcom Fairley what he can do with his job.

I squeeze out of my seat and lift the crumpled pile that is my coat. 'I'm going to make a dash for the bus now, guys,' I say, slipping the coat onto my shoulders. 'You know what a lightweight I am when it comes to alcohol.'

'Get a taxi with me,' says my mother, but I don't think I can face being on my own with her. There will be the inevitable quiz, featuring questions that I can't answer and penalty points for anything that's wrong. Difficult, when you're not sure what your specialist subject is supposed to be.

'No. You stay and finish those bottles,' I tell her. Then I make a quick exit before she can argue. 'See you soon.' I blow a kiss to no one in particular, then step out into the bite of a January evening.

A bus arrives as soon as I get to the stop. It is almost empty, so I sit near the front and listen to the driver telling me about the lack of road-gritting and streetlights out at the edge of town. When we finally arrive exactly at the place he's been moaning about, a quick glance tells me that there seems to be plenty of streetlighting. Because I can see someone sitting on the bench, just to the side of the bus stop. It's Jay.

I climb down the steps and check the road, before crossing towards him.

He stands up. My stomach flips.

'Evie,' he says. 'When you weren't at the cottage, I could only think of waiting for you here.'

'I've been at the cottage every night for the past week.' A snap of words that I don't mean, fuelled by a shot of adrenaline.

He lowers his head, then reaches for my hand. 'I'm sorry.'

'I was worried,' I say. 'I've got no way of getting in touch with you.'

No response.

'Jay? I don't even know where you live.'

'I'm not sure what you want me to say. I'm here now. Isn't that enough?'

I press my lips together and take a deep inhale of the sharp night air. So, I'm expected to say nothing about the last time he stormed off, or about his lack of contact. Without even stopping to think about the reasons he might have, I fly at him again. 'Enough? If you're having to ration your company, give my slice to someone else, will you? I'd hate to think you were spreading yourself too thinly.'

I'm not sure why, but I start to walk away, when all I really want to do is put my arms around him and check for wounds. Which means I'm very surprised when he snatches at my hand and starts to drag me in the opposite direction from the cottage.

'You want to see where I live. I'll show you.' There is an edge to his voice that I haven't ever heard, a coldness, and his eyes are hard. I try to pull away, but his grip is tight, and I don't want to fight him. We cross the road, then make our way towards the housing estate where my mother has her bungalow.

I am breathing heavily, and have to run to keep up with Jay's long angry strides.

'You don't live here, do you?' I ask. 'You've been this close all along?'

'No.'

It's all he says. Although he has tightened his grip on my hand, I could free myself if I wanted to. With words. But part of me is intrigued. Why is there this drama around the place where he lives? I'd been under the impression that we were in a relationship, and one we both wanted. So why hide anything? After all, I've decided to tell him all about Ian Turnbull, haven't I?

We make it to the far side of the estate, where there is a parade of shops, opposite which is a terrace of scruffy houses, probably Victorian, with one-up, one-down windows and just a front doorstep separating them from the pavement. A couple of them have been whitewashed, but the one at the end of the row is in a particularly bad way, with hunks of its concrete façade missing completely, so that the underlayer of crumbling brick shows through.

We stop outside this house, and Jay lets go of my hand. He fishes in his pocket and pulls out a large key attached to a wooden fob. 'This is me, Evie.' He spreads his hand wide on his chest. I keep my face impassive. 'What? Nothing to say?'

I peer at the front door. It is made from dark panels of wood, with a pane of bubble glass in the middle and a brass handle that looks out of place.

'It gets better,' he growls, then slots in the key. 'After you.'

Inside, there is a tiny vestibule and an open arch into another room. Jay flicks on the lights and I gasp.

'Welcome to my home,' he sneers. 'I hope you like what you see.'

The first thing I notice is a large table, covered with art paraphernalia: paintings, sketches, tempera palletes, brushes, cloths. Everything melded together, nothing cared for. There is an easel in one corner of the room, and a filthy armchair in another. A low table sits just in front of an empty fireplace, and everything is covered with a layer of greasy dust. Some old-fashioned venetian blinds hang at the small window. They don't look like they've ever been opened.

'Batchelor pad?' I grit my teeth.

'Hardly,' he replies.

'What I don't understand,' I tell him, 'is why you've been hiding this place from me? It's your home.' My eyes scan the room. 'Needs a bit of attention; you think I care about that?'

He runs a hand across his face, then steps towards me. I slide my arms around his waist and feel him relax into me.

'I'm embarrassed.' His words are a whisper. 'You're so organised and smart. The way you've sorted out Tunnel Cottage, got yourself a job. With friends. I don't have any of those things. I'm just treading water, trying to keep myself mentally well enough to function, and earn a little money to stay solvent. Why would you want anything to do with me?'

'Because I love you,' I say.

Jay

Love?

Jay thinks he's misheard. He can feel Evie shifting against him as she speaks, can't quite believe what she's telling him. And he's ashamed of his behaviour to the point that he almost tells her everything. Then she's stepping away from him, looking into his face, so he slides his hands down the sides of her soft cheeks and says he feels the same. Then they are kissing, and he can't find any more words.

When she steps away again, she looks at him, and asks if he is feeling okay. A shake of his head makes her lead him to the armchair and tug on his hands until he sits. Then he has to suffer the humiliation of her digging around in what he calls his kitchen, to make him a cup of tea. That the kettle is grimy, and the cabinets are full of nothing, is bad enough, never mind that his mugs are chipped and stained, and he hasn't washed up for weeks. But she somehow manages to bring him tea.

This woman is not fazed by anything. He has learnt; under her soft beauty is a core of absolute steel, magnetic and completely alluring. And he's not going to be able to free himself.

Just days ago, he'd had a taste of what his life might become if he couldn't see her. Escaping had felt like the only option. Why he's let himself become involved is something he can't understand. For almost twenty years, since he'd lost his mother and then his aunt, he's lived in the shadows. Tunnel Cottage and its landscape have been the only sustenance he needed. Now, a light has been aimed at those shadows and he sees them for what they are, the hiding place of a coward.

So, he has a plan: he will let Evie lead him out of the shadows and he will bring with him some of the pain that lurks there. But not all. That would be too risky. And with his artist's eye for detail, he paints a picture for her, of his life in Tunnel Cottage.

Chapter Twenty-Five

'So, it's not a coincidence that you were in the garden that day?'

I am sitting on Jay's only chair, while he kneels at my feet. He shakes his head, his mouth a line of grim embarrassment. I want to hold him, to ask about his family, but there is a distance between us, one that I can't quite understand.

'Tunnel Cottage feels safe to me, that's all,' he says. 'I'm so sorry, Evie. I wish I'd told you from the start that I'd lived there.'

'Why didn't you? It would have been easy enough to just say it.' There is an edge creeping into my voice. I can hear it, but I'm not sure where it's coming from. This isn't the first time I've been lied to, after all. But from Jay, a lie feels like the worst kind of torture.

'If you want the real truth, I hoped you wouldn't stay long. Having people living in the cottage stops me from getting close to it. I've even pulled down the *To Let* sign once or twice. Said to the estate agent that it was vandals.'

'That's so messed up,' I tell him. And when he rocks back on his heels and drops his gaze, I add, 'I don't mean it as a dig.'

I take his hand. 'But you need help, should have had help long ago.'

'Help from who?' His words have a bitter undercurrent, and I can see he is hurting. 'Who, Evie? Tell me who you think would have helped. I doubt you've ever known what it's like to be this lonely. The cottage is the only stability I have.'

That's when it comes at me, head-on, like I'm in the path of a speeding train. I've been singled out for his attention *because* of the cottage.

'What exactly is going on here, Jay?' I cover my eyes with my hands. Seeing him upset is killing me. Then I remember those early days in the cottage, when I had the distinct feeling that someone had been inside. 'There's more, isn't there?'

He gets up and walks away from me. Watching his slim outline and hunched shoulders causes a visceral feeling, like a punch to my guts.

'Jay?'

'I have a key. To the French windows,' he says as he turns to face me. 'I was going to – I don't know – set things up to scare you. Pathetic, isn't it?'

'Did you actually let yourself in without me knowing?'

'I did.'

'God, Jay,' I whisper. 'What the fuck?'

His head snaps back and he can't meet my eye. 'I know. And I'm sorry. I couldn't do much, in the end. Because it was you. But I have done things to other tenants: smashed crockery, left taps running. That kind of thing.' Now he's looking at me again. Waiting.

I'm on high alert. This guy has a serious problem, but I can only feel sympathy. Every instinct I have is telling me to get myself out of this situation. My heart is overriding them all. When I look at Jay now, he's wearing his vulnerability the way he wears his clothes: without apology for the ragged edges. It makes me want to slide my arms around his waist and take him in. I wonder if I'm strong enough to deal with these emotions, but I don't wonder for long. Suddenly, he moves to the front door and yanks it open. The handle smashes against the alcove wall.

'Feel free to leave,' he spits. 'So much for love.' But when he says that last word, it comes out as a crumble of sadness, and he covers his face with his hands and sobs.

I go to him. What else can I do? Because whatever has happened between us, whatever his motives, I'm not wrong about my feelings, and I completely trust his. I reach up and take hold of his wrists.

'Look at me, Jay,' I whisper, then try to pull his hands away. 'Look at me.'

And when he does, I can see the truth shining from him. It's all I need.

'I'm going nowhere,' I tell him. 'Not without you, anyway. Let's go back to the cottage. You'll feel better there. And I have some things to get off my chest, too.'

He doesn't argue, and we are soon stepping back out into the January evening. The air has a smoky taste, cold and bitter. I slip my arm through Jay's as we walk. And I tell him about Ian Turnbull and Malcom Fairley, and my suspension, the civil court case and my intention to quit. There is no interruption, no judgement; speaking it without these things clarifies my thinking completely. No matter what the cost, I am going to have the last word with Ian and Malcom, and I'm going to be the person that helps Jay get his life back.

We are just approaching the ruin as I finish. It stands silent and watchful, illuminated only by the weak yellow light from one streetlamp.

Jay stops in front of the railings and slips an arm around my shoulder. 'You know,' he sighs, 'this place has seen more than 800 years of human comings and goings. Ours are just a tiny snapshot, aren't they? Standing here, mulling that over, has helped me through so many–' There's a crackle in his voice, and his throat constricts.

'Let's go home,' I tell him, and he smiles just a little.

'Let's,' comes the reply.

———

We spend the rest of the weekend together in the landscape. We walk by the beck and across the low fells, enjoying the drift of light rain on our faces. There's an optimism in the way wild daffodils' stems push through the mush of last year's decay; a joy at the end of the day when a few minutes' more daylight allows us to sit outside after tea. And while we cook in the cottage's small kitchen, Jay stands over me, tasting everything and talking with his mouth full.

He tells me about how much he wants to make a new start with his life, and I tell him about how I lived mine at White Platts; about adult tantrums that were harder to deal with than anything the kids could pull together, and about that day in the canoe with Ian and Danni.

'Things happen that no one sees,' Jay says to me. We are sitting on an old garden bench, watching two male blackbirds vying for territory. 'That doesn't make the truth any less vivid.'

'What bothered me the most, when I heard about Ian Turnbull's accusation, was how many people were ready to believe it had some degree of validity.'

Jay leans forward and runs his hands over the muddy knees of his jeans. 'Even the people who should have known better,' he says.

It's not a question. He doesn't have a very high opinion of the human race, doesn't Jay. Which is perhaps why he has lived a large part of his life in a reclusive way.

'Even them,' I agree. I want to ask him more questions, about his mother's death and his father's rejection, but there is an almost physical reaction when I get anywhere near to it. So, we stay rooted to the ground we have in common and dig deep only there. And I still haven't told him that Tunnel Cottage is to be sold.

While we are talking, a car pulls up at the top of the drive. Unusual, considering it's Sunday teatime, and cold enough for the sky to be taking on that metallic blue sheen before it drops to black. Then my mother appears in the garden.

'There you are.' There's a wail in her voice. 'I've been telephoning for the last hour. Don't you keep your mobile on you?' She nods at the pocket of my coat. Then lets her eyes flick over to Jay.

'Mine's inside,' I tell her. 'And Jay doesn't have one.'

He stands up and smiles a hello. Something fizzes between them.

'I thought I'd pop down,' she says. 'See if you've planned any more about outfits for the wedding. Sheila and I are going to have a Manchester trip. I wondered if you wanted to come.' She puts her index finger on her chin. 'Yellow. I ask you.'

'I won't, if you don't mind.'

She frowns, more at Jay than me. 'What will you do, then?'

'About what?'

'Wedding outfits. Our town centre's a no-no.'

Jay is standing rigid, hands deep in his jacket pockets. She still hasn't acknowledged him.

'You could have phoned me, Mother,' I say. 'Why are you really here?'

'Do I need a reason to drop round?' Another dart towards Jay. 'Now?'

Then I realise what is going on. She's keyed into the fact that Jay wasn't with me during our Friday night drinks, and has read something in my tone. That was her speciality. Adding up the clues and making them fit her answer. She could pass for a television detective.

'You don't need a reason, of course you don't. And Jay's living here with me now. That'll be more company for you, won't it?'

I keep my voice light, focussing on the change in her face. It starts with her lips, which set themselves straight with a dimple in each cheek. Then her eyes close while she rolls them, so that when they open again, the whites flash for a moment. Jay shuffles beside me.

'Do I get a cup of tea, or what?' she says finally.

'I'll put the kettle on.' Jay. Helpful as ever. He walks towards the kitchen door and lets himself in. His ponytail reaches almost to his waist.

'I hope he's paying some of the rent,' my mother hisses once he's out of earshot. 'And look at that hair.'

I stretch my eyes and start to walk away.

'Like he's homeless,' she says. 'He's on to a good thing with you.'

That's when I flip.

'What is wrong with you?' I screech. 'Jay is the loveliest guy I know. The fact that you've decided to take against him says an awful lot.' My hand flies to my throat. 'Go home, Mother. It's the only way we can stay on speaking terms.'

Jay

There's a layer of corruption beneath the soft shiny exterior of Evie's mother; Jay wants to dig it out and show it to the world. And all she can focus on is the look of things. He's been judged and found wanting just because he doesn't *look* like her idea of a partner for her daughter. How little the woman knows.

Jay's own mother had loved him unconditionally until the

day she'd died. The burden of *blame* had come squarely from his father. But after Jamie's death, she was never the same.

His favourite memory fixes her in the kitchen of Tunnel Cottage, back towards him and arms thrust deep into a large white sink. A table and two long benches have been set up in the middle of the room. Plates and cutlery lay neatly, side by side, with plastic beakers set in a line in the middle of everything. Another door stands open, letting in slants of sunlight and a view of the garden. He and his brother are sitting, heads together, waiting, as they always were, to be fed.

When he'd come home from school one afternoon, to find her gone, her place on the sofa empty of blankets and cushions and her medicine, there had been a moment of panic. Though he was used to fending for himself, she'd always been there.

You've drove her fucking mental, his father had said when Jay wanted to know where she'd gone. They'd been standing at the mouth of the tunnel. There was rain, he remembers: so heavy it came down in white sheets, making his duffle coat sopping wet. He'd watched the pickaxe swing in his father's hands and the water running off his oilskin mac. And he'd hated him more than he'd ever hated anyone in his life.

Later, Liz had explained how his mother hadn't been well enough to be left on her own, and how a special *home* had been found for her, where she would be safe. That she was in someone's home had been a comfort to the thirteen-year-old Jay, until the day he'd been taken to visit.

The trees on the driveway had been a flare of red and gold and Jay remembers collecting smooth brown conkers as he walked along with his aunt. They'd felt like treasure in his pocket, and he could hardly wait to get home and look at them properly. Though he was living at her place, by then.

The building itself did look like a house, with its huge bay windows and slabs of neatly cut stone, but the inside had a funny smell; nothing like a place where people lived. Jay remembers the smell as a mix of rotten vegetables and the stuff his mother used to tip down the drains at the back of the cottage, *to get rid of germs*, she'd said.

And when he'd seen Mam, sitting in an armchair and wearing clothes she'd never have chosen herself, he didn't recognise her. Liz had taken his hand as he'd backed away, and talked to him like he was a little boy again. But there was nothing to his mother's expression; she wasn't there. It felt like trying to make contact with yourself in a mirror; same face, but it's not you.

Living at the cottage with Evie feels like a dream, one that had been building itself on the edges of his consciousness for many years. She was never in it, of course, but happiness was, and she's filled that gap. Thinking beyond each day is something he tries not to do. Life will catch up with them, eventually, but as each day passes, he feels more and more able to face up to what that might mean and what he's going to do about it. Now, though, she's storming into the kitchen and growling about her mother again, and he can only take her into his arms and let her rant.

Chapter Twenty-Six

I am sitting at my desk, with coffee and a head full of thoughts, when the letter arrives. The postman pushes open the front door of Swarbrick and Murray, breath steaming and cheeks aglow. There is a moment of conversation, mainly about the leaflet delivery that blights his life. He flips our bundle of post onto the countertop and steps back out into the sunshine, then uses his long-legged stride to cross the high street and makes his way into another office.

I wonder what Jay will be doing today. Thinking about him wandering the fellside, drinking in the simplicity of an early spring morning, brings a smile to my lips. It's his therapy as much as his art.

In the back office, Alex and Paul are heads down and scanning documents. Their concentration is a palpable thing, and I don't want to intrude. When I lay the packet of letters on their desk and try to creep away, Paul takes his attention away from his work for a moment and looks up at me.

'Everything okay?' he asks, then leans back in his chair and gives a small yawn. I catch the faintest scent of his aftershave. Something different today; green and tangy.

Alex turns towards the post and pushes his glasses to the top of his head. 'Let's have a break, shall we?' he says. 'My legs have turned to stone.'

He pulls the letters towards him and rolls the elastic band away, so that the pile slips across his keyboard, and a couple drop to the floor. While I pick them up, he starts to sift through the others.

'Can I get you a drink,' I say, 'as you're having a break.'

'You're an angel,' comes the reply. 'I'll be through in a mo.'

'Paul? Do you want anything?' I wait.

'Coffee for me,' he says, 'and thanks.'

While I'm loading up the coffee machine in reception, Alex opens the door of his office and calls to me. 'You've got mail, my darling. It's from your camp.'

He's waving a handful of white envelopes at me. My stomach gives a small lurch. Has one of my old colleagues written to me privately? Rob, perhaps? But when I take the letters from his hand, I notice they've been forwarded: each has my name, but my camp address scored through and replaced by the Swarbrick and Murray one.

'Well?' Alex gives me a lopsided grin. 'Open them, at least.' He tucks his white shirt into the back of his trousers, then walks towards the armchairs. He sits down, stretches out his legs and waits. When I've torn open one of the envelopes, I pull out its contents and begin to scan. It's a letter, printed in a large font and signed by a Daniella Woodburn, with a heart over the *i*, instead of a dot. And what she says makes me shudder. Alex notices.

'What?' He sits forward.

'There was a girl in the same group as Ian Turnbull,' I say to him. 'Danni. Not that I can remember her surname. But *Daniella Woodburn* is likely to be her, isn't it? Have a look.'

I flatten out the letter and pass it over to him, then watch as he stretches his eyes.

It's the date of this letter I can't quite fathom. November thirtieth, last year. Only a couple of weeks after I'd left the camp. One phrase has jumped out at me, something that Ian Turnbull had said on the coach trip home, apparently.

He said he wanted to get you done.

'God, Evie. The little shit.' He covers his mouth with his fingertips. 'Pardon me, but–'

'I could have done with this letter a couple of months ago,' I snap. 'Sorry. That wasn't a dig at you. White Platts just haven't bothered to forward my mail, have they?'

'Does this Danni say whether anyone else heard him?' Alex gets up and passes the letter back to me.

'No,' I tell him, 'and from what I remember, there was a lot of friction between the two of them. He was quite nasty.'

'So, she could be making it up?'

I shrug. 'Possibly. But why go to all that trouble? I could do with talking to her. They came from Apollonius School in Stratford-upon-Avon, that group. I'm sure I could track her down.'

'Don't do that.' Alex shakes his head. 'We can use what she's said in our script for the mitigation meeting, depending on how things are going. But chasing after the kid would look desperate, wouldn't it? And you need to be squeaky-clean and at the highest point on the moral high-ground.'

Paul comes into the reception area and walks towards the stairwell. Alex gives him a quick explanation of the letter situation, running his hand through his stubbly beard and squinting thoughtfully.

'Can I make a suggestion?' he says at last.

'Again?' says Alex with a giggle, and I almost spit out my mouthful of coffee.

'Behave.' Alex laughs. Then, 'Sorry, darling. Of course you can.'

'Well,' Paul begins, 'I guess she's a juvenile, so couldn't be summoned directly anyway. But a reply from Swarbrick and Murray, thanking her for her concern, letting slip that everything will hopefully be sorted for Miss Cooper fairly soon, date and venue included... She might just take it upon herself to be there.'

Alex lifts his brows. 'We could do that, but I don't think we should. The very fact that the Turnbulls want this preliminary meeting tells me something is a bit shaky.' A tilt of his head. 'Do it, if you like. Just a thank you, though. The kid will probably enjoy getting a letter from a solicitor.' He turns to me. 'Don't you get involved. Paul and I will copy and file this one. Even buy the stamp.'

At lunchtime, I decide to take a walk in the local park. It is laid out on a gentle slope between the town centre and a large comprehensive school, recently built in the eco-cladding-and-glass style on the site where brick-built grammar schools once dominated the landscape, and the thinking. Neither of these was my school.

I wander between twiggy borders and neatly clipped box hedges, enjoying the feel of winter sun on my face and my heart's race. Sitting in an office is never going to suit me, and the best of times at the moment are when Jay and I march across the landscape and climb any slopes that have a view.

A shout interrupts my daydreaming; a female voice, then something lower, rough.

A woman in a navy-blue coat, with a lanyard around her neck, waves her arms at a group of large children in grey blazers and black trousers. She's quite young, more of a girl really. Her face is pale, her hair flat and blonde.

'And don't be telling me you're year elevens,' she is saying. 'Especially not you, Patrick Semple.' A finger-point at the tallest boy, who towers over her.

I'm about to walk right into them, and without performing a half-turn, I can't see what else I can do. I dip my head but can't resist flashing her a smile as I pass.

'This is what they call dinner duty,' she says weakly. 'Their dinner and my duty.'

'Can't get the staff,' I reply.

'Tell me about it.' She nods towards the group. 'Hurry up.' The snap of her voice scares me, and it's enough to get them moving. 'Sorry.' A stretch of her lips.

I could do that, I think.

And I'm still thinking about it when I get back to the office and find Alex and Paul sprawled across the armchairs in reception, picking at packeted sandwiches and flipping through a scrapbook of what look like wedding invitations.

'Nice lunch?' Alex asks, without looking up.

'Yes, thanks,' I say. 'What's on for this afternoon?'

Paul pats the space beside him. 'We have something to ask you, Evie.'

'Oh?'

'Two things, actually.'

Alex butts in. 'Are you still seeing that Jay fella?'

Paul flashes him a look. They've had a conversation about this, I can tell.

'I am.' I fold my arms. 'Why?'

'We're just wondering if we should invite him to our wedding, that's all.'

'It's up to you.' I'm being played.

'We don't want to force you to bring him.' A pause, while Alex finishes his mouthful. 'If it's fizzling out.'

'Fizzling out?'

'You know.' His face remains impassive. 'The relationship coming to an end.'

'Well, you'll be pleased to know, it's not.' I let out a small sigh. 'In fact, Jay's pretty much moved into Tunnel Cottage with me.'

'Moved in?' Alex runs his hands over his thighs, then across his lips. But there are still a few crumbs stuck to the place where they join his cheek. 'You don't even know where he lives, and he's moved in?'

Paul groans. His chest sinks inwards. 'Al. Stop.'

'Yeah, Al. Stop,' I repeat, but not without a little humour. 'And what was the other thing?'

'Will you be one of our witnesses?' Alex is smiling.

'Please?' asks Paul. 'My sis is going to be the other one. We wanted two women. Perfect symmetry, I feel.'

Then we are hugging and kissing, and I'm saying that I'd be happy to do what they've asked.

When I pull away, I can't resist saying, 'And I do know where Jay lives, for your information.' Then I get up and move towards the cloakroom. There's work to be done, after all.

Later, when I mention the wedding to Jay, he finds many different reasons why he shouldn't be a guest. He has no formal clothing; no money to buy it, or indeed a wedding gift; he's not good with people; he hardly knows Alex and Paul, so why would they want him there; the excuses go on and on. We are sitting together on the sofa, listening to the news and the heavy lash of rain that started just as I was returning home for the evening. The lounge is full of the smell of unseasoned wood, and the fire snaps and crackles, sending out spits of wet bark that stop glowing the moment they hit the hearth. I don't want an argument.

'No worries,' I say, and enjoy the way his shoulders relax and his smile loosens. 'Alex and Paul will understand. But you wouldn't have to be outgoing and sociable. You could just fade into the background. Some of their friends will more than make up for it.'

'I'm not sure, Evie.' He stretches his legs, then leans over to take my hand. 'Can I think about it?'

'Course you can.' I move nearer. 'And one of your watercolours would make a perfect gift, whether you come to the wedding or not. You could do something especially for them, couldn't you? There's about six weeks to go. Is that enough time?'

This idea he likes.

If there's one thing I've learnt about him, it's that he finds safety within his art. When he's hunched over a sketch or examining something he's found in the landscape, brush in hand, his jaw isn't so tight, and the shadowy parts of his face disappear. He becomes a boy again. But this era of his life is something we never talk about, and I don't mind. I'd really rather not talk about the youthful mistakes and ridiculous scrapes that Alex and I got into, either. Though I'm sure some of them will be relived at his wedding.

'I could do an ink drawing for their office,' he says. 'If you think they'd like it. Something from nature, but in artificial colours, to match in. Have they got a colour scheme?'

'I'll take some photos with my phone,' I tell him, 'when I'm in work next. See what you think.'

We talk for a little while longer, about inking techniques and some of the pieces Jay has sold over the years. When the fire finally burns down, he pulls out the damper and pokes the last of the embers until their glow has gone. Then he sweeps away the ash, takes a last look out at the garden, before flicking off the lamps and leading me out of the room. And all the while, I am thinking about how I'm going to break the news to him that the cottage is to be sold.

Jay

Liz had given him a photo of Jamie; of both of them, actually, and he has it still. It was taken on a day-trip to the local beach. Jay has vague memories of a bus journey, looking out from the top deck as they crossed a bridge to the sea, and the sandy heat of the place.

He and his brother are wearing matching outfits in the photo: pale-blue collared T-shirts with a dark stripe, and navy-blue shorts. Jamie's legs are chubby, and his knees touch each other in a way that brings a tight feeling to the back of Jay's throat. Each of them holds a bright plastic bucket and spade. Each of them is smiling. At day's end, he'd collected so many fascinating items that his mother had made him choose only ten to keep; none of them had been alive, so he hadn't understood why it mattered. But he'd been happy with his choices: a sharp razor-clam, striped and lined with pearl-white, four tiny, delicate, pink shells that looked like fingernails, and an assortment of driftwood and coloured sea-glass. In his room at Tunnel Cottage, he'd laid out these treasures and memorised their detail. Then his brother had died, and Jay didn't see his collection for a while.

At the new school, when his teacher had asked the class to do a painting of the seaside, his had been singled out for its vibrancy, and hung on the classroom washing line for all to see. Just for a moment, Jay had felt better, had felt the hollow gnawing in his stomach shrink back a little. Punchy-Boy had torn down the painting when the teacher wasn't looking, and whipped his fist out of his pocket, knocking Jay to the ground with one blow.

And Evie was asking Jay to go to *his* wedding.

That he was going to have to face up to this Alex, or whatever he was called, Jay understood. But not yet. Not when everything between him and Evie felt so new and untested. The guy obviously hadn't recognised the sad little boy he loathed so much. By the time Jay got his height and his stature, Punchy-Boy was out of his life, gone to another school, a better one. Jay hasn't forgotten, though.

Chapter Twenty-Seven

It is a bitter-sweet morning for me: crisp air, bright sunshine, and the possibility that my professional credentials to date, will be found wanting. I slip Alex's spare crash helmet over my head and wonder again if I've dressed warmly enough for the journey.

Jay hasn't come out of the cottage to wave us off. Though I'd offered to drive the three of us to my court meeting in Stratford, he felt he'd be in the way. It is much faster to go by bike, anyway, and I am relieved to have the distraction of an interactive journey, rather than the worry of negotiating the M6 while he and Alex snarl at each other. Not that there would have been any snarling, but there is something. Jay won't change his mind about the wedding, and Alex is using this as a reason to give free rein to his suspicions.

'Ready?' Alex slips his files into the pannier on one side of his bike, then locks it. 'I have everything we need. Which could be nothing, if my instincts are right.'

I nod. He's convinced the Turnbulls are about to back off.

It's eight o'clock in the morning, and our appointment isn't till three. This is what's called overplanning, and it's a habit we both have.

Once we're moving, I tuck in behind him and enjoy our slow chug up to the motorway. I keep my visor up, watching as the townscape shrinks quietly, and the pastureland of Low Furness gives way to craggy outcrops and tourist signposts. Whatever happens today, this landscape will always welcome me back, and that knowledge makes me smile.

Paul has closed up Swarbrick and Murray for the day and is treating himself to a shopping trip with his sister. I don't doubt that he will come back with the perfect outfit for a spring wedding. If only he could have persuaded Jay along. But if I'm honest, I can't really imagine him dressed formally and making cheery small talk.

I flick down my visor again and call a halt to my idling thoughts. We have reached junction thirty-six of the M6, and this will require my full concentration.

The motorway is solid with traffic. Ducking and weaving in between it, while staying just under the speed limit, is something that Alex is good at. I huddle down behind him and think only of our next move. There's a tangible therapy in living for each second, and that's what I find so appealing about the zoom-and-fly of motorcycling. I was even going to put in for the motorcycle test myself, then the job at White Platts came up, and everything else in my life fell away.

On balance, it has been a fascinating and absorbing place to work, though it could make the outside world disappear from your psyche, if you weren't careful.

By the time we reach the M42 junction and pull off the motorway for the final time, my teeth are chattering, as much from cold as from the adrenaline that comes from flying along the tarmac at more than seventy miles per hour. And I need a pint of coffee. Alex pulls into a lay-by so that we can stretch our legs for a moment. It's almost lunchtime, and the traffic here consists mainly of cars, but they are nose-to-tail.

'It'll probably be another half hour until we hit Stratford,' he says as he lifts his helmet off. 'Shall we find a café or something, before then? Or just press on?' The skin around his eyes is filmed with salt and smut. Which means mine will be, too. I'm thankful for the washbag and make-up that I packed in the pannier.

'Let's get to Stratford. Park the bike, then check out the facilities. Once we're there, the pressure's off, isn't it?'

He agrees, and we're soon nudging our way back into the flow of traffic. Beautiful period houses in immaculate gardens are set in the landscape here. And when we chug through the small village of Henley-in-Arden, as the welcome sign proclaims, I am reminded of just how different this flat verdant part of England is to the place I call home. Home. Where Jay is. However I look at it, whichever future I see myself in, there he is, in Tunnel Cottage, lighting the fire, or boiling the kettle for the endless hot drinks that he loves.

What surprises me about Stratford is its industrial suburb. There is a large Tesco and row upon row of building-supplies units, and blocks of flats. It's only when we get nearer to the Avon, that the town's true heritage shows itself. Although there are shops and restaurants like any other town, many of them are housed within crooked terraces, timber-framed and tiny. And every signpost advertises one Shakespearean experience or another. It's like I'm on holiday. Especially when Alex brings the bike to a stop right by a canal lined with brightly coloured barges, and flanked by the most beautifully cared for parkland I have ever seen.

'This do you?' he calls over his shoulder.

I nod my approval and climb off the bike, scanning around the park for signs of coffee and a loo.

It's midday, and everywhere looks busy. School children in

bottle-green blazers, all elbows and striding their way along the various paths. Most of the benches are taken up by families with toddlers, or people in suits and overcoats, clutching coffee cups and brown paper bags.

Along the edge of the park is a row of shops that don't look anything like the ones in the centre of town. And one of them is a café. I wait while Alex locks the bike and hands me my bag.

'That's our first stop.' I tilt my head towards the row. 'Coffee, sandwiches and toilets, I hope.'

He follows me across the neatly clipped grass, our helmets slung, one on each arm, and we are soon inside the café, and joining the lunchtime queue. By the time I come out of the ladies, Alex has our provisions on a tray and is standing just outside the door.

'I thought we'd be better sitting outside.' He gestures towards a few wrought-iron tables and chairs that have been carefully arranged to catch the noonday sunshine. 'People are giving me funny looks. What with the helmets and leathers.'

We settle ourselves at a table. Alex stretches his legs out and reaches upwards with his hands. His joints crack. 'I haven't done a journey like that for a while,' he says with a laugh. 'Paul gets too cold.' He lifts his cardboard cup. 'You enjoyed it though, didn't you?'

'I did. It's a shame we're not here on a day trip. I'm too nervous to really explore the place properly.'

'No need to be nervous,' he says as he picks open one of the sandwich packets. 'We'll be driving back to Barrow knowing this is the last we'll hear from these wretched Turnbull people.' He bites off a corner of the sandwich. 'Then you can get back to your instructor's job. That's what you want, isn't it? Deep down?'

I take a sip of my drink but keep my eyes locked with his.

My cheeks feel hot now that I'm warming up a bit. A shake of my head makes him frown.

'It's this guy, isn't it? You hardly know him, and you're smitten.'

I'm not taking that; I've had enough from my mother. 'This *guy* has a name. And I'm not some teenage kid.'

A roll of his eyes.

'Honestly, Alex, I don't understand your problem with Jay. I thought you'd be glad for me.'

He splutters a little, spraying his mouthful of coffee. 'I don't have a problem with him, if you recall. He's the one who runs away whenever he sees me.'

'And now you're sounding petty,' I say. 'He doesn't run away. This is a guy who's terrifically nervous around people. Especially smart lawyer-type people. He's had a few problems in his life, that's all.'

'Well, I think he's taking advantage, Evie.' He looks out across the park, then back at me. 'Sorry. But there it is.'

I'm about to lose my cool, to tell him to mind his own business, to defend Jay to the hilt. Then we are interrupted.

'Hello, miss.' A small girl in bottle green. 'What you doing here?'

Danni.

'Woah,' I say. Then, I'm not sure why, but I stand up. She lunges at me, squeezes her arms around my waist. I return the hug. What else can I do? 'How are you?'

Two other girls are hanging back at the edge of the outdoor area, scrolling between phones and eye-darts. A wry smile from Alex.

Danni moves away from me. Her dark hair is caught back in a ponytail that leaves a scalp-white line across the top of her head, and the sleeves of her blazer hang past her hands.

'I'm all right. Did you get my letters?'

'I got the letters,' I tell her, 'but only last week. When did you send them?'

She thinks about this. 'When we got back to school, you know, after the camp. That idiot Turnbull was bragging that he'd got a teacher done. Thinking it was hilarious, and stuff. So I got the address of White Platts off the internet and sent the first letter. When I got no answer, I printed it off again, and sent the second one. My mum had a letter – off a lawyer, she said.' A shrug. 'I didn't really listen to her once I realised it wasn't from the camp.'

'I haven't been at the camp since your group were there, Danni. And they didn't send the letters to me until last week.'

'Soz. I didn't know,' she says, shuffling her feet.

'I'm not moaning,' I tell her. 'Far from it. You're the proof that Ian Turnbull has been telling lies.'

'I tried saying that to my teachers.' She is stuttering now. 'Because that idiot was sitting at the back of the bus, bragging. About how he'd gone up to your cabin thingy, and… stuff.' She winces. 'But they said I had to keep out of it. Mind my own business, and stuff.'

Alex has fallen silent. Danni swings her face towards him. 'Who's he?' she asks, in that demanding way teenagers have when they're set free from the constraints of authority. 'Your boyfriend? Better than that Rob guy, at White Platts. He was creepy.'

She's got good instincts, this girl.

'You mean Alex,' I say with a knowing smile. 'He's my solicitor. We've come down for a court case.'

'You're in court?' A stretch of her eyes. 'Real court? Is it because of dickhead Turnbull?' The other girls are all ears.

'Not the *prison* type of court,' I reassure her. 'This one just decides if there was anyone to blame for what happened. Don't you start worrying.'

'I'm there,' she shouts, punching at the air while her friends stare, phones redundant now.

'No, you can't be. But your letter, and what you've told us, will help, that's for sure.'

'You have to swear on the Bible and stuff, don't you?' She winks at her friends. 'That'd be ace.'

I need her to stop. 'This afternoon will be more of a meeting. Like you have when your parents come to talk about your schoolwork. No swearing on the Bible then, is there?' I take a quick glance at my watch. 'And hopefully, that will be it. We'll add in what you've said to the people who'll be listening. Then they'll say Ian Turnbull is a mixed-up kid, and we can all go home.'

Danni leans her head against my shoulder for a moment. 'Not fair though, is it, miss? You got kicked out of your job.' She's not so easy to fob off.

'What makes you say that?'

She taps two fingers to her temple. 'Duh. You just told me you haven't been at the camp since Apollonius were there. I'm not stupid.'

That makes me laugh. Stupid is the last thing she is.

'Anyhow,' I say. 'I haven't been kicked out. After today, I can go back anytime I like.'

Danni chats for a while longer, sprucing up her experiences at White Platts, decorating them with a sprinkling of pike biting her canoe paddles and the way she traversed a huge mountain without the aid of any ropes. Her friends show a mild interest, then turn back to their phones once again.

'Good luck at court, miss,' she suddenly says, grabbing my waist again. 'Is it the one on Rother Street?'

'Clever-clogs,' Alex says over his shoulder. Then he winks. Danni moves back to her friends then gives me the coolest of waves.

'See ya,' she mouths.

An unexpected ball of tears forms in the back of my throat and all I can do is return her wave. This tiny girl has just made me realise how much I miss working with children.

The courthouse is oddly stark, next to the rich texture of Tudor architecture in the town. It is not unlike the Victorian Gothic I am used to. In the middle of its stone-slab frontage is a wide double door, whose lintel has the standard-issue Latin motto carved into it. Cars are parked on a slant, and I wait while Alex puts the bike on its main stand and locks on our helmets. Then he takes my hand and in we walk.

There's a cold echo in the reception area, from which a stone staircase twists upwards. Eight panelled doorways stand, closed and dark. When we announce ourselves to the receptionist, she presses something on her telephone and one of those doors opens.

'Hello.' A woman with shiny chestnut-coloured hair and black-rimmed glasses peers at us, then steps through the doorway. 'I'm Jane Hunt, court mediator.'

I shake the hand she is holding out, then she turns to Alex.

'You must be Mr Swarbrick. Miss Cooper's solicitor?' She is eyeing his leather outfit.

'I am.' Alex accepts her hand. 'Is there somewhere we can gather ourselves? A cloakroom or something?'

She gestures for us to follow her into the room, then closes the door behind us. 'You're early. But don't worry about it.'

I wasn't.

'There's an annex, with a restroom. Just through there.' A tip of her head towards another door. 'I'll come and get you when everyone is here.'

There's something about this woman that is already grating on me. It's like we're an utter inconvenience. But didn't she use the title *mediator*? A lack of anything conciliatory rolls off her shoulder as strongly as the smell of her perfume.

We make our way past a large oval-shaped table, laid out with notepaper, pens and jugs of water. Its chairs are neatly tucked.

We peel off our bike gear and get ourselves looking presentable. Then comes a light knock on the door. When I open it, Jane Hunt is there again, and this time the room is full of people. Most are seated around the table, but one is slipping her shoulders out of a waterproof coat and bunching up her hair. Pip Joy.

'Hi,' she says as we lock eyes. 'Mal's not here, only me.'

Mal? That tells me a lot.

'Hello, Pip.' I can't think of anything to say, that wouldn't be overheard by everyone in the room. I've already had my instructions from Alex. Say as little as possible and let the complainants fill the silence. Then strike. He is just behind me and selecting our chairs. Pip sits next to us. She rummages through her rucksack and pulls out a plastic wallet. I cannot imagine what paperwork will be in there, but before I can think about it anymore, Jane Hunt begins to speak.

She welcomes us all and wants us to introduce ourselves. I haven't done this since university, and it makes me want to slide down in my seat and disappear under the table.

What surprises me is the glossy look of Ian Turnbull's parents. I'm not sure if I'd got them marked as a bit rough, but he's smart in a grey suit and sharp-cut hair, and she's taken time with her make-up and is very pretty. But their expressions are strangely cold, and they don't meet my eye when I say who I am.

Their solicitor is an older lady, with sharp shoulders, who introduces herself as Jackie Odell. But she doesn't stop there. While Jane Hunt watches, pulling in her two chins, Jackie starts to make a case for the Turnbulls' mental health status. Or at least that's what it sounds like. There are some sentences about how difficult Ian has been since *the incident*, and how much the Turnbull lifestyle has been disrupted by his behaviour. When she finally pauses to breathe, Jane Hunt jumps in.

'Can I remind everyone in this room that there hasn't been any conclusive proof of what Ms Odell is calling The Incident.' She turns to the young man who appears to be taking minutes, and taps his notebook. 'In fact, the reason we are here is to allow for Miss Cooper's version of events to perhaps put us all at our ease. And give some kind of closure to everyone. No one is on trial here.'

'Yet,' mutters Jackie.

Across a short slice of silence, in which Alex puts his hand on my thigh and pats me into not responding, Jane takes control again.

'As I said.' She coughs lightly. 'The purpose of this meeting is to establish whether there is any arena for a civil court case to be pursued by the Turnbulls. Or has the whole *episode* been blown out of proportion by the natural reaction of parents wishing to protect their child?' Her eyes dart to Alex. 'Would you like to start, Mr Swarbrick?'

'No,' he replies, his smile giving nothing away. He's already told me that he wants to be the one to finish; have the last word, so to speak, though I know he won't force the situation. I shift position, let my eyes roam around the room and try not to look at a large water stain that has spread across one corner of the ceiling. It's so bad that the plaster cornice has started to crumble away with it.

Jane Hunt lets out the smallest of huffs, then turns to Jackie. 'That's fine. Ms Odell, perhaps you can give us an understanding of Ian Turnbull and his recounting of the trip to White Platts last winter.'

When Jackie begins to sift through her papers, Jane adds, 'Please remember this is not a court. There will be no accusations or counter-arguments. Just what you know to be factual.'

And so, I have to sit through a description of everything Ian got up to in the week that Apollonius School came for their camp experience. Once or twice, there is an implication, lifted directly from Jackie's notes, that something of a flirty relationship was developing between him and me.

Jane soon stamps on that.

What pains me is that Ian has specifically stated that I invited him up to my chalet. He says that the conversation went on while we were out on the lake, paddling our canoe. He has completely overlooked the fact that Danni was there with us. Surely she would have heard, and mentioned it later, when accusations started to fly. He also insists that when he'd got to the front door and seen me, he'd realised he was doing something wrong. His backing away had made me angry, apparently. I'd used some cruel words. This scared him, so he'd headed back to camp again. Then had to face the wrath of various staff members.

Ian Turnbull, scared? I doubt that. But I say nothing.

According to Jackie Odell, Ian's treatment at the hands of the White Platt's staff has had a detrimental effect on his mental health, and has led to a recent suicide attempt.

I look across at Mrs Turnbull at this point, and what I see makes me shudder. The sneer painted across her lips holds no emotion, according to my gut and Alex's sideways glance. I almost feel sorry for Ian Turnbull. I'm finding his mother extremely unsettling. It dawns on me that the *suicide attempt* is the extra thing, the thing they thought would perhaps add weight to their incredible wish to get me to a court of some kind, yet they don't seem upset. I don't believe a word of it.

Jane is shaking her head. 'We are all sorry that your son's life has become problematic. Who'd be a teen, these days, eh?' A nod to us all. 'And we should, of course, remember, that we have been given just one version of events. From one perspective.'

She stops short of mentioning the word *truth*. I want to stand up to shout at everyone in the room that Ian Turnbull's perspective contains not even a whiff of that word. But I don't. I gaze around the room at the vanilla décor and the gleam of polished wood, and I press my lips together.

Time seems to have slowed down. There's no natural flow to the conversations we are having; each word is measured, and drags painfully. And now it's Pip's turn.

Firstly, there's the characteristic hair-fiddling. It's not in a plait today, and she reaches up to twist it into a ponytail, then tucks it into the collar of her checked shirt. Though why she's straightening her pile of papers I can't fathom, because she meets everyone's gaze as she talks and never refers to the papers again.

She explains that she's gathered evidence from everyone who worked at White Platts during the weeks Apollonius had their camp, from every member of staff who had contact with the group. She's even spoken to some of the teachers from the school. None can recall any inappropriate behaviour between Ian Turnbull and myself, none had any negatives about my professionality.

Nice of them, I think.

It's when she passes on Rob Bardwell's comments about Ian's return to camp that evening, after a brief spell of being missing, that I almost shout out.

Apparently, the poor lad was visibly shaken and could only say that he'd been up to my chalet. It was much later when he began to make claims about being invited, coerced. This was when Malcom Fairley had intervened and contacted the Turnbull parents. Though, as I recall, he told me Ian had sent a text home.

It's at this point that I realise I've been set up for a fall. As much by Rob as by Malcom. I imagine them both, heads together and tutting as Ian stretched his story to suit. Taking that one action, and following Ian back down to camp, would have had a profound effect on the position I now find myself in. Once again, I have no answer for why I didn't do this. Except that fear stood in my way; not a credible excuse from a person who thought nothing of hanging from a 200-foot rock face with only a rope for company. But fear, nonetheless. And the most ridiculous thing of all? I would never have brought any charges against Ian Turnbull, had the tables been turned.

'So, it is quite clear,' Jane is interrupting, 'that Ian went to Miss Cooper's chalet that evening. With no other evidence of motive, the matter should have been dealt with in-house. What worries me is that a civil case, brought for purely vindictive reasons, would help nobody. Least of all Ian.'

Hallelujah, I think. *Someone finally gets it.*

Alex chooses his moment. 'Can I remind everyone that Miss Cooper hasn't been able to work, because of this incident. It's likely that she won't return. How can she?' He clears his throat and tilts his head dramatically. 'Without being fully exonerated?'

'Should never be allowed near children again.' A snarl from the lips of Mr Turnbull. But he won't meet my eye, even though I fix on him.

'Miss Cooper could have remained in post,' says Jane Hunt. 'Her apparent *suspension* was a choice. One made by her employer, perhaps to give confidence to his other clientele.' She shrugs. 'My personal opinion is that suspension has to have a very clear and purposeful motive, if it isn't for reasons of law.'

Alex inhales deeply, as though sucking his anger back in. 'Miss Cooper needs to clear her name,' he says. 'Not for reinstatement or to gain the upper hand with her employer, or with the Turnbulls for that matter, but just because she wishes to prove she would never act in an inappropriate way.' He looks at me. 'It seems her word is not good enough, so we are happy to proceed to civil court.'

No one has heard my side of the story yet. I'm wondering if there will be any chance for me to speak, with all this legal banter. But I have to agree with Jane. What would be the point when there is nothing to back up my story?

Suddenly, there is a loud knock on the door, and the receptionist comes in, sheepish and searching the faces seated around the table. When she locates Jane, she shuffles around to whisper in her ear. Then in barges Danni.

'I told you to wait out there.' An icy tone. The receptionist moves, as if she's going to throw her out.

'Danni,' I say. 'This is cheeky.'

'Sorry, miss.' She's still wearing her Apollonius uniform. But the spark is there. 'I've been worrying all afternoon about you getting done. It's not right.'

The receptionist is closing in.

'Hello, Danni.' Jane Hunt smiles, clearly used to dealing with children. 'Do you know Miss Cooper?'

'From White Platts, yeah,' comes the reply. 'And I know Ian Turnbull. Twat.'

'Oh?' says Jane. Then there is the faintest trace of a smile. It flickers then melts back into her face.

'Yeah. I've been in double chemmy with him this afternoon. He got chucked out. Again.'

The Turnbull parents are staring at her, all frowns and steepled fingers.

'He's in school?' Alex has sniffed something out. 'Hasn't he been… unwell recently?'

'You mean when he took that stupid photo? He was out for a day.' She's sharp, this kid.

'What photo?'

'Filled a bath with water and got under it, didn't he? Then took a selfie, one arm out, and posted it, saying he was going to kill himself. Thank Christ he had all his clothes on.' Danni's cheeks flare red.

'What happened?' Alex is deadpan.

'Well,' says Danni. 'He got into trouble. Got *exo* for a day. He thought it was hilarious. Now he's got to see one of those psycho-thingys.'

'Psychologist.' He turns to Jackie Odell. 'You didn't explain very well. That was hardly a suicide bid, was it?'

But Danni hasn't finished. She puts both her hands on the table and leans into us all. The receptionist rolls her eyes. 'It's not right, this court case. Miss Cooper didn't do anything. That dickhead told everyone he was going to get her done. Even bragging about it on the back of the bus home, he was.'

I'm watching the Turnbulls. I can't help it. Their faces are solidifying right here in front of me. It reminds me of that mythological story where seething Medusa sees her truth in the shiny surface of Perseus' shield, then turns others to stone. Except the Turnbulls are not hissing.

'We've only got your word for that, Danni,' says Jane Hunt.

'No. That's not right. We all heard it. And I even told my teacher.'

Alex has his tongue firmly in his cheek.

'That's why I wrote the letter,' she continues. 'To miss.' She shoots me a smile. 'Wasn't fair, was it? She lost her job, and she never even did anything.'

It's at this point that the Turnbulls stand up and storm towards the door. Then exit, leaving us all in silent contemplation of Danni's words.

'That should be the end of it,' Alex whispers so that only I can hear. Then, louder, 'If I could have a copy of all minutes made today?' He fixes his gaze on Jackie Odell. 'And I want a full letter of apology from *Ian Turnbull*, written directly to Miss Cooper and copied to all other parties. Including his parents and school.'

Jackie lifts her shoulders and starts to gather her papers.

'Well. That was easy,' Pip whispers to me.

Later, when Alex and I are hunkered down and speeding towards home, I mull over Pip's comment, and how much she seems to have changed. Did she really have no idea how difficult it's been for me over the past few months? Did she even care? Holding my nerve is something I'm good at, though there have been a few shaky moments, that's for sure, but I would hardly have called the meeting today *easy*.

Had Ian Turnbull not come into my life, there would have been no entanglement with Jay, so there's got to be serendipity in there, somewhere. But I do worry about a teenager who has to make false allegations and create fake suicide attempts for attention: there'll be no *easy* for him.

I'm also sure now, that Pip doesn't want me to waltz back into White Platts, to pick up everything I left behind: my credentials, my work ethic, the sessions that someone else has had to cover. She'd lose her footing. There'd be no *Mal* then, would there? That comment had been a gloat, a pat on the back to herself. Like I needed her to save me.

Then there's the fact that Malcom wasn't at the meeting in person. It tells me everything I need to know about their relationship: there's no gap in it for me. And there had been no need for sending me off-site, either. I vaguely remember Alex telling me the same thing. The whole thing stinks of a corruption that doesn't match the blandness of its players. So, I'm not going to become one of Malcom Fairley's choices. He's lost me. But I want to see his face when I tell him.

By the time we're chugging down to Tunnel Cottage, it's eight o'clock. My thighs are tense and cold, and I just want my bed. We are greeted by huge piles of garden rubbish: twiggy tangles and shadowy mounds of leaf litter and wet moss. Jay has been busy. The driveway feels wider, and I can actually see over the fence and into the ghost-grey meadow. The cottage is in darkness, but there is warmth when I push open the front door.

'Come in,' I whisper to Alex. 'Sit and have a drink with us. It'll give you a chance to meet Jay face to face.'

He mouths an *okay*, then follows me inside.

An orange glow lights up the lounge. A crackle of fire, and Jay, fast asleep with a blanket over him and his knees hanging off the sofa's edge.

Alex backs away. 'Don't wake him up.' His voice is low and hesitant. 'There'll be other times.'

We creep back out into the hall, and I put my arms around Alex, allowing my body to relax into the pleasure that comes from sheer relief. 'Thanks so much for everything,' I murmur. There is comfort in the smell and sense of him, of leather and intelligence, and I lean in.

'No worries.' His chin is resting on the top of my head, then he pulls me away and holds my shoulders. His face is shadowy but there is a glint in his eyes. 'You've been dealt a shitty hand, my darling, but change it for a new one, now. These things happen for a reason.'

As he closes the door behind him and I listen for the sound of his bike starting up, I wonder if Jay is the reason. My reason. And I decide that he is.

Chapter Twenty-Eight

J ay has agreed to accompany me to White Platts. Though it's a weekday in late February, I know spring activity camps will be in full swing, and there will be hordes of schoolchildren on the site. I've decided I'm not going to warn Malcom or Pip of my visit. Better that they don't have any time to prepare. I, on the other hand, have a mental list of everything I have to say.

It is one of those mornings where the sky is radiant, but the air is so sharp it could cut your cheeks. Jay climbs into the car and buckles up his seatbelt. He has let me trim two inches from his ponytail and he is freshly shaven for the occasion.

'Are you nervous?' he says as he settles himself into his seat. 'I know I am.'

'Because you don't trust my driving?' I laugh.

'Because I've hardly been out of Barrow since...'

I push the key into the ignition and turn to look at him. Then wait. Chasing the detail of his past life is something I never do, but each unveiling fascinates me. The instability he'd experienced as a child has given him a depth of understanding that can be unsettling but is also extremely tantalising. On occasion, I can't resist him.

'Well, since Kew,' he says eventually. 'That sounds pathetic, doesn't it?'

It's a word he uses a lot. *Pathetic*. Mainly about himself.

'Not at all. I hardly ever left White Platts, as it happens.'

'You were working, though. That's different.' He stares out of the window as the car pulls onto the main road and I nudge us into the traffic. 'I just couldn't bear to be away from the cottage.'

And suddenly it hits me: he might not cope with travelling to the Lakes. It will take him thirty miles out of his comfort zone, after all. Not many of us stretch our bonds that far.

'Are you going to be okay with this? Today, I mean.'

'You'll be with me. I'll cope.' He lets out the faintest of sighs. 'Now, can we talk about something else?'

We chat as the landscape changes. The fells of Low Furness are starkly beautiful in these early spring months, but inside the national park the quality of light changes: trapped between high peaks, and scattered back from the lakes and rivers, it gives everything a shine, turning slate to sapphire and brown to bronze. And everything makes Jay gasp with delight.

When we get to the camp, he asks, no, begs, to be allowed to walk up into the woods near the chalet while I seek out my revenge with Malcom. Then he kisses me goodbye and tells me he'll come back within a half hour and wait for me by the car.

I smile as he hurries away, though my stomach is doing somersaults at the thought of seeing Malcom Fairley again. There's something quite affecting in the way Jay interacts with the landscape. It's his safety net: I can sympathise with that.

As I turn and make my way towards the office block, I'm struck by how quiet the camp is. At half past ten on a working morning, I would have expected it to be buzzing with groups of waterproof-clad teenagers dragging paddles and life jackets down to the lake, and the usual array of delivery vans being relieved of supplies. Then I catch sight of Rob Bardwell. Pip is with him, and they are heads together over a clipboard. To my surprise, both are togged up in the White Platts fleece-and-trousers outfit reserved for what we used to call the *land-brigade*. Have they been promoted?

'Hi, both,' I call, over-loud and with a smile set in concrete. 'You okay? Guess who's back.'

'Evie.' He gives Pip a side-eye. It's quick, but I see it.

'Been demoted?' I scan over their clothing.

Rob matches my banter. 'In your dreams. Does Mal know you're coming?' He's looking so rattled, I almost back off. Then I remember what he'd called me when I wouldn't join in with his little bed-hopping games and my compassion slides away.

'No. It's a surprise,' I say. 'Good, eh?' I add a flounce to my step as I walk away.

When I reach the main office, I hesitate, and wonder if I should just go back to the car and wait for Jay. Malcom will have had the meeting minutes and apology letters by now. That he's received no other word from me or Alex, will be worrying him, I'm sure. Though not enough for him to contact me by telephone, or even pay a visit. So, here I am.

The place smells very clean, and there are hoover stripes on the carpet. Nothing has changed; I'm not sure what I expected. There is a light on in Malcom's office. I take in some gulps of air then knock on his door.

'Hello,' he calls, then I'm in.

'Hello,' I say. 'Remember me?'

He tilts his head quizzically and for a moment I think he's going to say that he doesn't.

'Evie.' He gets up from his seat. Too quickly. And he's not dressed for a day in the outdoors. 'You're here. I was only saying to Pip last night that we'd have to get in contact.'

'Saved you a job then, haven't I.' I walk up to his desk and lean my thighs against the metal edge. 'So. Where do you want me first?'

That confuses him. I enjoy the moment.

'Meaning?' A frown.

I tug at my sweater. 'Meaning, what am I rostered on to? You must have realised I was coming back. You've been told the outcome of the meeting, I take it?'

'The meeting?' He scratches at his beard. It's greyer than I remember. 'Oh, yes. With the Turnbulls. Pip filled me in.'

Who's running this bloody place? I think, then use Alex's weapon of silence.

'Well,' he mumbles, after a moment. 'There's the induction process. As you know.' He looks for my agreement, but I'm not playing. 'Then there's a question of finding you a chalet. And... erm...'

I still say nothing. Just peer at him.

'Erm. You'll have to bear with me, Evie.' He runs his eyes over my clothing. 'And you're hardly dressed for it. I thought you'd be having a few weeks off. You know, before you came back to work full-time.'

He's got me, finally.

'A few weeks off,' I spit. 'I've been "off", as you put it, for nearly fourteen, thanks to you and your cock-ups.'

He steps around his desk and moves towards me. I get a whiff of male sweat, gone off.

'Now, hang on,' he growls. 'I'm not sure I like your tone.' He eyes the open office door. And for a moment, I actually believe he's going to try and guide me through it. But he doesn't. Instead, he tries to use his proximity to back up what he's saying. A rubbish move, and a predictable one. I step towards him.

'Well, you'd better get used to it, though you've never really liked my *tone*, have you?'

'Look,' he says, deliberately placating, 'if you're coming back to work here, we have to get our relationship on track. Stop this sniping.'

I can't believe he actually thinks I'm going to be his employee again. The man's an idiot; has he not realised there is no way back?

'Sniping?' I cry. 'You've ruined my life with your incompetence, and you can't see why I'm sniping?'

He huffs and tries to move away. 'I'm not having this.'

'Truth hurts, Malcom, doesn't it? Ian Turnbull was a gift, wasn't he? Wrapped up in bloody shiny orange paper. With a bow on the top. Am I right?'

'As always,' he sighs, as he shrinks back, 'you're talking cryptically. Something I never really had time for.'

We lock eyes now, and I can tell he's not enjoying this. I, on the other hand, am. 'Let me simplify things for you then,' I spit. 'Malcom. Ian Turnbull caused his mayhem, and you saw your chance. To be rid of me. The only senior instructor who posed a serious threat to your position. I was bloody good at my job, wasn't I? And you couldn't handle it.'

And when he stretches his expression so that his fillings are on show, I add my final touch.

'Yes. I said *was* good at my job. If you think I'd ever work for you again, that tiny shred of intelligence you think you've got, must be fake. I'd never work for someone who is, quite frankly, beneath me.'

Then I surprise us both by pushing forward slightly so that he jumps back, startled. And off I go.

Once I'm outside, I start to laugh, quietly at first, then wildly, and finally I burst into tears. But they are tears of relief. Closing the door on White Platts hasn't wounded me half as much as I thought it would.

Jay

There's a strength to Evie. One that makes Jay realise how she could easily have become the fixation of a mixed-up teenaged boy. It's something he can hardly put into words, only that she's the spiders' webs he sees on spangly winter mornings, beautifully held together, featherlight, but with the might of tensile steel.

So, he knows she'll be okay when she meets this Malcom Fairley, despite the fact she seems stewed up about it.

He can't tear his eyes away from the intricate detail of the area, though, and he's glad of the time to roam a little and run the place through his hands.

Up a steep, rocky escarpment, he finds an area of woodland with nothing but deciduous trees, though their bare branches tangle together so that hardly any light filters through. In spite of this, on the floor, dotted between patches of moss and mud, are many clumps of wild snowdrops, shining white in the gloom like a thousand Christmas lights. They have nothing going for them, these plants: no sunshine and very little water. Yet here they are. He smiles to himself. What they do have is the nurturing soil and an instinct for survival. That fascinates him.

When he'd taken the job at Kew, his own instincts had overridden everything trying to keep him rooted at home. He remembers his aunt, standing on the dirty platform, looking at him through the window of the train. When he'd settled into his seat, a beat of sadness tightened in the back of his throat, and he'd almost got up again, wanting to throw his arms around her and say that he wouldn't go. But he couldn't: too much in his life was broken. Staying wouldn't fix anything.

He'd waved his hand, then blown a kiss from his palm. His aunt, a sag of summer dress and crinkly arms, returned both. Her problems were as big as his. They hung, like the terrifying heat of the day, end to end and suffocating. Since the death of his mother, Liz had changed. There had been no more evenings, talking about what the future held, no waking pleasantly groggy and thinking about the day ahead; optimism was as rare as gold.

When a slam of the train doors told him it was time for that final farewell, the churn of his stomach had become uncontrollable. Anxiety, a doctor had called the persistent panic that was beginning to affect his health, and he'd torn off a sheet of tranquillisers, which had gone in the bin, along with the bank statements reminding Jay of just how far his account was overdrawn.

As the train pulled out of the station, Jay had stared at the graffitied underpass and the grey gravel of the railway embankment and tried to steady himself. Travelling light had been his only option: money flowed through his hands like the water in the beck, beautifully cool, then gone. He owned little more than the clothes he was wearing. And now he was going to see Tunnel Cottage for the last time, through the window of a train.

In the tunnel, he had sucked in his breath, and counted the seconds. Then the train burst into daylight again, and the first thing he saw was the froth of pink clematis lying along the top of the cottage's fence. Then a flash of blue-grey roof tiles and the blank eye of his bedroom window, the cool green shade of the beech trees along the drive, and the scene was gone, leaving only the haze of the meadow, and the beck shimmering out its lament. The place was in his blood, even back then, but it felt tainted. The train was carrying him away from that, away from Jamie and his baby-soft hair, from his parents' bitter disappointment in the son left behind. And from his life of sneaking and lying and convincing himself that he could win his way out of pain.

At the top of the pathway, the line of trees drops away, and

Jay has a view of the lake. With the fells behind and the sky stretching away, he feels like he has walked into one of his paintings. And then it comes. Starting in his belly, and spreading upwards, along his arms and through his chest. Like a pulse of soft light. It'd be pale pink, if he had to put colour to it. There are no words. Evie has done this to him. When he sees her, he feels free, like she's reached inside him and taken away all the syrupy darkness. Except for Jamie. She'll have to dig deep to free him of that.

Chapter Twenty-Nine

The changing rooms have that familiar smell: sweat and rubber, overlaid with mouldy towels. I walk behind the guy who is showing me around, watching his calf muscles contract and relax, and trying not to look at his tanned biceps. Could I be one of these teachers? Wearing sports gear to work, and crawling under desks to wrestle problem kids? I am willing to try, and I've got this far: a tour of the school prior to interview next week.

We step into the disorientating expanse of the sports hall, where an echoing roar makes me stretch my eyes.

'Handball finals,' says my tour guide. 'Emotions always run high.' His jawline is lean and tanned, but he's losing his hair. 'Reckon you could work here?'

I give him an enthusiastic nod. There's no doubt in my mind. To join in with the handball game, right now, would be bliss. To work with a team again, that is something I crave.

Jay had been thrilled when I'd told him what happened in the meeting with Malcom. Especially when he realised I'd burned my bridges, and would be staying local to look for work.

'I'll show you the equipment room,' the guy is saying, 'as you'll probably be asked about how you'd use our resources. In your interview, I mean.'

'That'd be good,' I reply. 'I'm used to PE equipment, but I've never worked in a school setting before.'

He frowns at this, then leads me to a huge set of double doors with a keypad at the side. With a tap of his fingers, he lets us into the storeroom and flicks on the lights.

'Woah.' I let my gaze dart around the lower walls, then upwards. The place is immaculate and kitted out with every kind of sports apparatus I could ever imagine. And some that I couldn't. He pulls out a triangular-shaped ball and gives it a spin.

'Bet you've never seen one of these before.' He slams it to the floor, and it bounces in a completely unpredictable direction. 'Reaction balls. Great fun, but vital for handball game training.' He waits.

'And for volleyball routines.' I collect the ball. 'This place is amazing. Your kids are getting a great experience, I'll bet.'

'They are,' he says. 'Up to a point.'

'Oh?'

'The bottom line is, Evie – can I call you Evie – is that some of my staff don't *model* enough. They're good educators, don't get me wrong. But sometimes, in sport especially, you have to show rather than tell and coach. Did you find that in your last job?'

'I wasn't working in a school,' I tell him, 'but I agree with you. It's even more important in outdoor ed. You have to get in among it. Kids get confidence in themselves from the teacher being completely immersed. Well, that's what I found, anyway.'

He smiles. His teeth dazzle. 'Exactly. I like you already.' He throws the reaction ball back into its tub and presses the keypad again. 'Coffee?' he asks.

'Desperate.' I laugh.

Later, when I've driven back to the town centre and found somewhere to park for the rest of the day, I wander back to Alex and Paul's office. The wind is up. It has a salty freshness and is chasing away the last of the morning's drizzle. Being trapped in an office every day is making me twitchy. Today, I just want to follow the smell of the sea and cut loose. But I owe Alex and Paul for the support they've given me over the last few months. Alex in particular, with his broad reach and wide shoulders. Though what the vibe is between him and Jay, I cannot fathom.

Alex thinks Jay is hiding something and I'm the fool who's letting him; and Jay is just plain scared. None of it adds up. If I could just persuade them to meet face to face, there would be so much common ground, I'm sure. Me, for starters. But every time I try to engineer something, it falls flat.

Inside the office, I find Alex manning my desk. There is an empty sandwich wrapper next to the computer keyboard, and an open can of Pepsi.

'Evie,' he says as I step towards the cloakroom. 'How was it?'

'Oh, Al.' I move to stand in front of the desk. 'It would be perfect. There was such a buzz about the place. Kids everywhere. And the sports hall was fantastic.'

As I continue, his smile grows, until it's big enough for both of us.

'What?' I ask.

'You.' He gets up and hugs me. 'Nothing gets you down, does it? I could do with some of your energy, right now.'

I lean into him, inhale his spicy scent and allow myself a moment of self-indulgence. Am I allowed to feel as happy as this?

'What's bogging you down?' I step back and catch his eye. 'Anything I can help with?'

'You cannot, darling. I'm trying to organise our stag party, but nothing's coming together.'

'Does that matter?'

He holds me away from him. 'Have you forgotten I'm marrying Paul Murray? Everything matters.'

'Can't he help you with it?'

'He wants to be surprised.' A flick of his hands. 'Imagine that.'

It's difficult to reconcile my image of Paul – laid-back and open to suggestions – with what Alex is implying.

'I always thought you were the fussy one.' My comment makes him splutter. 'Well, not fussy. That's not quite the right word. Meticulous? Is that better?'

'I'll take it,' he says with a laugh. 'But I so love the guy. I want everything to be perfect for him.'

'I'm pretty sure,' I say as I walk back towards the cloakroom, 'that it already is.'

'Your Jay's invited, by the way,' he calls, 'to the stag.'

I glance back over my shoulder. 'I'll tell him,' I say.

When I park my car at the top of the cottage driveway, there is a thin layer of fierce sunset just behind the ridge of the fells. The beauty of this place can sometimes overwhelm me, with its watchful trees and silent history. It can tear me open, then pour its green salve on my wounds.

I breathe deeply, tasting burnt wood and earth. Jay has been gardening again. Along the sides of the drive are tangled piles of twigs and crisped leaves. The ones that have clung on all through the winter, though they're useless, dead, in fact.

When I push open the cottage door, I can smell cooking:

something meaty and rich – the pan of stew I made at the weekend and decanted into a plastic tub, perhaps.

'Jay,' I call, and he appears in the doorway of the kitchen, hair pulled back and a stripe of pink across his cheeks.

'How was it?' That smile. 'The school thing, I mean?'

I slide in for a hug. 'It was so good, Jay, honestly. I'd work there in a heartbeat. Just got to get through the interview now.'

He rests his chin on the top of my head. 'You'll get through,' he murmurs. 'Only an idiot wouldn't give you a job.'

'What are you cooking?' I ask, stepping away.

'The stew. From the fridge. Hope that's okay?'

I slip my arms out of my anorak, and open the scullery. 'Why wouldn't it be?'

I'm half listening as I kick off my shoes and hang my coat from one of the new pegs we've put up.

'I don't want you to think I'm taking advantage, that's all.'

This has caught at my interest. Taking advantage? 'What are you talking about?' I look at his face. He's frowning. I step towards him again and take his hands in mine. 'You know I like it when you take advantage.'

'I'm being serious,' he says. 'So, today, I've taken a trip into town.'

I follow him into the lounge. The curtains are drawn, and he's lit a fire, which snaps and hisses, and sends flashes of orange light into the gloom. I switch on one of the lamps while he is rummaging around on the coffee table.

'I'm giving you this,' he says suddenly as he hands me a large, padded envelope, open at the top.

I can't help staring at his face. There are shadowy places, across his nose and under his chin but his eyes shine.

'What's this?' I laugh, but I'm worried. When I look into the envelope, then slide in my hand, I realise this is a packet of money. Lots of it. Crisp notes, twenties, mainly. 'Cash? Jay? What's going on?'

He walks across the room and stands by the fire, leans his hands against the mantlepiece and doesn't say anything for a moment.

'Jay?'

'It's difficult, Evie.' A whisper. Finally. 'I'm living here without contributing anything. There's no regular wage as you know. But I still have some of my aunt's money in the bank. I've never wanted to touch it. I want you to have it.'

'I can't take your only money,' I say. 'We were managing all right, weren't we?'

'We were better than managing. I love being here. With you. But I don't want your friends to think I'm living off you.'

Alex. My first thought. 'Who's been saying that?'

Silence.

'Jay? Who's put these ideas into your head?'

'No one,' he says. Then, 'Everyone. I know your mother doesn't think I'm good enough to be in your life. And your boss. Alex. The way he looks at me whenever he's seen me with you. I know what he's thinking.'

I step towards him and pull his arm away from the fireplace, then take both his hands. 'You are so wrong,' I tell him. 'My mother is not a pleasant woman. Sorry. I know that sounds harsh. And Alex isn't what you think. Trust me.'

'He doesn't rate me though, does he?'

'What's he got to go on?' I ask. 'You've not really even met. Alex has supported me through this whole mess with White Platts. He's a good guy, Jay. You just need to stop worrying about how he looks and seems, and dive in. Get to know him.'

He shakes his head.

'Honestly,' I continue. 'He would never judge you. He's not the type. And he's had enough of that in his life anyway, to know not to do it to other people.'

But Jay's face is as hard as stone, and I can see that my

words aren't enough. I have a creeping sense of unease, but I choose to ignore it.

'Take the money though, will you?' He pulls me towards him. 'Put it in your bank and use it for our living expenses. Don't refuse me this. Please, Evie.'

I think about this for a moment, while I lean into him and inhale his smell. It's his spicy soap tonight, but something else, too. Something that makes me think of water and summer meadows. A warmth.

'I won't refuse,' I say. 'But you can do something for me in return.'

'I can?' A small laugh.

'You can. Come to Alex and Paul's wedding with me.'

Jay

He can't think how to refuse. Evie asks nothing of him and gives everything. The money is just a token, one that could be wheeled out and waved at the cynics who pretend to care for her. But they can't care more than he does. And so, he will have to try and go to this wedding.

When he returns to the kitchen, she follows him and tells him more about her time at the school, about the size of the sports hall and about the buzz of being in the centre of frenetic human activity. In that respect, they are very different. He only wants peace and solitude. And her. But he'd never hold her back. Better to let her go and find what she needs, and hope she'll always want to come home to him.

To have had this small slice of a life he's craved for so long, is enough and more than enough. Grasp it too hard, he thinks, and it will crumble in his needy hands. Simple things, like eating a meal together, hacking at the garden, Evie combing his hair or putting his clothes through a cycle in the washing machine, they mean everything. While others are seeking out their next piece of happiness, thinking that it will come in solid form, he only wants what they cast off as ordinary and mundane. It's all he's ever wanted.

Later in the evening, when they are walking by the beck, with only a swathe of moonlight to keep them from straying off the path, he almost tells her the rest of his story. But then she has this crazy idea that they should take off their shoes and socks and dip their toes in the water. Paddle even. And it is icy cold, and there's that smell, of wet clay and bitter regret, and all he can do is hold her as she laughs with pure joy, and he lets her think that his shaking shoulders and gasping are him laughing too.

Chapter Thirty

When my interview is over, and I realise I had the job before it even started, I pop back to see Alex and Paul and break out my news. The town centre is very quiet, but there's the promise of an early spring in the way the air feels. It's so soft I could catch it between my finger and thumb and use it as hand cream. That thought makes me laugh, because I've lost the calluses and ragged nails that stood for my time at White Platts. And I couldn't care less.

'You're looking at the academy's new PE and recreation tutor,' I call as I push my way through the street door and into the back office.

Their eyes dart up from their computer screens. Paul claps his hands together and Alex makes a dive for me. I let him crush me in a hug for a moment then I wriggle away.

'Easy,' I say with a laugh. 'You'll kill the new teacher before she's had her first day.'

'And when will that be?' I know why he's asking.

'Not until after their Easter break.' I grit my teeth, embarrassed. 'Is that leaving you in the lurch?'

'Darling girl, you've done more than enough for us.' He flicks a look at Paul. 'Hasn't she?'

'More than enough,' Paul echoes. Then puts his hands behind his head and stretches a little. 'But we've a few weeks to train up your replacement. If that's okay with you?'

'Course it's okay,' I say. 'And I can keep the training going while you are on honeymoon, if you like.'

It's not long until the wedding, now. Though there's been no mention of what the two of them will be doing afterwards.

'No honeymoon for us,' says Paul. 'At least, not yet. We've got too much on.'

Alex walks away from me and stands behind his fiancé, clasping the lilac-clad shoulders. 'Don't sound so sad, my love,' he tells him. 'Australia is booked for the New Year.'

Paul lays a hand on his. 'Ignore me, Evie. This one's booked us a month of touring in Oz. Must have cost a fortune.'

The banter continues, but all I can think about is Jay. He will be waiting to find out whether I've managed to get the teaching job. I've only dropped into the office on my way back to Tunnel Cottage.

'Pity your guy wouldn't come on the stag,' Alex is saying. 'We had a wild time.'

Though Jay has agreed to accompany me to the wedding, I couldn't persuade him to even meet up with the stag party for a drink. And I understand that, in a way. Pubs and dancing, crowds and strangers – everything that gives him anxiety. The wedding will be different. He'll be able to stay close and let me ease his way. That he's agreed to attend at all makes me very proud, considering the level of fear he feels in polite company.

'He's coming to the wedding,' I reply. 'That's progress.'

Alex turns away. 'You need more than *progress*,' he mutters. 'You need a guy who doesn't skitter away at the first sign of trouble. That's what you need.'

'Al. Stop.' Paul's voice cuts across from where he's standing.

'Sorry.' Alex raises his hands and catches my eye. 'The whole thing baffles me, that's all.'

'What whole thing?' The tone of my voice surprises me. I don't want to argue with Alex.

'Keeping this *Jay* hidden away. Him hiding away. Don't you find it a bit weird?'

If Alex knew some of Jay's truths, he'd struggle. Which is why I am letting him hold onto the simplicity of *weird*. Paul steps towards him and folds his arms in a way that tells me everything I need to know about their relationship.

'Sorry. Sorry.' Alex sidesteps, sits back down on his office chair. 'I'll keep my mouth shut.'

'In other news,' Paul says, leading me back to the reception area, 'we've started sifting through the gigantic heap of paperwork Rosina Kerr gave us, about your cottage.'

'Oh?' I thought we'd have more time to find somewhere else.

Paul seems to read my mind. Or my expression. 'Don't worry,' he says. 'It's going to take an age to get through it all and make sure everything's in order, ready for a sale. One slip-up, and the whole thing could come crashing down.'

'So we've got a while?' I ask.

'Yep.'

I let out a hugely exaggerated sigh. 'That's a relief.'

'We've not had a proper look through the files yet. Everything's on paper. There's been no transactions on the place since the digital age. It's just parcel after parcel of smelly old paper. There's all sorts of stuff.'

'Like what?' I pull open the front door of the office. A waft of pizza-base comes in and my stomach fizzes for a moment. I haven't been able to eat today, but now that the anxiety's gone, I find I'm starving.

Paul lifts his shoulders. 'Receipts of work, drainage plans, maps. There are even some old photos in there. And newspaper clippings. The place has a story to tell, that's for sure.'

I don't know why his words suddenly resonate, but they do. To be inside Tunnel Cottage is to get a sense of that story, that mystery. I haven't been able to acknowledge the feeling, until now. The thought of leaving has crystallised, for me, the sudden urge to make the place my own. To buy it, and to keep it close to me forever. Jay is part of that landscape. There's no way we could live anywhere else.

'I'd love to have a look. When you've got time,' I tell Paul. Then I step away with a wave of my hand. 'I'll see you both in the morning.'

My car is parked just off the high street. It isn't late. The last dregs of homeward-bound children elbow their way past me, aloof and untouchable, and I wonder again if I'm really going to be up for coping with their type, in a situation so unfamiliar. But physical education, school-style, might be the bridge between classroom stuffiness and the real outdoors. Let's hope I'm right.

While I'm driving back to the cottage, I open the window and take in the rising season. There are flowerbeds on the roundabouts, with yellow-and-cream primroses in neat lines, and garden hedges are aflame with forsythia and flowering currant.

The trees around Tunnel Cottage are still bare, but their boughs have the promise of unfurled buds. Which means that the landscape is beginning to look different. It has changed colour. Through the winter months, there has been grey and wet brown, and muddy pink. When I pull my car up at the top of the drive, I can see the silver-green of whitebeam buds, and the beeches have already begun their juvenile fluttering.

Jay isn't downstairs in the cottage, but the front door is unlocked so I know he is somewhere about. There are no new piles of garden debris, and no smells of cooking or coffee. Some thick paper lies on the kitchen table, with a small palette of watercolours and a delicate brush. He's been working on something to give to Alex and Paul as a wedding gift, but he hasn't told me what.

I call up the stairs and hear him say he's in the bedroom. I take off my coat, then head up to tell him my news.

'I got the job,' I say as I push open the door.

His usual clothes are on the bed: jeans and a sweater, and his socks. He turns as I walk in.

'I knew you would.' He looks at me with a wry smile. 'What do you think?'

He is wearing a charcoal-grey suit and white shirt. With bare feet and his hair scraped into a topknot. My hand flies to my mouth. From somewhere deep in my body comes a shot of what feels like concentrated adrenaline. It makes my knees shake.

'What I think.' My voice has become a croak. 'Is that you better take that suit off. Pretty darn quick.'

His eyes show confusion, until I step across the room and reach up to kiss him. Then he understands.

Jay

He is hard in an instant. But he stays still, lets Evie take the lead. She reaches up and slips the jacket from his shoulders. Where her hands skim, he feels a burn. What he wants to do is undress as quickly as possible and get her skin on his. He watches as she dips her head and pulls open each button of his shirt. Then her palms sneak inside and run up his chest. He tries to kiss her again, but she won't let him, just slides the fabric away, so that he is half undressed and shuddering with it all.

How he'll hold on, he doesn't know, only knows that while he's with this woman, the other places in his life, the painful ones, cease to exist. And now she's unbuttoning his trousers and running her hand over the length of him, and he can't stand it any longer.

He climbs onto the bed and drags her with him, and everything else falls away.

Chapter Thirty-One

I can taste dust. And the dry clog of paper that has been locked away for years. We are sitting in the upstairs conference room of Swarbrick and Murray. Spread across the table are about thirty documents linked in some way with Tunnel Cottage. Just thinking about the place brings a smile to my lips. Alex sees it and reacts.

'Share the joke, Miss Evie Cooper.' He giggles slightly. 'I'm going to be a married man, tomorrow. And you know what that means.'

Paul leans back from the table and glowers at him. He's wearing a pair of white cotton gloves, and the fingertips are already grubby. 'Let me think,' he says. 'Does it mean you'll keep your nose out of other people's business?'

Alex snorts.

'Oh wait,' continues Paul, 'everyone's business except Evie's?'

Both men are edgy today. Which is understandable, with their wedding less than twenty-four hours away; and there's the possibility that some won't accept it. My mother included, though she loves a *good wedding*, she says, and she'll definitely be there.

'I don't have a joke to share,' I tell them. 'Sorry guys.'

Both sets of shoulders slump.

'But, in other news, Jay has bought himself a suit for your wedding. So at least I know he's coming with me.'

The memory of that suit causes a sizzle in my stomach that translates to a flush so hot, I can feel it burn. It causes me to lean across the table and pretend to be separating the delicate documents from one another, so I don't have to meet their eyes.

'Told you we'd have a job on our hands with this one,' Alex says as he joins me. 'What we need to do first is separate off anything not directly related to the sale.' He slides his hand over some tatty photographs. 'Like these, for instance.'

I pick them up. A crumble of dust falls away as I sift through. Some have a scrawl of faded handwriting on the back. The cottage was built at the end of Queen Victoria's reign, from what I can gather, when the railway line was brand new. One of the photos, in sepia and white, shows the place in a clean and bare state, with no growth of garden or jumble of outbuildings.

'Look at this,' I say, and slide the photo across to Paul. 'It must have been taken with one of the first cameras.'

He is skimming through an oversized piece of parchment. It has *Land Registry* printed across the top, but the rest of the page is handwritten.

He glances up at me.

'The cottage was definitely built for railway workers,' he tells me. Then he picks up the photo. 'Pretty snazzy for a basic company worker, wasn't it?' He wafts the photo towards Alex. 'What do you think?'

'The Furness Railway Company made a lot of money.' He huffs slightly. 'It's not like now. Investing in rail transportation was cutting edge, back then. Everyone wanted a piece of it. And I guess if money's coming in fast, it's got to go out fast.'

He tilts his head, waiting for a response.

'Oh. You mean it was put into property,' I say. 'Like the cottage?' I can follow his logic, but there is no Furness Railway Company now. Nor has there been for many years, according to another one of the documents. I read about how Tunnel Cottage went into private ownership for a while in the 1950s, but then was purchased by the local council. I want to know why.

Alex is busy sorting through all the planning permission documents. There aren't as many as there should be, so he says.

He thinks about my question for a moment. 'Probably because the railways were nationalised at that time,' he tells me, 'so snapping up property connected with the lines made things easier for them. That's what I'm guessing, anyway.' He sighs. 'Most of the outbuildings tagged on to the place don't have planning permission. Nightmare.' He looks across at Paul. 'This lot could take some time to unravel. I hope the buyer wasn't looking to move quickly.'

The buyer. Of my home. Mine and Jay's home. I'd love to know who it is. I'd go and kick their legs out from under them. But I mustn't be stupid. I'm only a tenant, and I'm never going to be anything else. Soon, there will be a new owner, wanting to get the measure of the place: they'll want quotes for heating and rewiring, new kitchen and bathroom, tree felling and paving slabs. I wonder what this person will be like. Probably some rich kid from the local aeronautical firm, or a property developer wanting to make money from someone else's romantic desire to live in a cottage in the country. That's not what Tunnel Cottage is. To my mind, it's a place for living close to nature and trying to become part of it. No thatches or wood-burners involved. Or Agas.

'Who's *selling* it, though?' I wonder out loud. Alex won't tell me who's buying the place. He can't. I don't actually think he knows. Rosina Kerr just asked for the legal work to be done. That request did come with a warning, as I remember. Of murk.

'Not sure,' he says. 'Ms Kerr is acting as sole agent, so that's really all we need to know. Someone bought it from the local council in the 1980s, I think she said.'

I let my mind wander for a moment. Tunnel Cottage wasn't in a derelict state when I moved in. Rosina said it'd been rented out a few times when her agency took it on. But it hasn't been modernised; it certainly has a look of the 1980s. Perhaps that is when it'd last been loved. I'd love it. If I could afford the place. But at more than two hundred thousand pounds, it's going to have to be someone else.

I pick up a bundle of newspaper clippings and more photographs. They are held together with a crumbling elastic band. It pings away when I try to remove it, and everything scatters.

The photographs are those small square ones with a white border and faded colours. Tunnel Cottage again. Probably in high summer, with honeysuckle and clematis around the garden gate and a family standing by the front door. A man and a woman, squinting awkwardly. She's wearing a short sleeveless frock and he's in some kind of uniform. Two children stand in front of them. Boys, though their hair is softly styled. They wear shorts and T-shirts, and one is holding something up for the shot. It looks like some kind of doll. I find I'm a bit emotional when I imagine a family living in Tunnel Cottage. The place has had a happy life, I'm sure of it. I'd love to know more.

Alex is staring at me. 'Evie,' he says. 'Look at this.' He has picked out one of the newspaper clippings and is sliding it towards me. It is yellowed with age, a small squared-off piece with the headline cut neatly so that it hangs away from the main text.

What I read makes the hairs on my forearms and the back of my neck stand on end. A child drowned in the beck next to Tunnel Cottage. In 1984. A James Frederick Pickthall, local lad from a local family. No, not local. A family who actually lived in the cottage.

'Oh my God, Alex,' I whisper. 'That's awful.' I drag my eyes away from the newsprint and look at him. 'Poor kid. Poor family.' Before I have time to register anything about that surname, Alex takes my attention again. He is reading from another clipping.

'The father worked for the railways at the time. There was a brother. John Pickthall. He was with the little lad when he drowned, apparently.'

I shudder. The beck where Jay and I have walked, enjoying the play of light on its surface, its gentle gurgle.

John Pickthall? Is that what Alex is saying?

'There's more.' He slides another photo towards me. His face has taken on an expression I can't quite read. And he's gone sickly pale.

My hands shake as I pick up the photo. It's black and white and has been cut from yet another newspaper. It shows the laughing faces of two boys. Together, as though they had pressed the sides of their faces close, for the photo and from love. These are the faces of John and James Pickthall. But one of them looks exactly like Jay.

When I've recovered enough to be able to speak again, Alex offers to drive me home. That word. Home. Until an hour ago, that's how I'd thought of Tunnel Cottage. Jay will be there, waiting for me. We'd planned to have an early tea and a walk, so that we would be fresh enough to rise above any tension the wedding might cause, and just have a lovely time. I'm wondering now if I know enough about him to even stay in the same room.

Some of the stories he's told me, about his life before we met, they make perfect sense. But why wouldn't he have mentioned a little brother who'd drowned? And why am I assuming that this John Pickthall is in fact, my Jay? One thing is for sure: I need to see him and talk to him.

'Are you ready?' Alex is standing in the reception area of the office, holding Paul's helmet and my handbag. 'You're not fully kitted out, but I'll let you off. Just this once.'

I don't want to be *let off*. Alex has already made me feel ridiculous about trusting Jay. There is an air of *I told you so* in the office, so thick that I can smell it; the reek of mistrust and desperation.

'I can get the bus,' I say, without looking at him.

'No. You can't,' comes the reply. 'You've got things to sort out. And I want you at my wedding tomorrow. So, you need to get a head start.'

While Alex chugs through the afternoon traffic, I hunch down behind him and let my mind wander again. That Jay is connected to the Pickthall family's story is something I've already accepted; that he's withheld the most devastating part of that story, I cannot connect with at all. Why? There's an obvious answer to that question. He's got more to hide.

Earlier, in utter confusion, I'd begged Alex to telephone Rosina Kerr. To see if he could find out anything about who owned Tunnel Cottage. In my mind, I'd started to invent some creepy story where I'd become embroiled in a crazy family dispute. Which is ridiculous, when I consider Jay. He's the most unsophisticated person I know. All Rosina could say was that the cottage was being sold on behalf of an estate. A way of recouping some of the costs entailed when there is a death without benefaction. I'm not brilliant at understanding the language of the law, but I'm pretty sure that meant the owner of Tunnel Cottage was dead and had no living relatives. And considering that owner was a Frederick Pickthall, father of John and James, he most certainly does have a living relative. Jay. But that doesn't make any sense. What it does do though, is make me feel like I've been used, and that's not something I'm dealing with very well.

We stop at the top of the cottage's driveway, and Alex turns off the ignition. Neither of us moves for a moment. From here, I can see the dark glitter of the beck as it cuts along the edge of the meadow. Jay's brother died in that water. How could he have held that back from me? Is the reason more sinister than a simple desire to block out the past?

'See you in the morning,' Alex says as he helps me down from the bike. 'And Evie.'

'What?' The brightness of the sun is grating. And my head pounds.

'Do me a favour. Put yourself first, okay?'

I nod. What can I say to that? It's not fair of me, but I hear gloating.

'Will do,' I mumble. Then, 'Thanks.' I hand him the helmet and set off walking down the drive.

When I get inside, I find Jay kneeling at the coffee table in the lounge. He has a paintbrush in his hand. The curtains are flung wide, and all of the windows are open. On the breeze that drifts in, is the scent of turned earth and grass.

'Oh, hello.' He beams, laying the brush down very carefully. 'They let you out earlier than planned?'

I crouch down beside him and loop my arms around his shoulders. His hands come up and press against me.

'Is everything all right?' he asks. Then, before I can say anything, 'It's not, is it?'

'Something happened at work today. I need to ask you about it.' I stand up and lead him to the sofa.

'You've got me worried now,' he murmurs. 'What's happened, Evie? Is it something bad?'

I smile thinly and nod my head. Then I tell him about what I've seen this morning, in Alex's office. What I've found out. What I think I've found out. He listens, elbows resting on his knees and his face covered by his hands.

When I am finished, he lets out a long sigh, and stands up. Then positions himself in front of the fireplace. His face is ashen.

'John Pickthall is who I *was*,' he spits. 'As I've told you before.' Then he punches a fist against his chest. 'This is Jay Elliot.'

Am I going to get anything else, I wonder? It's been one lie after another with him, and now he's not going to explain the latest two?

'Why haven't you told me your father owned the cottage, *Jay?*'

'Because I didn't know. He's been dead to me, these last twenty years. I told you that.'

I don't like his tone. There's the implication that my lack of understanding the situation is the problem here, not his lack of telling me. Negativity towards him isn't something I'm comfortable with feeling, and I want it to go away. But I have to know the truth.

'You did,' I say, and I'm surprised at how calm I sound. 'But you never mentioned a brother. One that drowned in the beck by the cottage. Why didn't you, Jay. Why didn't you?'

He doesn't give me an answer, only a look that chills me to the bone. Then he storms out of the room and the front door slams.

Jay/John

Summer 1984

Glitter on the water's surface makes John want to dip his hand and scoop. His head is hot with the sun, his throat a choke of cardboard dust. But Mam will give him one of her looks if he brings Jamie back with wet socks and sloshing shoes. And if John goes into the water, his brother will have to follow. There are pieces of crumbly stone by his feet. Throwing them in might relieve the itch. Just the sound of them, hitting that bright surface. He scuffs them with the toe of his plastic sandal, then kneels to lift a few. Jamie narrows his eyes. Green slits against the soft tan of his face.

'We're not to get dirty, Mam says.'

'Not getting dirty.' John checks the sandstone crumbles. 'Just my hands.' With a swing of his arm, the stones are launched across the surface of the beck. They scatter widely, then drop out of sight with a gentle plop.

'Again. Again.' Jamie jumps over the heat of the afternoon. John turns his head towards the cottage. Mam and Dad will still be taking plates and cups out of those dry-smelling boxes. Only one downstairs window looks out across the meadow and down to the beck, and he can't see them standing at it. Plenty of time for a few more handfuls to be chucked. Jamie hunkers down and watches. Clouds of red dust form around John's feet as he grabs more of the stone. The sun beats down.

Then comes the whistle. Loud, with two familiar notes. Dad. John swings his head towards the sound. By the time it comes again, he has grabbed his brother's hand, and they are running across the meadow, jumping tussocks of scorched grass, swerving patches of nettle and thistle.

Dad leans against the cottage gate, shirtsleeves rolled to his elbows, the usual slick of his hair undone.

'In now, you pair,' he growls. 'And clean them hands.'

John squints up at the cottage, taking in the slabs of red sandstone and long chimney stacks. He wonders if the tiny window under the eaves will be his. They will have a bedroom each, his mam says. Not like in the last place. And there's no rent to pay now, what with Dad being the tunnel-man and everything. So, he and Jamie have new beds. Come flat, in cardboard boxes, the man in the shop told them. Just needed fixing together, and Dad was good at that. As long as they didn't get under his feet, he said, and Mam brought him a brew or two.

The front door stands open, and Jamie scampers up the path, disappearing inside. Dad glares at John's hands.

'Told yous not to get filthy, didn't I?' He cracks a hand around John's head, not enough to do damage, but enough for keeping quiet. 'Get 'em washed before tea. Your mam's ready to dish up.'

The hallway of the cottage is dark and cool, and nothing like the outside. There are tiles of carpet on the floor, in grubby shades of red and green, and a telephone sits on an orange pine table. Shoes and boots spill out of a half-packed tea chest. John's shoes and Jamie's wellingtons. They really have moved here then, if they've brought their shoes. The air smells of cucumber and something tinned. Salmon, perhaps, and John's mouth waters. But what he really wants is a tall beaker of cordial.

Mam is in the kitchen, putting flowers in a vase. Ones she's picked from the garden. John has never had a garden before, let alone a meadow and a beck, and this thought makes his stomach do a flip that shakes right down to his knees. The time he is going to have. Outside, with water and warmth and light. No concrete grey or broken glass or dogs anywhere in sight.

And all dad has to do to keep them here is look after the tunnel, keep people off the crossing and check the signals now and again.

'There you are.' Mam is all softness and buttery hair. 'Give us those hands, John Pickthall. Jamie's gone to find the toilet.' She nods towards the hallway. 'Fancy having it upstairs. We've gone posh, haven't we?'

John plunges his hands through the white suds in the sink, and feels the warm water lurking beneath. He is just tall enough, at eight years old, that he can see the view through the kitchen window, see the tall firs, the felt-roofed outhouse and the stretch of the meadow. The sky is a rich blue.

In the space between tea and bed, he'll have to help unpack boxes. Or so Mam has told him. That, and keep his brother entertained with plastic soldiers and wars.

Dad appears at the kitchen door, growly still, his arms full of scrunched newspaper. 'Take this off me, lover,' he shouts towards Mam. 'Get a binbag or sommat.'

She unpeels a crunchy black bag from a roll on the countertop, and shakes it until it opens itself up, gaping and hungry. Dad shoves in the dirty newsprint, then rinses his hands under the trickle of water coming from one of the brassy taps joined to the sink.

Jamie skips into the room and Dad bends to put his hands around the little waist, and lift him high. 'Down you go, lad.' He beams, plonking Jamie, brown cotton shorts and all, onto the end of one of the kitchen benches. 'Hope you washed your hands.'

John slides in quietly beside him, watching Mam as she carries plates of triangle-cut sandwiches to the table.

'There's crisps, too.' She smiles. The Tupperware bowl is the crowning glory, and John dips his hand straight away. Crisps. Salt and grease. What adults eat in pubs. He and Jamie have to stand outside those places sometimes, waiting for Dad and his rugby mates.

'Manners.' Dad slaps him away. 'Let little lad get his first.'

'Fred, leave him. They're both hungry, and there's plenty.' Mam's soft smile, especially for him. But John drops his chin and waits.

Later, when more boxes have been emptied, and John has shared three inches of lukewarm bathwater with his brother, Mam towel-dries their heads and pulls out mismatched pyjamas from a battered brown suitcase.

'How did I get two lads with such different hair?' she asks. 'A little blond angel, and a dark, clever wizard.' A gentle tutting sound, then she kisses them both. The fire grate lies undisturbed, though she has placed her special clock on the wooden mantle, along with two green bottles stuck with half-melted candles. Dad is sprawled, eyes closed, on their new green sofa. It has cream patterns cut into the cushions, and John wants to trace their shell-like spirals, but he dares not disturb his father. With his pyjama top tucked in, John stares out through the large glass doors that take up a whole wall in this room. Mam has pushed them open slightly, and the scent of sweet honeysuckle slides in.

Behind the hedge lies the railway line, and he can hardly wait to see his first train trundle by. The summer light is starting to fade. It's way past the time when Dad would send him scurrying for his bed. Only Jamie gets stories now, from Dad, anyway. John reads so well; he can do his own bedtime story, or that's what Dad says. And if Mam sometimes creeps into his room and talks to him about what he's reading, John can live with that. He's the big brother. Jamie hasn't even started at school; he needs all the fuss of stories and tucking in and patting.

'Can I go and get in, Mam?' John asks. Sleep will make tomorrow come quicker. More than anything, he wants to zoom across that meadow, drinking in the taste of grass and freedom. She has Jamie on her knee, pink-faced and smudge-eyed.

'Go on then.' A dazzling smile. Mam doesn't need make-up, Dad says. She purses her lips, this time for John alone. 'Kiss-kiss, Johnny.'

He leans in, careful not to knock against Dad's huge legs.

'Goodnight, darling.' A whisper in John's ear, then he skips away.

The hall is dark. John doesn't know where the light switches are in this house, but he won't allow himself to be scared. Not like Jamie. Monsters of the night don't worry him: he'd like to meet one, if they really existed. There is no carpet on the stairs, and John has to tiptoe around the cold spikes of wood and saw-tooth runners. On the landing are five doors, all made from rough orange wood, and all closed. He takes a quick peep into Mam and Dad's bedroom. Stacked with boxes and crates, but her perfume, too.

A rush of soapy air from the bathroom makes his nostrils curl. The floor is tiled in black and white, and the red spotted bag they take on holiday is propped against a tall white basin on the wall opposite. He rummages for his toothbrush and some minty paste, and wipes his mouth with his fingers after, as he can't find towels. Then, it's off to his own room.

He tries the door, and sees the plumped-up quilt cover he chose, spread across the small wooden bed. His books are there, splitting the sides of a cardboard box. Above the slats of the headboard is the tiny window he'd seen outside. His window. Not Jamie's, not Mam's or Dad's, just his. He springs onto the bed to look at the view. The sky is silver-blue, with just a whisper of moon. Across the sleeping grass of the meadow, the beck is a line of liquorice-black. Above it, behind the grainy outline of trees, a train whistles by. One that he'll always remember. His first train at Tunnel Cottage.

One morning, Mam has a scarf wrapped around her head, with a roller poking out at the front. A sign that she and Dad are doing grown-up things, later on. A trip out to a pub, perhaps, or someone coming for tea.

'I want you boys out the way,' she says. 'Aunty Liz will be over later, to see how we've got the place.'

Liz Elliot: silver hair and marshmallow-soft skin, more like a mam than a sister, in John's opinion. But she always talks to him, doesn't fuss Jamie so much.

John is becoming used to the way Mam polishes and vacuums the cottage. Every day, whether it's needed or not, so his dad says. But he's as bad, out in the sheds all the time, sharpening tools and messing about with hunks of wood. Four weeks into their life at the cottage, and Dad acts like he's been in charge of this bit of the railway forever.

Mam drags open the back door, and the fragrant heat stalks in. She stands in silhouette for a moment, running a hand across the back of her neck.

'It hasn't been as hot as this since the summer you were born, Johnny. 1976. I remember it well.' A hand rests on her belly. He has heard this story before. The one where she's as big as the side of a house and twice as heavy, and where she guzzles so much orange cordial that she's sure he'll pop out with a bottle of Corona in his hand.

'Can we take some sarnies with us,' he calls, working on a distraction, 'and a drink? Over to the beck, I mean?'

This is how he spends his days, these high days of summer.

In the shade, on the banks of the beck, dipping for the silver fish with bulbous eyes that appear from nowhere and have no place to go, other than the bucket that he and his brother found in one of Dad's sheds. Jamie is almost blond now, with a tideline tan at his neck and sleepy eyes. John's own hair has taken on a dusty shade of brown tipped with orange. And sleep has become a treat. The nightmare that used to come repeatedly, about wolves hiding behind threadbare curtains, has gone.

'You can, son,' Mam says, dreamy, and tucking at her hair. 'But I'll be over at lunchtime anyway, just to see how you are. Dad's got some repairs to do on the other side of the tunnel.' She leans over the table and picks up their cereal bowls. 'Teeth done, then.' A thumb towards the hallway. 'And I'll make your pack-ups.'

John has plans for today. Everything he's been working on should come together. Jamie can stick with his Action Man Frogman, who takes hundreds of dives in the beck every day. The duck-trap that John has invented and laid out has to have worked. Not to have harmed the birds that bobbed on the edges of the water, but just so that he can make friends. There are three pairs of the creatures nesting in the overgrowth of grass and reeds at the water's edge. He loves their yellow eyes and harsh greeting-call, the oily, teal feathers of the males, and the pretty faces of the females. They are quick enough to snap up his bread-crusts. Perhaps today, one of them will be snared.

He and Jamie clatter up the stairs, knees jabbing and wanting to be first. Mam's bedroom door is open, letting sunlight slant onto the landing. No sun gets into his room until the middle of the afternoon, and then it has to fight its way past a giant red-trunked tree. One that Dad keeps threatening to chop down. It'd keep the fires going for at least a year, he says.

John can catch a glimpse of the beck from his window, if

he kneels on his bed. That's worth more than any dazzle of sunlight. And every time he presses his face to the glass, he wants to lay down that view in his memory and keep it there forever.

'Get your wellies,' he tells his brother as they jump down the stairs again, 'and don't put any socks on this time.' He shrugs. 'No point, is there?'

Jamie does as he's told, peeling off his socks and leaving them on the floor of the scullery. Their wellies are royal blue, with a layer of bendy yellow plastic at the top that has something like shoelaces threaded through. That way, you can pull them tight underneath your knees and no water slops in. But it still does, through the lace-holes.

'Keep an eye on our Jamie.' Mam hands him a pack of sandwiches, wrapped tight in silvery plastic, and a Tupperware beaker with a lid. 'And stay in sight of the cottage, please.'

He shuffles out through the kitchen door and into the shady promise of the garden. Jamie is already flying Frogman through his first adventure of the day. John doesn't wait. He flings open the garden gate and runs, wellies slapping, into the meadow.

A small group of scribble larks fly upwards from the thistle patch, golden heads hammering out their seven-note song. The breeze is warm and thick and ruffles the surface of the beck. Frogman takes a dive, while John scans the bank for any sign of his mallard friends. Mam told him the name of the ducks and that the males have beaks of solid gold. He doesn't believe her, but he'd like to get close enough for a look and a feel. The basket he wove from twiggy ash and hazel die-back is just visible from its place on the opposite bank, but he sees at once that it has no ducks trapped beneath. Instead, it bobs gently against the surface of the water, as though it could be carried away at any moment.

John doesn't hesitate. He jumps into the beck and wades

across to save his basket. The water is never more than as high as his knees, but it floods his wellies soon enough. Jamie jumps in too, and Frogman is rescued, ready for his next mission. The mallards are nowhere to be seen, but John knows they will be along eventually, in search of a crust, unable to curb their curiosity. This is what he loves about them. Their nosy nature is stronger than their fear. A bit like him, really.

There is no damage to the basket. John pulls it out of the water, and it soaks his clothes. He has spent weeks collecting and weaving and planning, but the ducks never come near. Or they probably do the same thing that he does, in the local swimming pool. A surface dive, Dad calls it. A way of swimming underwater, avoiding dangers on the surface. John is a good swimmer, but Jamie hasn't learnt yet.

Across the meadow, heat rises in fragrant plumes, scattering buttercup pollen and making the hoverflies drowsy. John notices none of this. Instead, he lets the beck flow by while he thinks. If he can fix his basket to some legs, these could be whipped away if a mallard happened to swim by, perhaps seeking out a sandwich crust. The plan will take some hard work, some thinking about, but the morning stretches out like the rolled-out ball of his mother's pastry: elastic and sweet and full of possibilities. Punctuated, every half hour, by the screech of a train.

And suddenly, Mam and Aunty Liz are stepping towards him. Smiling at first, and Liz wearing a pink frock with a tiered skirt. Then they are running, and Mam's face has been taken over by the wide black gape of her mouth, and she is screaming. His brother's name.

'Jamie. Jamie. Jamie.' Over and over. Then Liz is in the beck, and she has Jamie in her arms, shaking him while Mam continues her screaming.

John watches, basket in hand, wondering what is happening. Wondering why Jamie is pretending to be asleep, why he stays asleep while Liz lays him on the banking. And then Mam is striding towards him and grabbing at him and hitting him.

'Why weren't you watching?' she shrieks. 'He's only five. My Jamie.' A clutch at her stomach. 'My Jamie.' Then she falls to the ground.

'Fetch your dad,' Liz calls. 'Now.' Not her normal voice. That's soft. This comes from a place in her that John doesn't recognise, but he runs anyway. Dad will be a mile away, through the tunnel and down the track, but oh, how he runs.

———

When John gets back to Tunnel Cottage, his father at full pelt behind him, white spittle at the corners of his mouth, Mam is still screaming. There is a trail of muddy water through the hallway, and she is sitting on the sofa, cradling the sleeping body of Jamie, while Aunty Liz stands and watches, her expression flat and sad.

'He's gone, Fred,' she whispers, putting her hand on Dad's arm. 'But I've called for an ambulance. It's on its way.'

Dad falls to his knees in front of Mam and begins shaking Jamie and slapping his smudged face. 'Wake up, son,' he wails. 'Wake up. Wake up. Wake up.'

John isn't sure why his brother seems so floppy. And why is Mam leaving him in wet clothes? The noise in the room, and the shaking, it's enough to scare anyone awake.

'What's happening, Mam?' he shouts, crossing his legs, fearful now. Aunty Liz grabs him and forces his face into her soft hip. 'It's all right, lad. It's all right,' she murmurs, but John can tell she's lying. The way her bottom lip trembles, making her words stick together.

The high-pitched screech of a siren splits the air. For a moment, everything in the room pauses. The shaking, the slapping, the wailing. It all stops. Liz drags him with her to the front door. Two men in white-shirted uniforms are racing down the drive. One is carrying a large case. It makes John think of their holiday suitcase, the one pushed under Mam's bed.

'In here. In here,' Liz screams, shoving him to one side. Heat crawls in behind the men, and John thinks he might fall over, there's so much punching going on in his guts.

One of the men has slicked-back hair and a moustache that droops down both sides of his mouth. He takes Jamie from Dad's arms and lays him flat on the living-room floor, on the swirly pastel-pink rug. But his brother's face is far from pink. It is grey. And his lips have taken on a greenish colour, like the algae that covers the boulders in the beck.

Then suddenly, the men are shaking their heads. More shaking. An ear is lowered to Jamie's green lips. His wrist is lifted. Mam is shrieking again, but Dad is looking at John. Staring. Dark brows drawn into a line, above angry eyes.

'Get him out of here, Liz,' he growls. 'Get that little bugger out of here.'

Jay

March 2019

That summer, at Tunnel Cottage, had been the best – and the worst – in Jay's life. Making a better one, with Evie, isn't going to happen now. When she'd spoken to him earlier, there had been fear in her eyes. Fear, and something else. Loathing, perhaps? He didn't look at her for long enough to find out; could only leave. With him, for most of his life, he's carried the burden of killing Jamie, the burden of his mother's decline and his father's hatred. Finding Evie had given him the confidence to relive that tragic day again and begin to compose it into words that he could offer her as an explanation. One that she might be able to shine her light through, and change.

Not now, though.

Walking back to his aunt's house has given him time to think. There can be no future with Evie. The trust is gone; he's been given so much, despite the stupidity of his actions, but he's still managed to lose it. But what's gnawing away at the last shred of his sanity is the way she found out the truth. That boss of hers, he's been after getting rid of Jay from the beginning. It's as though he remembers.

Jay/John

June 1985

John holds his breath and pushes his hand into the plastic bag.

'Come along now, Master Pickthall, it's not a fashion show.'

Mrs Lavender is standing right behind him, in her floaty skirt and whistle necklace. She reaches over his shoulder and gives the bag a shake. And up comes the rubbery smell, overlaid with something that reminds John of rotten meat.

'I need a size five, miss.' He thinks about manners. 'Please.'

The plimsols all look the same. Black and tatty, with that mocking gusset of elastic. He hates the things. And he hates what they stand for. PE lessons where he's picked last for teams, and usually ends up on the floor, cradling his shins.

'We can't all have what we need,' Mrs Lavender tells him, then thrusts a pair into his hands. There is a number four bleached into the heels. 'Now hurry up and put them on. Our class are going out to the field right now.' The telling voice becomes a shout. 'And put on a red band.' She nods towards a basket on her desk, then walks away, meeting a line of children by the door.

John thinks about taking his socks off. That way, the plimsols might fit. But he knows the soles aren't clean and he'd have to lay them on his chair. Where everyone would see. It's bad enough having to wear last summer's playing-out shorts and a T-shirt that's too small. When every other kid has an outfit especially for the sports day: gleaming white polo-shirts, shiny navy shorts, and stretchy skirts for the girls. He doesn't have those, except in his dreams, where he imagines himself to be the child of a king or queen. Or the Prime Minister, perhaps. She's a lady. She'd understand about wearing the right sports clothes.

Mrs Lavender is clapping her hands together in the way she always does when she's nervous. Then she steps into the corridor, and the rest of his class follow.

Punchy-Boy, white shirt gleaming, is at the front of the line because he's the class captain. But his red band worries John more. It means he's going to want everyone wearing the same colour to be a winner. That's not something John thinks he can be. Although the morning kicks and thumps are something he's got used to, got clever at swerving, Punchy-Boy is always looking for the next thing to make him feel bad.

The playing field is a haze of heat and faces. John drags his feet across grass that is so dry it snaps at his ankles and prickles the back of his legs as he sits down.

Mrs Lavender is flapping her hands at him. 'John Pickthall,' she says, 'do we smell or something? Why are you sitting all the way over there?'

The other children laugh, Punchy-Boy louder than the rest of them.

'Sit up straight, Zan,' she says to him. 'And give your mummy a wave.'

John's not quite sure what sort of name Zan is, except that it makes Punchy-Boy sound like one of the superheroes from a Marvel comic.

When the headteacher speaks a tinny welcome to the parents and toddlers who have come to enjoy the afternoon, John puts his hands over his ears. The clapping and the smiling faces and the smell of suntan lotion is giving him a sickly feeling in his stomach. A year ago, he had a proper mam and a toddler brother. They'd have been cheering for him and waiting at the school gates with the safety of family, and an iced lolly. If he doesn't win his race, those same gates are going to be deadly.

The afternoon wears on in a muddle of skipping ropes and orange cordial and tears. John can feel the sun burning the back of his neck, but he dares not say anything. Better to be invisible, in his opinion. Especially when the red team are not winning, and Punchy-Boy's lips are getting more and more pouty.

By the time John's race is announced, he has almost fallen asleep. The black plimsols have drawn his feet into a shape that reminds him of a bridge. And now he's got to get up and crawl through a set of obstacles, while the world looks on.

Most of the children are up on their feet as he waits on the start line. Ahead are benches to be jumped, hoops to be wriggled through and then the final humiliation: four tyres, hanging on ropes from a heavy frame, at a height that seems unfair for the other kids who line up with him. He can win this race, he knows it.

On the whistle's sharp blast, he sets off, elbows pointing, and fists clenched. He can feel the inhale of the crowd, and wishes Mam was there to see him. But he will tell her about the win. If he gets it. And he might just, because he is flying ahead. Only the tyre to do now.

He decides to go through feet first. With a grab of the rope, he heaves himself up. The others have caught up now and are diving like they're in a swimming pool. Their hands hit the grass on the other side of the tyres. But John is stuck. The backs of his thighs, sticky with afternoon heat, have wedged themselves into empty space. When he tries to free himself, there is a sucking pressure that won't give. While he holds onto the rope and feels himself swinging, he watches the other three racers reach the finish line almost together. Time stops. His tyre begins to turn slowly. Then there is cheering and clapping. And laughter.

Mrs Lavender trots across the grass, with some of the red team. Including Punchy-Boy.

'Now, don't you cry, John Pickthall,' she is saying, but he can't help himself. His head is pounding, and he wants Mam. But all he's got is Punchy-Boy, spinning the tyre around with one hand, and holding himself between his legs with the other.

Later, when the sports are over and the winning team has lapped the field holding high their silver trophy, John drags himself along the school driveway in the direction of home. Most of the other kids have gone with their mams and dads, all pink-faced and whining for ice creams. He swings his bag of uniform and shuffles his feet in the too-small plimsols. Mrs Lavender has said he could keep them, though what use they'll be he can't work out.

'Loser.' A voice just behind him. Punchy-Boy and his two friends.

John walks quicker, even though his feet hurt.

'Oi. Pee-your-pants. I'm talking to you.'

There is no one else about. No mams and dads, or teachers. Not even Mr Wardman, the janitor. He sometimes sweeps up on the street outside the school, especially on hot days when there's choc-ice wrappers, freshly dropped. Lazy, in John's opinion, even though he wishes he could have a mam and a choc-ice, right now.

'Get lost,' John mutters. But it's all he gets to say.

Punchy-Boy is on him in an instant, swinging his fists against John's shoulders and pushing him to the ground.

'You lost us the whole sports day,' he snarls, waving a *V* sign he has made with his fingers. 'Scratter. I hate you.'

His face is bright red, and John can smell the cleanness of him. And almost tastes his anger. He tries to push him away, but the other two boys take hold of his arms and pull them out so that he has nothing to gain leverage with.

'Get off me,' John cries. 'Get. Off. Me.'

'Did you pee in that tyre?' Punchy-Boy is saying. 'Is that why you got stuck? You dirty pig.'

John watches as Punchy-Boy's face moves nearer to his. It reminds him of when Aunty Liz homes in for a kiss.

Their eyes lock, then Punchy-Boy coughs, somewhere in the back of his throat, and spits in John's face.

Jay

March 2019

He isn't a violent man. So many things in his life could have caused him to react in a physical way. But what would have been achieved? Only more trouble, and he's had plenty enough of that. Losing Evie, though. That has made him breathless with anger.

He lets himself into the house. It smells of old paint, and misery. In the middle of the living room, he stops. This isn't his home; it's never been. There's a weight pressing down on his shoulders, and he has to sit. It isn't the first time he's thought about stepping away from his life. If that means he's what people call *mentally ill*, then so be it. Over the years, he's prided himself on keeping physically well, and if there have been dark days, he's stepped away and watched them pass. Connecting with nature has helped: it has never judged him and has an unflinching beauty. Like Evie.

And suddenly, every scrap of emotion he's ever held inside, every need he's ever ignored, join together in his belly. One gigantic ball of searing energy that can no longer be controlled. He has to let it escape. A growl comes first, a small one, but then it grows. It forces him to his feet and changes into an almighty dry sob where he feels his face crumple. His hands clutch at his hair and rage shakes him. Then he's calling Evie's name over and over. And the only other thing he can think about is knocking Punchy-Boy to the floor and stamping all over him.

Chapter Thirty-Two

When I blink myself awake, a stream of bright sunlight is coming through the bedroom window. I haven't slept well, waiting for Jay to come back. But I don't think he has. I swing my legs over the edge of the bed and shuffle downstairs to check. He's not there. What I'll do about going to Alex and Paul's wedding I can't work out. I feel too wretched. Jay's suit is still hanging in the lounge, pressed and ready. My yellow dress is next to it, and the sight brings me to tears.

I sit down on the sofa and let myself cry. What else can I do? Betrayal isn't what I feel. Broken would be a better description. Like I've been sliced four-ways, my insides scooped out. That Jay hadn't felt he could trust me is bad enough. That he may have had a hand in the death of his brother is terrifying. Have my feelings for this guy been wrong from the start? My slip-up over Ian Turnbull's character should have warned me that I was losing my touch.

By the time I've done as much crying and thinking as it's taken to be able to function, it's ten o'clock. The wedding is at eleven, and I've promised Alex I'll be there early. There's a meeting for the two grooms and their witnesses, apparently, about twenty minutes before the ceremony, which will take place at the registration offices, in their purpose-built wedding room, with enough space for eighty guests. There won't be that many, Alex has told me, and for that I am thankful.

What I'm going to use is a technique I had at White Platts that will allow me to get through the day without alerting anyone to what I'm feeling. My colleagues and I perfected it when we had stuff going on in our personal lives but had to lead an expedition on the water, or up the side of a fell. It involved lots of deep breathing and cups of tea, and a mental meditation that took your unsettled self out of your body and left it somewhere safe for the day. A kind of out-of-body experience. Crazy, but it worked for us then, so I'm going to try it now.

In half an hour, the diamond me is washed, dressed and stepping out of Tunnel Cottage, while the real me is still lying in bed, and watching.

I struggle to find a parking space in the town centre. A sunny Saturday, with daffodils opening in the planters, and the chance to shop without wearing thick coats, has filled the main areas with couples and families and groups of shrieking teens.

Alex and Paul are both wearing white. Well, cream actually. Ivory. They make a stunning couple. Alex in his yellow shirt and sunglasses, and Paul, smaller, and with a white shirt and marigold tie. I dart between the traffic and catch up with them just outside the offices. That first glimpse brings a choke of tears and longing, but there is no time to say anything: Alex gives me a questioning look, then ushers me away.

When the deed is done and the register is signed, I make my way back towards the rows of waiting guests, so that Alex and Paul Swarbrick-Murray can be formally introduced. I flick my glance across to my mother, but she is talking to Sheila Swarbrick, and doesn't see me. Or maybe she chooses not to.

I slide myself into the empty seat next to her. 'All done,' I whisper. 'They're married; signed, sealed and delivered.'

She lifts her chin slightly and gives me a chilly smile; there is a conversation to finish and I'm being *inconvenient*. Alex's mother isn't quite so rude.

'Evie, my love,' she says, looking fresh in her primrose-yellow suit. 'Don't they make a gorgeous couple.' She glances past me. 'Where's your fella? Not over already, is it?'

My mother barks low in her throat; a shark, scenting blood. 'Let me guess,' she says. 'He didn't have anything to wear.'

This woman. She has no idea. I can feel myself slipping back into damaged-mode, and we haven't even made it to the reception yet.

'He'll be here,' I say, before I can stop myself. 'No need for a feeding frenzy yet.'

We are saved from further decline by a demand from the registrars that we applaud the happy couple, then escort them out of the building.

Outside, people blink in the sunshine, then follow Alex and Paul as they stride through the town centre. Saturday shoppers stop and clap and smile at us all, and one of Paul's college friends runs ahead, snapping photographs and sending out vulgar comments. This lightens the mood even further, so that when we reach the hotel, the whole group is fizzing with excitement. I just feel rotten.

More guests greet us at the front door, and though the interior of the place is in the grand Gothic style, we are shown to a room that is airy and light and full of white linen and vases of daffodils.

The tables are laid out with place names and silver service and small mementos of the day. I sit next to an empty chair, and with four members of Paul's family. His sister, small and dark like him, and with the same brand of humour, is soon chatting to me. But all I can think of is Jay. I've lost the *out-of-*

body me, and the miserable one is back. I try my best to join in with the frivolity of it all, but in the end, Paul's sister gives up and turns to someone else.

While speeches are made and more wine is drunk, I start to think up the sentences I am going to use to explain why Jay isn't here with me. Alex should understand. He's the one who told me to put myself first: code for getting rid of this *John Pickthall* character. Strange then that he's caught up with me a couple of times during the afternoon, wanting to talk about Jay.

I don't think I can. Not to Alex, anyway.

The afternoon fades into evening. More people turn up, flamboyant and outrageous and everything Jay would have found difficult to handle. I'd have agreed with him on that one. In my head, I veer between flagging down a taxi and driving to his house, and getting up on the dance floor and smooching with the first straight guy I can find.

The guests are working their way into a lather, and I wander away to find somewhere cool to sit. There is a quiet saloon at the front of the hotel, with small booths and a scatter of red-topped tables. I've only just sat down when there is a shout from the doorway. Alex. Yellow shirt unbuttoned to the waist and the blur of drink across his expression.

'There you are.' He stumbles towards me. 'Not had a chance to speak properly yet, have we? There's stuff I need t'tell you, darlin'.' His words tumble over his lips with their beginnings and ends missing, so that it's difficult to tell exactly what they are.

'You're drunk,' I say with a sneer, and he looks shocked.

'S'my weddin',' he drawls. 'Got a right t'be drunk.'

I search over his shoulder for Paul, but he appears to have given up chasing his dangerous toddler.

'If you're wanting to know about Jay,' I say. 'And I guess you are, well, it's over. You'll be pleased about that, I'm sure.'

Alex slams his hands down on the table and sticks his face forward so that I can't avoid looking at him. 'Not pleased,' he mumbles. 'Far from it.'

I sigh and look away. How my business has suddenly become his, baffles me. And on his wedding day, too.

'Are you listenin' to me, Evie?'

'No.'

'Well, I'm tellin' you anyway.' He pauses and draws himself up to his full height. 'Been digging aroun'. Haven't I. Into that… bloody… drownin' story.' His arms are waving frantically. 'It was pure accident, you know. Did you know that? Pure accident.'

I shake my head. 'You can't stop yourself, can you? Digging around? What the hell does that mean, Alex?'

'It means,' he slurs, spitting slightly, 'that I've read the inquest notes into young James Pickthall's death. Your Jay… John… whatever you call him, he was there. But the kiddie just fell in the water when no one was watchin'. Accident, like I said.'

When I fling myself upwards and move towards him, he sways a little and stands his ground. I have never felt so angry. It's like a red-hot flare of energy, pounding at the base of my neck so that I can hardly breathe.

'How dare you,' I shriek. 'How bloody dare you.'

Alex's hand grips my arm, and we stand in rigid silence. Which is suddenly broken by the swish and scrape of the swing doors at the side of the bar. And in walks Jay.

'Get your hands off her,' he says, cold as ice.

'Jay. Buddy.' Alex staggers a little then holds out a hand. 'Glad you could make it.'

I want to frame the moment: Jay, somehow wearing his wedding suit and an open-necked shirt, tall and elegant and so tense he might snap. And Alex, smiling and offering his hand and his good humour.

But Jay isn't playing.

At first, when he dips his head, I think he's going to take himself out of the situation, then the two of them are chest to chest, eye to eye.

In the moment that I'm thinking about how I can defuse the situation, Alex says, 'I know you.' The words are laced with hostility.

'And I know you,' spits Jay. 'Zan.'

The air between them shimmers with anger. I can feel it. My attention is snagged but I can do nothing.

'You tried to chase me away once before,' Jay is snarling. It scares me. 'Remember that? Big tough Punchy-Boy, kicking lumps out of the kid who killed his brother?'

Punchy-Boy? What is Jay talking about?

'Guys,' I say, moving towards them. My mother and Paul are in the doorway. But no one is listening to me.

Alex growls deep in his throat. Then slaps his hands against Jay's shoulders, making him stagger back slightly.

'Fuck off,' he says. 'I could never stand you. No one could. What were you even doing in our school?' Then he pushes again.

'Alex,' I shriek. 'Stop it.'

My mother steps into the room. Paul is behind her. The flow of time is altered. There is no movement, only the muffled throb of music. My breath catches, and I wonder if the scene is real.

Then Alex launches himself at Jay and lands a punch that sends him staggering backwards. I stare in horror as his head smashes against the corner of a table, snapping forwards, chin to chest. He hits the floor. His eyes roll upwards, and he twitches. Just once, then he is still.

Alex and I stand and stare. Only for a few seconds, but it feels like forever. Then my mother is kneeling beside Jay's head and calling for clean towels, and Paul is shouting for someone to get an ambulance. And all I can do is cover my whole face with my hands and peep at the scene from between my open fingers. There's so much blood gushing from the back of Jay's head, and his features have softened. Like he's melting away. That's when I start to scream.

———

Within a few minutes, while my mother presses towels to various places around Jay's skull, and before Alex has moved from where he is now rooted, a team of paramedics arrive; two women and a hefty man carrying a large case. He clears the room with one shout and one of the women, frizzy-haired and muscular, kneels down next to my mother.

'Who is this, please?' she asks gently.

'Jay,' she whispers. 'Jay Elliot. I've applied pressure to the back of his skull where the worst of the damage is. And kept his airway clear, though his breathing's very quiet.'

Then she stands up, and lets others take over.

I realise that I am shaking violently, and my mother takes me by the hand and sits me down.

'Never mind about me,' I stammer. 'Help him.'

'He's getting the best help he can from the guys over there. You just calm yourself, dear.' Then she slides a hand across my shoulder, and I can't help but lean into her.

I can only see Jay's legs. And the shoes he hated so much. They are long and shiny and jerk from side to side, so I'm sure he's moving.

'I can't get him back, Simmy.' A deep frown from the face of the male paramedic. 'Can you come over?'

The three of them continue to work on Jay, blocking my view and sending waves of nausea through me with every grunt and groan and move they make. If I could stand up, I would. But my legs feel as though the muscle has been stripped from them.

My mother's face is raw and teary. I catch her eye for a moment, and she gives me a grim smile. 'He'll get there,' she whispers. To us both.

Then Alex appears in my vision. 'What's happening, Evie?' A dense whisper. 'Aren't they taking him to hospital?'

'He's got a name, you know,' I hiss. 'He's somebody.' I turn away. The fault here lies squarely on Alex; of that, I'm sure.

The paramedics are muttering to each other. They've stopped holding tubes to Jay's mouth and waving pencil-thin torches across his eyes, and are instead loading him onto a stretcher.

Then the frizzy-haired woman stands up and walks towards me. 'It's not looking good,' she says. 'We're going to blue-light him in.'

I want to go in the ambulance with Jay, but the space isn't there. Instead, one of the paramedics suggests I call a taxi and follow behind. This isn't what I do. My reptilian brain takes over, and I run: through the soft twilight, past groups of hideously smiling people, in front of cars with headlights on low beam, and back to my car. If there is any residual alcohol in my bloodstream, I figure it must be gone after that sprint and I strap myself in and just drive.

I'm right behind the ambulance, and the paramedics are just wheeling Jay through the accident and emergency department when I get there. He is wrapped in an acid-yellow blanket that looks like it's come from a baby's crib, and is just a collection of holes joined together by soft wool. There's some kind of clumsy bandage around his head but blood has soaked through at the side. Then he's whisked away and the only thing

I can do is lean against the reception desk and try to give Jay's details, such as they are. When Jay Elliot comes up on the system, I am surprised. I was ready to call him John Pickthall. He'd meant what he'd said, about leaving that particular guy behind. No words come when they ask me for next of kin, though, so I call myself his wife and they write that down.

Most of the seats in the waiting area are occupied; it's a Saturday night, after all. I sit opposite a young guy with his leg elevated on the magazine table and pressing a wad of bloodied tissue to his nose. He is flanked by two others, whose heads loll in a way that makes them look bored rather than drunk. But I can smell the alcohol on them. In fact, the whole area reeks. Who'd be a nurse on a weekend shift in A&E? Give me a night-walk with a group of Haringey teens any day.

When White Platts had fronted a camp for twelve kids whose deprivation index marked them out as unique, it had been a turning point in my learning. They'd been brash and East End and the most characterful youngsters I'd ever worked with. They'd taught more than they needed teaching. Their survival in the lives they'd been given left us awestruck. This is how I'm feeling now, about Jay. What had my last words to him been? Had I rejected him, or had he simply taken himself out of the situation? I'd accused him of lying; but is omitting the truth the same as an outright lie? Hadn't I treated him in the same way? In the middle of trying to escape from the pounding of my thoughts, a name is being called.

'Mrs Elliot? Is Mrs Elliot here?'

It's a young man wearing what looks like jade-green pyjamas. He shuffles towards me in his clunky plastic shoes, and I realise I'm *Mrs Elliot*. He is looking at his clipboard. 'Do you want to come with me,' he says with a weary smile, then pushes himself through a pair of Perspex doors, holding them open while I follow.

'We're going to have to take your husband up to high

dependency.' Eyes snap to mine. 'Oh, don't worry. It's only that we can't bring him round and we don't want him to be too far away from a ventilator, should he need one.'

A curtain is pulled back and there is Jay.

'He's taken quite a blow to the back of the head, Mrs Elliot. How did that happen?' the young man is asking. I have to presume he's a doctor now, though he hardly looks old enough. 'Mrs Elliot?'

'There was a bit of pushing and shoving. At a wedding, where we all were. He fell against a table edge.'

Why I am protecting Alex, I don't know.

'Was anyone else hurt?'

I shake my head. 'No,' I tell him. 'It was just a silly accident.'

I can't stop staring at Jay. His face is so pale, and the collar of his wedding shirt is soaked in blood. The bandaging is looking more professional though, and it's clean.

'Can I touch him?' I so want to touch him.

'Course you can. Hold his hand. The porters will be here in a mo. I'll have to love you and leave you.' Then the guy slips away, his shoes squeaking across the linoleum floor.

Jay's hands are ice cold; just like always. Being so tall means the heat and blood has a long way to travel, is what he says when he lays his cold feet and hands on my bare skin. If that never happens again, I don't think I'll be able to cope. I put my lips against his cheek and whisper to him that I'm here, but he doesn't react. I could be watching a film, so unreal does the whole scene feel. And the worst of it is, there's no magic moment when the lead character wakes up and everyone lives happily ever after. Instead, there is the smell of vomit and someone's late-night takeaway, and a harsh white light that doesn't allow for the hiding of anything.

When the porter comes lumbering in with a joviality that doesn't belong to the middle of the night, I follow him back out into the waiting area. My mother is there, sitting by herself, and with a smear of blood across the front of her gold-coloured jacket. And that's when my tears come.

She stands up. 'Evie,' she hisses. 'What's happening? I thought you'd have phoned.'

I want to ignore her. Who thinks about themselves at the scene of someone else's crisis? She does. But then I remember how she'd been the one to help keep Jay stable as he was bleeding out on the floor of that grim saloon bar. So, I step towards her and hold out my arms.

'We're going up to HDU,' I tell her as she falls into my embrace. 'But he's going to be okay, they've said.'

'Well, tell them he needs a brain scan,' she says. 'At the very least.' Then she steps away so that I am free to follow Jay.

'Alex is with the police,' she calls, as though it's an afterthought.

'Good for him,' is my reply.

Chapter Thirty-Three

MAY 2019

'I'm bloody terrified, if you want the honest truth,' Alex says as he climbs out of my car. A blustery wind lifts his hair and sends a group of spindly plane trees into swaying overdrive.

The hospital car park is full, and a traffic-management officer is eyeing us suspiciously, as though she thinks we're trying to avoid buying a ticket.

I reach into my pocket and pull out a handful of coins. 'Jay won't be a problem. I'd be more afraid of her, if I was you.'

He follows my eyes to the fluorescent-clad woman who is striding towards us. Agreeing to come and make his peace with Jay is something I've had to work on. The police had given Alex a caution, but that's nothing compared to what he's been giving himself.

When I've paid for my parking ticket, we walk together towards the main entrance of the hospital, lifting our coats around us and squinting our eyes against the bite of the wind.

Jay is on an ordinary ward now, though it's been a long journey to get him there. My mother had been correct in her diagnosis of a brain bleed. It had only been a small one, but the damage had been done. A full recovery is predicted but not guaranteed, and at the moment, Jay has been left with a slight twist to his left leg when he walks, and a weakened grip in his left hand. But his character hasn't been affected at all. His first words, when he'd opened his eyes after almost a week of being out of it, were *I'm starving*.

I'd kissed him then, and he'd cried.

There'd been no loss of memory. Jay remembers squaring up to Alex exactly as it happened. He's not denied that he wanted nothing more than to kill when he'd barged into the wedding. Losing me, he said, was like being plunged back into the claustrophobia of a dark tunnel, and not being able to see light at the end. It made him want to fight.

We've talked a lot whilst I've been sitting at his bedside, and it's helped. He's come to realise the things that happened in his life to cause him hurt, have also created a person of whom he's quite proud. Having someone to show him this, was like finding the lock to fit that elusive key: the one with no label.

But knowing that he actually owns Tunnel Cottage is the one thing he can't quite get his head around. There will be no reconciliation with his father now. He's gone. But there could have been, and that thought hurts Jay more than anything. He'd no idea his father had somehow *purchased* the cottage, no idea when this would have been. He can only imagine it happened when Fred Pickthall had found himself alone in the place, longing for the time when it was filled with his family.

'What should my first words be, Evie? Tell me.' Alex is pressing his fingers to his temples. His lips are very pale. 'I can't think.'

Our footsteps echo on the antiseptic stairwell. I stop for a moment to get my breath back. 'The great Alex Swarbrick. Lost for words,' I say, giving him a grim smile. 'Start with a sorry and let him do the rest.'

We finally reach the upper floor of the hospital, where Jay's ward is. Alex takes my hand and stops me. A small woman in a set of navy-blue scrubs comes up behind us, and we stand aside to let her through. She brings with her the smell of steak-and-kidney pie, and fatigue.

Alex waits for her to go, then says, 'I was a little shit, back then. Like your Turnbull kid. I've got no excuses: I had decent parents, unlike him. Thank Christ there's Paul to rein me in, now.' He gives me a shrug. 'Nothing from the past can be changed, can it?'

'Nope.'

His voice lifts. 'Help me out a bit here, Evie. Please. I'm dying slowly.'

'It's what you do now that'll count, for Jay. You don't need any insider knowledge.' I push open the door of the ward. 'Just use your instinct. It's a pretty powerful thing.'

As we walk towards the nurse's station, I can almost *feel* him rolling his eyes. We are greeted politely enough, though the nurses are always too busy to talk much, and even when they do, their focus is moving on to the next thing.

'You know the way,' one of them tells us. 'He's fretting at the window today.'

And he is.

Though the ward is three floors up, the view is level with the top of the valley where Tunnel Cottage lies. It is a patchwork of freshly ploughed fields and spring-green treetops, and Jay has his hands and face pressed as close as the glass will allow. There's a bare patch of skin at the back of his head and he's told me that I'll have to get him to a hairdresser when he gets out, to *level things up.* That I'm being included in his plans is something I'm grateful for. How it'll work out for us, I'm not even going to imagine. My new job is on hold for a few months. The place could hardly refuse my request for compassionate leave: they're desperate for my input. That scares me and thrills me in equal measure.

When Jay turns to face us, I can feel Alex's tremble as if it were my own. The air shimmers with a strange energy. Then the two men step towards each other and fall into an embrace. It has a power to it that I've never seen before; they melt into one another. I can do nothing but stare, until I have to look away and press the heels of my hands to my eyes.

'Break it up, you lads,' calls the man sat up in bed at the end of the row. There's not much to him, and he's wearing a hospital gown rather than pyjamas, but his voice holds a quiet power. 'Or we'll all want a go.'

The moment scatters, like a million tiny sunbeams on the surface of the beck, and then we are talking and laughing, and I know everything is going to be all right.

Jay

When Evie walks Jay back to Tunnel Cottage, wild garlic is just coming into bloom. It spreads along the track like a swathe of bridal confetti. They hear the train before they see it: the low thrum, a pulse that seems to come from deep in the earth, then the ear-splitting screech of metal moving over itself, and the tunnel end is punctured.

They stand together and watch from the gate, as the bright lights of the train burst from the darkness.

Jay is far from his whole self, and he wonders if that's what he really wants to be, anyway. To lose any of his story feels plain wrong. It doesn't weigh as heavily now, that's all. Thanks to Evie. She's shown him how to shine light into dark places, so that the bad stuff scuttles away, like an aged, nocturnal insect. And all that's left are its shed skin and droppings: her words, though they're right enough. What he wants to do more than anything is to paint that image, set it onto a page so that he never forgets.

The train has passed now, and they carefully pull back the gate and step across the tracks. They don't walk up to the front door of the cottage. Instead, Evie leads him towards the meadow.

Today, it is full of brown-and-white sheep, which he thinks look like goats. Some are quietly grazing, others drink from the beck. The air is fresh in a way that only comes with early summer: there's May blossom and trampled grass and a sweetness that brings tears to Jay's eyes.

He rubs them away and leans on Evie, so that he can kneel and run his hands through the clear water of the beck. It sparkles, cold and clear, then flows away.

THE END

Acknowledgements

The spectacular Furness Abbey – a nine-hundred-year-old Cistercian ruin – holds a special place in the hearts of people local to the area; I am one of those people. The place has an energy and vibrancy, an essence of stories untold. On its southern flank, just across the railway line, sits Tunnel Cottage. Its garden is overgrown, and the house has no outward signs of life, though it has a beautiful outlook across a meadow and a shallow beck. During the terrifying lockdown of 2020, I walked around this area on a daily basis with my husband. It's how we kept each other sane. Each time I looked at Tunnel Cottage, I invented a story about people who might have lived there. Evie and Jay are the product of those stories. Once I'd let them loose in my imagination, they wouldn't go away. I hope my readers fall for them in the way I did.

Once again, I would like to thank my writing team: my family for their cheerleading skills, and especially my daughter, Rosie Hillman, for her beta-reading skills and book talk. Bloodhound Books – Betsy Reavley and Fred Freeman have been the most supportive publishers. Thanks especially to Clare Law, my editor, who completely understood Evie and Jay, and to Abbie Rutherford for her critical eye on the final versions of *The Cottage*. Also, thanks to Keiran and Joe, whose wedding I stole for my final scenes.

The Cottage, my second novel, is dedicated to my husband, Steve Hillman. We have walked some miles together since I started writing, and worn out many pairs of trainers, but he has been more than happy to let me ramble on about my story ideas. He knows my books as well as I do.

A note from the publisher

Thank you for reading this book. If you enjoyed it please do consider leaving a review on Amazon to help others find it too.

We hate typos. All of our books have been rigorously edited and proofread, but sometimes mistakes do slip through. If you have spotted a typo, please do let us know and we can get it amended within hours.

info@bloodhoundbooks.com